Instructor's Manual
and Test Item File

to accompany

Environmental
Science
A Global Concern

Fifth Edition

William P. Cunningham
University of Minnesota

Barbara Woodworth Saigo
Saiwood Biology Resources
Saiwood Publications

Prepared by
Amanda Woods McConney

WCB
McGraw-Hill

Boston   Burr Ridge, IL   Dubuque, IA   Madison, WI   New York   San Francisco   St. Louis
Bangkok   Bogotá   Caracas   Lisbon   London   Madrid
Mexico City   Milan   New Delhi   Seoul   Singapore   Sydney   Taipei   Toronto

WCB/McGraw-Hill

A Division of The McGraw·Hill Companies

Instructor's Manual and Test Item File to accompany
ENVIRONMENTAL SCIENCE: A GLOBAL CONCERN, FIFTH EDITION

 This book is printed on recycled paper containing 10% postconsumer waste.
RECYCLED

1 2 3 4 5 6 7 8 9 0 QPD/QPD 9 0 9 8

ISBN 0-697-41249-0

www.mhhe.com

CONTENTS

PREFACE

Note to Instructors by the authors of the text

Environmental Science: A Global Concern is designed for use in a one-semester or one-quarter length course in Environmental Science or Human Ecology. This text first covers principles of natural science and ecology, making them accessible to non-science majors as well as general science students (Part I). Questions of human populations and our interaction with our environment are addressed in Parts II and III. Part IV investigates our earth's resources and the ways we use and abuse them. Finally, Part V investigates ways we might build a society capable of living on earth with less harmful impacts. Throughout the text, examples, illustrations, and case studies apply science principles to both national and international topics of environmental importance, making clear the immediate connections between classroom learning and the world around us. While the material covered is scientifically thorough and up to date, presentation is clear and straightforward, so that students may get a solid grasp of concepts and their significance.

Throughout *Environmental Science: A Global Concern* a special effort has been made to guide students into patterns of independent thinking and evaluation of issues and problems. Chapter 2 includes an in-depth discussion of critical thinking skills. This discussion is designed to help students consciously develop an orderly method of evaluating and understanding the often conflicting information they will gather about science and the environment both in and out of the classroom. In order to reinforce this practice critical thinking is referred to in the chapters and students are asked to reflect on their worldviews in *What Do You Think* boxes. Lists of Questions for Critical Thinking at the end of each chapter as well as the customary Review Questions are also designed to reinforce meaningful learning and critical thinking. These questions are designed to expand independent reflection of topics discussed in the text, but they can also be useful tools in initiating in-class discussions or as starting points for paper topics. Chapter Objectives are presented so that students can clearly know from the outset which central lessons they should focus on as they read. In addition, alphabetized lists of key terms and additional resources on the Internet are presented with each chapter. Suggestions for Further Readings are provided at the end of the text, listed by chapter. This Instructor's Manual contains full lists of questions, outlines, objectives, and key term lists for each of the 25 chapters in the text.

Note to Instructors about the preparation of this manual

The organization and content of the instructor's manual is similar to previous editions and again I focused most of my energy on developing higher order questions for the test item file. Because assessment is such a critical aspect of student learning, I attempted to construct questions that are not based solely on knowledge, but instead require students to apply their knowledge. For this reason I did not use true/false questions. I believe that true/false questions make guessing too easy since students have a 50/50 chance of guessing correctly. Further, with the high level of guessing, you, the instructor cannot diagnose where students *are* in terms of their grasp of the content. Hopefully, some of the questions in this manual will help you diagnose student learning and will in turn facilitate student knowledge. As you well know, constructing good questions takes time, and I find, revisions after administering exams. I welcome your comments and suggestions so please provide feedback on the test questions. I can be contacted through Western Oregon University, Monmouth, OR 97361.

I am excited about the fifth edition of this text because I recognize the authors' commitment to critical thinking. Critical thinking is an integral component of the text and is not merely "tagged on" at the end in a chapter. This helps students develop their critical thinking skills–which are so very important in unraveling complex environmental issues. I urge you to use the list of Internet resources provided at the end of each chapter. These resources provide the most up-to-date information and can be an excellent tool for you in preparing class activities .

Have fun, good luck, and great teaching!! AWM

EDUCATIONAL MATERIALS

Organization of the Instructor's Manual

Broadly, this Instructor's Manual presents additional teaching resources, followed by chapter outlines, objectives, questions, and key terms, and finally the test questions that are listed by chapter with an answer key at the end.

Correlation Guide for the Transparencies: A guide for the list of colored acetate transparencies from the 3rd edition that correlates with the 5th edition of *Environmental Science: A Global Concern.* The 3rd edition color acetate transparencies are available through your local William C. Brown sales representative or by phoning Educational Services at 800-228-0459.

Multimedia Educational Resources: This listing and brief explanation of useful, non-printed teaching materials is presented to expand available learning methods for students.

Sources of Films, Computer Programs, Databases, and Networks: Addresses and telephone numbers for repeated listings of multimedia material sources are collected and presented here. (Addresses for unique listings are included in the initial entry.)

Note to Instructors, Chapter Outline, Objectives, Questions, and Key Terms: The organization of each chapter is presented here, with the objectives, critical thinking questions, and key terms that students will find in the text of each chapter. Notes to the instructor are also included to provide tips in teaching or reflections on the topics in the chapters.

Test Item File: In the second half of the Instructor's Manual 50-70 multiple choice questions are listed for each chapter. Questions are given in the order in which topics are presented in the text, with correct answers at the end in an answer key. William C. Brown Publishers provides a computerized test generator for use with *Environmental Science: A Global Concern.* It allows you to quickly create tests based on these questions and requires no programming experience to use.

Printing an exam yourself requires access to a personal computer--a DOS, Windows, or Macintosh that uses 3.5" diskettes. Diskettes are available through your local William C. Brown sales representative or by phoning Educational Services at 800-228-0459. The package you receive will contain complete instructions for making up an exam. See the notes about Micro Test III on the first page of the Test Item File.

William C. Brown Publishers also provides support services, via mail (WCBP Technology Dept., Wm. C. Brown Publishers, 2460 Kerper Blvd., Dubuque, IA 52001) or by phone (800-258-2385) to assist in the use of the test generator software, as well as in the creation and printing of tests if you don't have access to a suitable computer.

MULTIMEDIA EDUCATIONAL RESOURCES

This section contains a list of multimedia resources (audiovisual and computer) that you may find useful in your teaching. A broad range of materials is included, from videotapes and video disks to computer games, and databases. Videotapes and disks are available from film and video collections at many universities and public libraries. Often prices from these public collections are lower than prices from commercial distributors. Many of the video disks are designed to be interactive, so that if you have a computer linked to your video disc player you or your students can view various segments in any order you wish. Some interactive video programs also come with computer simulation or database packages. Computer versions are usually designed for Macintosh or IBM-compatible personal computers (PCs) or both. The materials listed here are only a sample of the many resources available. The text has listings of current Internet resources and your library or audiovisual department may have additional listings, topics, and sources. For all materials listed here, addresses and phone numbers for ordering are listed either in the entry or in the next section, entitled "Sources of Films, Computer Programs, Databases, and Networks".

Computer resources can be excellent tools in teaching students of the twenty first century. Games, such as simulations in which students are responsible for designing and maintaining a sustainable ecosystem or planet, are excellent teaching tools because they give students "hands-on" experience with the variables and dynamics in natural systems. The Internet and databases are outstanding tools for student research projects, written papers, or simply brief explorations that will expose them to some of the resources they may find useful later in life. Both on-line and CD ROM databases are common library resources. You may need to order or subscribe to specialized databases.

The textbook has excellent lists of current Internet websites that pertain to each chapter topic. The principal advantage of these websites is that their information is far more current than that collected and stored in published databases. They can also facilitate project networking: many Internet websites are developed to spread news and gather support for important environmental issues. Database listings from on-line and e-mail sources can often be down-loaded into your own computer so that you can work with them without paying for extended telephone time.

All computer games, networks, and databases come with manuals or directions for installation and use. Specifications for needed memory and monitor types are also provided. Many commercial products and systems have toll-free help lines that you can call with questions. When you consider acquiring a computer resource, make sure that it is compatible with the type of computer your class will be using. Many are available for multiple formats, but some are not.

In addition to electronic teaching aids, this section includes a number of thematic atlases. These specialized atlases present detailed mapped and graphic information on environmental topics from population and demographics to water resources and development. They can be extraordinarily useful for in-class work or for independent student projects. Thematic atlases are available through the map libraries of many universities or from listed publishers. Again these listings are only a sample of the many excellent resources available. The textbook has a list of further readings for each chapter. Your library may have other similar, outstanding resources.

In the following pages, multimedia listings of general interest are grouped together first. Sources with more specialized applications are presented together in the order of chapter topics in the textbook. In many cases there will be significant overlap from one chapter list to another.

The following general reference publications may also serve as good resources for your own course planning or as student references.

Further Information on Computer Network Resources:

Ecolinking: Everyone's Guide to On-line Environmental Information. Don Rittner, 1993. Berkeley, CA: Peachpit Press.

General References:

These sources were used extensively in preparation of the text *Environmental Science: A Global Concern.* They will serve as strong references and basic data sources for class discussion and student research or writing projects.

State of the World, 1997. The Worldwatch Institute (L. Starke, ed.). New York: W.W. Norton and Company. An annual publication containing well-documented essays on major environmental and population issues. Thorough discussions with examples and statistics.

World Development Report 1994: Development and the Environment. The World Bank, 1992. New York: Oxford University Press. An establishment view of human, environmental, and economic development issues. Each annual issue relates major themes to current approaches to development thought; the 1992 issue, for instance, focuses on sustainable development as discussed at the Rio world environmental conference. Excellent tables and graphs.

World Resources, 1996-97. The World Resources Institute (in collaboration with the United Nations Environment Programme and the United Nations Development Program). New York: Oxford University Press. A biennial report containing extensive original data on natural resources, environmental quality, and development progress. Each year's report focuses on a series of central issues such as land use, food supplies, and energy resources.

World Resources: Teacher's Guide. The World Resources Institute, 1997. New York: Oxford University Press. A handbook designed to facilitate classroom use of *World Resources.* Includes introductions to the issues, practical lesson plans, student handouts and enrichment activities, transparency masters, and more. Individual chapter reprints and sets of colored slides or transparencies of illustrations from *World Resources* are also available.

The World Environment, 1972-1992. United Nations Environment Programme. M. K. Tolba, O. A. El-Kholy, eds. London: Chapman & Hall. An international review of major environmental conditions, including discussions, data, maps, and graphs covering such topics as agriculture, mining, fresh water supplies, land and coastal degradation, air pollution, tourism, and population.

The 1993 Information Please Environmental Almanac. World Resources Institute. New York: Houghton Mifflin. A good source of instant environmental statistics, with good graphs and tables. Includes a listing of major environmental indices for each of the United States and each of the world's countries.

The Environmental Encyclopedia. William Cunningham et al., eds., 1994. Detroit, MI: Gale Research, Inc. About 1300 short articles on important environmental topics. A good starting point for students working on research papers. Longer articles fully referenced.

Thematic Atlases on Environmental Topics:

Atlas of United States Environmental Issues. Robert J. Mason and Mark T. Mattson, 1990. New York: MacMillan. ISBN # 0028972619. Excellent general reference covering lands, agriculture, natural resources, waste disposal, energy, wildlife, pollution, and other environmental topics.

US Mapbook: Environmental Atlas. 1992. Cambridge, Mass: Interarts. ISBN # 1879856018. Nearly 200 pages of mapped environmental data; comprehensive environmental source book including climate, relief, and natural resource use.

Atlas of the 1990 Census. Mark T. Mattson, 1992. New York: Macmillan. ISBN # 002897302x. Presents data from the first-ever mapped decadal US census, including most census data topics (population density, population changes, housing, economy, education, ethnicity, and more).

Third World Atlas. Ben Crow and Alan Thomas, 1983. Philadelphia: Open University Press. ISBN # 033510259x. Excellent source on demography, environment, politics, economy, and history, with overall attention to development issues.

California: An Environmental Atlas. Bern Kreissman, 1991. Davis, CA: Bear Klaw Press. ISBN # 0962748994. Good comprehensive source covering California's ecology, conservation of natural resources, and resource availability as well as relief maps. Includes bibliographic references.

California Water Atlas. 1979. North Highlands, CA: State of California. Available from General Services, Publications Section, Box 1015, North Highlands, CA 95660. ISBN # 0913232688. Outstanding and beautiful volume with detailed environmental information including extensive presentation of critical water issues: water resources, aqueduct and dam projects, aquifers, and more.

Water Atlas of the United States. James J. Geraghty, ed., 1973. Port Washington, NY: Water Information Center. ISBN # 091239403x. A dated but comprehensive source with outstanding maps focusing on water quality, resource availability and consumption, water laws, and other major topics.

The Last Rainforests: A World Conservation Atlas. Mark Collins, ed., 1990. New York: Oxford University Press. A lavishly illustrated and mapped presentation of the world's remaining tropical rainforests, grouped by world region and covering cultural ecology, botany, ecology, population, resource extraction, and other environmental problems. Extensive text discusses issues in detail.

The Great Lakes: An Environmental Atlas and Resource Book. Environment Canada and US EPA, 1987. Toronto: Environment Canada and Chicago: US Environmental Protection Agency. ISBN # 0662151985. A jointly produced atlas of water quality, settlement, industry, and other environmental issues surrounding these international waters.

Environmental Atlas of Alaska. Charles W. Hartman, 1978. Fairbanks: Institute of Water Resources, University of Alaska. Good sources of mapped climate, resource, and other environmental data.

Atlas of Environment and Natural Resources in Appalachia. HRB Singer, Inc., 1977. Washington, DC: Appalachian Regional Commission. A dated but excellent source covering economic development, forest, mineral, and water resources of this economically important region. Also covers mine disasters, mine reclamation, solid waste conditions, and demographic data.

Additional Innovative Course and Classroom Resources:

Fast Plants & Bottle Biology. A source of insect eggs and plant seeds developed by the University of Wisconsin for in-class experiments, ecosystem simulations, and other hands-on projects. Plants and insects selected for fast germination and breeding in plastic soft drink bottles in less than five weeks. Venus fly traps, fruit flies, praying mantises, and a variety of flowering plants are available for simple demonstrations of predator-prey relationships, pollination, niches, and other ecological concepts. Seeds, instructions, and ideas provided. Write or call Fast Plants/Bottle Biology, University of Wisconsin-Madison, Department of Plant Pathology, 1630 Linden Dr., Madison, WI 53706, (608) 263-5645.

Cooperation and Competition: Theory and Research. David W. Johnson and Roger T. Johnson, 1989. (Interaction Book Company, 7208 Cornelia Dr., Edina, MN 55435, (612) 831-9500). Cooperative learning techniques. Intriguing research results and practical techniques in cooperative learning strategies and structured interactive projects. Included in this discussion are methods of recognizing and managing attitudes toward science, motivation, social skills, and self-esteem. Useful in developing effective learning methods.

How to Study Science. Fred Drews, 1992. Dubuque, IA: William C. Brown. Designed to supplement any introductory science text, this student workbook includes discussions and exercises concerning ways to learn and study concepts, organize note taking and set priorities in remembering ideas, and interpret lectures. Also contains discussions of overcoming science anxiety.

General Environmental Science Resources

Games and Simulations

Balance of the Planet. Students manipulate production of and investments in natural resources, health, technology, population control, and other variables in an effort to gain points by establishing a healthy, stable planet. Manual includes glossary, brief discussion of environmental hazards and benefits, and an annotated bibliography.

Global Recall. Lets players use a real-world environmental database, including over 300 maps, 600 data indicators for all countries of the world, graphing capabilities, and essays on development issues to direct a world development strategy. Macintosh. Source: World Game Institute.

CD and On-line Databases

Dictionary of the Living World. CD-ROM dictionary with text and graphics covering environmental topics and systems. Macintosh. Source: Educorp, #1566.

World Resources Database 1992-93. A tabular database and graphing program from World Resources Institute. Demographic and environmental data worldwide. 3.5 and 5.25 inch disks formatted for PC. Source: World Resources Institute.

Focus on Global Change. An on-line database covering more than 200 publications on subjects including agriculture, demography, earth sciences, ecology, economics, forestry, geography, natural resources, planning, and other topics. On-line databases, updated bi-weekly, are accessed with a program installed on either IBM compatible, Macintosh, or NEC computers. Source: Institute for Scientific Information, 3501 Market Street, Philadelphia, PA 19104.

Small Blue Planet. A CD-ROM full-color satellite atlas of the world. Allows students to zoom in and out, scan, use insert windows with political, physiographic, and other map themes. Macintosh. Source: Educorp, #2090.

Videotapes and Video Disks

Race to Save the Planet. WGBH Educational Foundation, 1991. A 12-inch interactive laserdisc with 7 excerpts from the public television series of the same name. Six-minute segments cover topics including the Colorado River, the Rhine River, wilderness and species diversity, garbage, pesticides, air pollution, and Chico Mendez and the Brazilian rubber tappers. Includes a Macintosh-formatted environmental database, user's manual, teacher's guide, and student worksheets. Scholastic Software.

Race to Save the Planet. The complete series of 10 hour-long video tapes of the public television series *Race to Save the Planet.* A dated, but useful resource. The tapes need to be reviewed before showing them. Topics include historical human relationships with the environment, atmospheric change, solid and toxic waste disposal, biodiversity, and more. Produced by WGBH Educational Foundation. VHS #UM-3007, Films for the Humanities.

Individual titles in the Race to Save the Planet Series:

Environmental Revolution (historical human-environment relations, ideas about nature)

Only One Atmosphere (potential climatic crises associated with human activities)

Do We Really Want to Live This Way? (advantages and disadvantages of modern consumer culture)

In the Name of Progress (reviews well-intentioned development efforts gone bad, asks if environmental preservation and economic development need to be opposing interests)

Remnants of Eden (looks at mass extinctions, our possible role in them)

More for Less (considers ways we might plan our future with less environmental exploitation)

Save the Earth-Feed the World (questions modern farming practices, reviews alternatives)

Waste Not, Want Not (chilling accounts of waste disposal problems, explores reduction and recycling options)

It Needs Political Decisions (explores the power of politics in environmental protection-in developed and developing countries)

Now or Never (introduces individuals actively working for environmental change, encourages others to take action)

The Greenpeace Years. A look at the early innovations and recent accomplishments of this highly visible, controversial, and committed environmental activist organization. Interviews founders, members, and participants in a Greenpeace training camp. 54 min. VHS, National Film Board of Canada.

Danger Ahead: Is There No Way Out? Is global warming available? Can we reverse it technologically? This film presents various projections of climate change. 26 min. VHS, Beta or U-matic #PD-2406, Films for the Humanities.

Preserving Our Global Environment. 1993. An hour-long focus on three major issues, population growth, biodiversity loss, and global warming, and their interrelations and implications. Presented through real examples of communities in Zimbabwe, Panama, and the United States. 53 min. VHS #EDPGV, World Resources Institute.

Part I: Environmental Science and Ecological Principles (Chapters 1 - 5)

Games and Computer Simulations

LIFEmap. A CD-ROM simulation with high-quality graphics and special effects demonstrating the process of evolution. Three volumes: 1. Organic Diversity (#1992); 2. Animals with Backbones (#1993); 3. Animals (#1994). Macintosh. Source: Educorp.

SimEarth: The Living Planet. Students direct the development of a planet, from the first emergence of land to the development of sentient cultures among different types of creatures or plants. Macintosh. Source: MacWarehouse Catalog, ENT 0356.

Ecology. Ecological simulations and games exploring relationships and dynamics in ecological systems such as the Amazon rainforest. Macintosh. Source: MacWarehouse Catalog, EDU 0298.

Predation Equilibria. A package that allows students to explore the effects of varying sizes of predator populations and to model the effect of hunting pressure in a stable predator-prey system. William. C. Brown.

Niche: An Ecological Game. Students use this program to explore the concept of an ecological niche. Cambridge Development Laboratory.

CD and On-line Databases

Discovery Environmental Data. Worldwide data on food, population, and agriculture, including general environmental data from *World Resources.* Source: PEMD Education Group, Ltd., 220 Hyde Street, San Francisco, CA 94109.

Environmental Bibliography: GeoRef. Journal abstracts on CD ROM from the American Geological Institute's GeoRef database. Source: SilverPlatter Information, Inc.

Science Citation Index. CD ROM version of printed index to 3300 major journals in 100 scientific disciplines. Search by title, author, cited author, cited work or patent. Updated quarterly. Available at many libraries.

The National Directory. A national listing of over 100,000 organizations, with phone and fax numbers. Source: Xiphias.

Videotapes and Video Disks

Diversity Endangered. A good, ten minute introduction to biodiversity. Smithsonian Institution Traveling Exhibition Service, Washington, DC 20560; (202) 357-3168.

Only One Earth. A series of tapes from the public television series. Each segment investigates one major aspect of living with our environment, such as efforts to provide organic foods, biodiversity and medicines, or the fate of the earth's forests. Each show 30 to 60 minutes. VHS (catalog numbers vary), University of Minnesota Film and Video.

Significant Hazards? The Sommerville DNA Debate. Documents the political and public debate surrounding the proposed building of a recombinant DNA lab in a densely populated suburb of Boston. Makes clear the importance of effective communication between scientists and the public, examines benefits and risks of technological development. 24 min. 16mm #7N1715, University of Minnesota Film and Video.

The Blue Planet. This video examines the development of life on earth and the ways the earth's environment shaped the way in which life-forms evolved. 26 min. VHS, Films for the Humanities.

Ecological Biology. This film describes the distribution of living organisms in space and time, why they live where they do, and how their populations interact. 16 min. 16 mm #10271, University of Wisconsin.

What Is Ecology? A film defining what an ecosystem is, with examples. 21 min. 16 mm, #05274. University of Wisconsin.

Matter and Energy. Describes the properties and states of matter and energy, and the law of the conservation of matter and energy. 14 min. #03250, University of Wisconsin.

Goddess of the Earth. This Nova show explores the controversial theory that the earth functions as a living organism, modifying conditions to create an optimal environment for life. 58 min. VHS #4937C, Coronet/MTI Film and Video.

How To Make a Difference Video: Wetlands. Audubon Productions 1992. Outlines the rapid loss of wetlands in the United States, the costs of this loss, and ways that individuals can take action to help preserve our remaining wetlands. 30 min. VHS. Source: Audubon Activist.

The Living Reef. Explores the composition and communities of the Great Barrier Reef in Australia. Looks at the many types of marine life that depend upon the coral reef. Laserdisc. Emerging Technology Consultants.

The Temperate Rain Forest. Examines the characteristics and ecology of the beautiful British Columbian coastal rainforest, looks at factors that make its balance delicate, and presents a case for its preservation. 16 min. 16mm #5N1714, University of Minnesota Film and Video.

The Everglades: Conserving a Balanced Community. Documents the political and public debate surrounding the Everglades, featuring aerial views of the swamps, forests, and prairies and close-ups of birds, plants, and alligators. The unique environment exists nowhere else but is threatened by population and industrial growth. 12 min. 16mm #5N1746, University of Minnesota Film and Video.

Antarctica. Still largely uncharted, Antarctica is already used as a garbage dump. Introduces the geography, beauty, and vulnerability of this remote region. VHS, Beta, or U-matic #PD2200, Films for the Humanities.

The Water Crisis. Although most Americans take water for granted, this segment of the Nova series shows that water scarcity could become the next national issue. Looks at supplies, pollution, and policies of water. 57 min. 16mm #1N14543, University of Minnesota Film and Video.

Water and Life: A Delicate Balance. This video shows the role of water in the human body, the cycles of water, and industrial water consumption and pollution. 13 min. VHS, Films for the Humanities.

Jungle. A segment of the *Living Planet* series, this video describes the complex ecological relationships in a tropical rainforest. 14 min. VHS or 16mm #1N1587, University of Minnesota Film and Video.

Part II: Population, Economics, and Environmental Health (Chapters 6-9)

CD and On-line Databases

Agricola. The National Agricultural Library's on-line database, covering worldwide journals and monographs on agriculture, soils, livestock, forestry, and other related topics. Source: Knowledge Index Databases.

Agrochemicals Handbook. Provides information on agrochemical products used worldwide, on-line via Dialog. Source: Knowledge Index Databases.

Economic Literature Index. On-line database run by Dialog. Covers book reviews and articles from 260 economics journals as far back as 1969. Source: Knowledge Index Databases.

The Chemical Referral Center. A public service providing health and safety information about chemicals and chemical production. An on-line database: to use it call (800) CMA-8200 between 9 am and 6 pm M - F. Free.

Food Science and Technology Abstracts. Provides access to research and innovations in food science, agriculture, chemistry, and other related subjects since 1969. Source: Knowledge Index Databases.

Pollution Abstracts. References to literature on pollution of all sorts, as well as sources and control methods. Source: Knowledge Index Databases.

Toxic Chemical Release Inventory. CD database of reports to US EPA of toxic emissions from manufacturing, processing, or use facilities. Available at larger libraries or through the EPA.

Films and Videos

World Population. A graphic display of the history of human population growth. 6.5 minutes. ZPG Population Education Program, 1400 16th Street, NW, Suite 320, Washington, DC 20036. (202) 332-2200.

Will the World Survive? Increasing populations need accelerated agricultural production, but rapid-growth, high-yield crops take their toll on soil resources. Considers the Green Revolution and other efforts to improve food production. 58 min. VHS #5136C, Coronet/MTI Film and Video.

The Silent Emergency Preventable diseases kill 15 million children yearly, a problem that could be largely prevented with monitoring and simple technology. English, French, or Spanish. 21 min. (3/4 inch U-matic videotape #193, UNICEF.

Nova: Child Survival-The Silent Emergency A full-length presentation of the "child survival and development revolution," a worldwide UN effort to prevent childhood mortality due to diarrhea and other common illnesses. English only. 58 min. 3/4 inch U-matic videotape #197, UNICEF.

A Population Story: Collision with the Future. Shows a frightening futuristic scenario in which life on a dangerously overpopulated earth finally becomes insupportable. 23 min. 16 mm #10025, University of Wisconsin.

Tragedy of the Commons. Portrays the problems associated with overpopulation; based on the essay by Garret Hardin. 30 min. 16 mm #08657, University of Wisconsin.

Scientific Eye: Earth LTD. Journal Films. Discusses the earth's non-renewable resources (metals, stones, fuels) and ways that we can use them more carefully and wisely. Laserdisc. Emerging Technology Consultants.

Forestry: the Science and the Art. Gives an overview of the forest products industry and its current controversies, especially the clearcut method of harvesting trees. 20 min. VHS #5N1753, University of Minnesota Film and Video.

Pollution: How Much Is a Clean Environment Worth? Defines the concept of "external diseconomy," shows the ways in which externalities can be calculated, and uses a cost-benefit analysis to determine the "optimum" level of pollution. 30 min. VHS #7A1027, University of Minnesota Film and Video.

The Toxic Goldrush. Cleaning up the environment has become a fast growth industry. But will companies hired to clean up air, water, and land really use appropriate technology and contain the poisons, or will sloppy methods merely transform and spread toxic substances? 26 min. VHS #NN-1871, Films for the Humanities.

Dioxin. Exactly what is dioxin? Where does it come from? What is its effect on humans? Working from the example of Agent Orange, this film looks at how links are scientifically established between a chemical and disease. 26 min. VHS #NN-1832, Films for the Humanities.

Environmental Illness: Bad Chemistry. This program examines the health effects of common chemicals from perfumes and aerosols to plastics. Environmental Illness (EI) has become an increasingly common and recognized result. 60 min. VHS #NN-3058, Films for the Humanities.

Environmental Toxins and Community Response. Includes 17 lectures on 6 videocassettes, taped at the Harvard School of Public Health. Accompanied by a 149-page study guide. VHS, Umbrella Films.

A Plague on Our Children. Two hour-long segments covering the debates and dangers surrounding dioxins and herbicides (part 1) and PCBs (part 2). Looks at regions where serious health problems have arisen and at EPA responses. VHS, Richter Productions.

Environmental Health: Are You Swimming in a Sewer? Waterways and oceans are receiving billions of gallons of waste daily. What sort of toxic chemicals are fouling our waters, and what threats do they pose? 58 min. VHS #5127C, Coronet/MTI Film and Video.

Introduction to Ecological Economics. Gaylord Nelson, Herman Daly, and John Cobb, Jr., present an introduction to the issues and ideas of environmental approaches to economics. 45 min. Griesinger Films. ISBN # 0961676256. 1991.

Investing in Natural Capital. Herman Daly and others investigate ways of altering our current ways of economic thinking to include the natural world as a viable priority. 45 min. Griesinger Films. ISBN # 0961676264. 1993.

Conversation for a Sustainable Society. Amory and Hunter Lovins, Dennis Meadows, and others explore the possibilities for building a sustainable society. 45 min. Griesinger Films. ISBN # 0961676272. 1993.

Good Books

Steady-State Economics, 2nd Edition. Herman E. Daly, 1991. San Francisco: Island Press. ISBN # 155963071x. Daly's classic 1977 argument for an economic paradigm in which, rather than "more is better," we can consider that "enough is best." A keystone in sustainable development theory, compiled with new essays.

The Green Economy. Michael Jacobs, 1991. San Francisco: Island Press. ISBN # 0745304125. Explores what it would mean to integrate an environmental perspective into economic theory, both in theory and in practice. Investigates the ideas of "sustainability" and "environmental protection."

Part III: Food, Land, and Biological Resources (Chapters 10 - 15)

Computer Games and Simulations

EcoDisc. CD-ROM simulation of a developing and working nature reserve; demonstrates principles and dynamics of maintaining a nature reserve (available in 9 languages). Macintosh. Source: Educorp, #1355.

Darwin's Dilemma. Students manipulate evolutionary dynamics to cause life-forms to evolve. Macintosh. Source: MacWarehouse Catalog, ENT 0338.

SimLife: The Genetic Playground. An advanced genetic simulation that allows students to design plants and animals, test adaptive abilities by altering the environment, and experiment with food webs, mutations, and natural disasters. Macintosh. Source: MacWarehouse Catalog, ENT 0457.

On-line and CD Databases

Standard Pesticide File. Lists approximately 3900 pesticides, with chemical structure, trade names, and classifications. On-line database from BRS/After Dark.

Tropical Agriculture. Worldwide literature since 1975 on methods and developments in tropical and subtropical agriculture. On-line database from BRS/After Dark.

Videotapes, Video Disks, and Films

Diversity Endangered. A good, ten minute introduction to biodiversity. Smithsonian Institution Traveling Exhibition Service, Washington, DC 20560; (202) 357-3168.

Pesticides: For Export Only. Documents production and export of agricultural chemicals that are banned in producing countries of North America and Western Europe. Ironically, continued use of these chemicals in Third World agricultural production leads to a "circle of poison" when wealthier nations import coffee, bananas, and other agricultural products. English or Spanish. 57 min. VHS, Richter Productions.

Will the World Survive? Increasing populations need accelerated agricultural production, but rapid-growth, high-yield crops take their toll on soil resources. Considers the Green Revolution and other efforts to improve food production. 58 min. VHS #5136C, Coronet/MTI Film and Video.

Fragile Harvest. New genetic engineering tools promise solution to world hunger, but they are increasingly in the hands of multinational chemical companies that have taken over seed companies and are breeding and marketing seeds to suit their agro-chemical interests. Filmed in Ethiopia, Peru, Turkey, and North America, this film records "development" programs that have driven farmers from the land, increased agrochemical dependencies, and eliminated indigenous crop varieties. 49 min. 16mm #1S2387, University of Minnesota Film and Video.

The Muck and the Mystery Man. Part of the *Only One Earth* series, this film documents the resurgent demand for natural, chemical-free foods in industrialized countries, and some of the difficulties of reverting to organic agriculture. 20 min. VHS #7G1011, University of Minnesota Film and Video.

The Law of Nature: Park Rangers in Yosemite Valley. Looks at the dilemma of park rangers, trained as naturalists, who must act almost exclusively as law enforcement agents. 28 min. VHS, Umbrella Films.

Can Tropical Forests Be Saved? A global examination of tropical rainforests from Indonesia to West Africa to Amazonia. Inspects global effects of deforestation, economic and cultural values of rainforests, and efforts to save both the trees and the people of these areas. Three segments, 35 to 45 min. each. VHS, Richter Productions.

Equilibrium in a Mountain Habitat. After millennia of human habitation and overtaxing of resources in India's jungle region and in the mountains of central France, government protection and regulation in each place is developing model examples of how humans can live in equilibrium with their environment. 28 min. VHS, #VJ-2337, Richter Productions.

Treasures of the Greenbelt. The nine counties surrounding San Francisco Bay contain some four million acres of parks and watersheds, farms and ranches, forests, and vineyards, making a "greenbelt" around urban San Francisco. Looks at lifestyles, land uses, and endangered species here. 28 min. (all standard video formats) #37989, University of California Extension Media Center.

STV: Rain Forest. National Geographic. Portrays the richness of a fragile ecosystem. Based on the National Geographic television series. Laserdisc. Source: Emerging Technology Consultants.

Genetics: Patterns of Evolution. Coronet/MTI. Illustrates modern evolutionary biology, including field studies of species adaptations in dynamic, interactive systems in habitats ranging from volcanic islands to temperate woodlands. Laserdisc. Source: Emerging Technology Consultants.

Eco-Insights. Interactive videodisk covering basic principles of ecology in the Kananaskis Region of the Canadian Rockies, including biological diversity, adaptations to winter, and forces of landscape change.

Baikal: Blue Eye of Siberia. Looks at environmental damage done to Lake Baikal, which contains one-fifth of the world's fresh water and is home to 2600 species. An international campaign-fraught with politics-is under way to save the lake after decades of toxic contamination. 107 min. VHS #NN-2791, Films for the Humanities, Inc.

Sea of Slaughter. In this film author Farley Mowatt chronicles five hundred years of European exploitation of marine life on the northwestern Atlantic coast. The decimation of walrus, seals, seabirds, fish, and whales is documented and discussed. Produced by the Canadian Broadcasting Corporation. 96 min. VHS, Bullfrog Films.

Part IV: Physical Resources (Chapters 16 - 22)

On-line News Sources and Databases

Power. A catalog record of books, journals, proceedings and other sources collected by the Department of Energy since the 1950s. On-line databases from BRS/After Dark.

Videotapes, Video Disks, and Films

Riches from the Earth. Our modern technological society depends as never before on the earth's resources, from precious metals to commercial ores and groundwater. A story of discovery, depletion, technology, and conservation. 20 min. 16mm #5N1485, University of Minnesota Film and Video.

Do We Really Need the Rockies? This segment of the Nova series investigates the pros and cons of a new industry, shale oil production, in the Rocky Mountains. There is more oil in the Rockies than in the entire Middle East, but every attempt to extract the fuel thus far has proven too costly and environmentally unsound, and processing produces enormous volumes of highly toxic wastewater. 57 min. 16mm #1G0933, University of Minnesota Film and Video.

Alterations in the Atmosphere. Discusses widespread effects of pollution in the troposphere, the lowest layer of the atmosphere. Examines evidence for the "greenhouse effect" and the roles of various "greenhouse" gases. 18 min. VHS #NN-2321, Films for the Humanities.

Assault on the Ozone Layer. CFCs spread in the atmosphere with great speed, reaching from the equator to the poles in weeks. Ozone losses around the globe are the subject of this film, which also shows the effects on living things of these events. 18 min. VHS #NN-2320, Films for the Humanities.

Emissions and Emotions: Challenges to the European Forest. Political revolutions have exposed ecological crises of astonishing proportion in eastern Europe. Subjects include the "Death Triangle" between Poland, Chechnya, and East Germany, where industrial pollution has decimated forests, resulting in soil erosion. 30 min. VHS, Bullfrog Films.

Rampaging Carbons. Since the industrial revolution we have been burning fuels at an unprecedented rate, and the result is high levels of carbon dioxide in the air. Looks at a group of scientists monitoring all aspects of carbon release and absorption. 20 min. 16mm #7N1632, University of Minnesota Film and Video.

The Climate Factor. Analyzes how climate affects populations and how past climate changes have caused whole populations to move or disappear. 25 min. 16mm #7N1724, University of Minnesota Film and Video.

The River in the Desert. Looks at how the Colorado River became "one of the most highly dammed, diverted, and regulated rivers in the world," and examines the consequences of this aggressive manipulation of nature from early settlement to modern speculative land development. 29 min. VHS or 16 mm, Umbrella Films.

The Ocean Planet: Death of the Mississippi. Although the Mississippi was declared a wild and scenic river less than two decades ago, much of its reach, especially its southern bayous, are heavily contaminated with oil, chromium, mercury, lead, and other toxic substances. 23 min. VHS #NN-2295, Films for the Humanities.

The Great Lakes: Troubled Waters. Examines the nature of the threat to water quality of the lakes, and the bi-national failure of the United States and Canada to fully address the problem. 48 min. VHS, Umbrella Films.

The Underlying Threat. Offers a penetrating look at groundwater pollution: how it happens, what contaminants are involved, why groundwater pollution is especially difficult to measure or manage, and what we can do about it. Produced by the National Film Board of Canada. 48 min. VHS or 16mm, Bullfrog Films.

Whose Sea Is This? How do nations divide rights to the oceans? Do they belong to all of us? If property ownership is unclear, environmental protection is difficult to develop. This program looks at the Law of the Sea and at the ways we are treating our seas. 26 min. VHS or Beta #ND-2293, Films for the Humanities.

Down to the Last Drop. Only during droughts do we think about water conservation; once the rain falls all is forgotten. But better planning may be necessary if we are to have reliable, usable water supplies. 26 min. VHS or Beta #ND-1831, Films for the Humanities.

Green Energy. This program examines some renewable alternatives to petroleum products and explains how biological and organic products like wood chips, corn, and garbage can become major sources of energy. 26 min. VHS #NN-1870, Films for the Humanities.

Chernobyl: A Taste of Wormwood. Provides on-site photography of the blast site and of the areas and people affected. Interviews with victims, physicists, and politicians. 52 min. VHS #NN-1264, Films for the Humanities.

The Energy Bank. Examines the potential of energy conservation to meet our energy needs and reduce both global warming and air pollution. Takes case studies from the Pacific Northwest and the Northeast, where pioneering energy programs have been developed. 38 min. VHS, Umbrella Films.

Energy: Less Is More. An energy conservation film that shows how energy can be saved in transportation, in building construction, and in industrial applications, including cogeneration. Presents the case study of a community that has effected remarkable savings through building codes and community involvement. 21 min. 16mm #5N1430, University of Minnesota Film and Video.

Part V: Society and the Environment (Chapters 23 - 25)

Computer Games and Simulations

SimCity. Students direct the development of a city, balancing investments in technology, pollution control, building, and human resources, in an effort to create a stable, livable urban environment. Macintosh. Source: MacWarehouse Catalog.

Videos and Films

Affluenza A humorous, thought-provoking look at what happens when a society becomes infected with Affluenza. Originally produced for public television. 60 min., Bullfrog Films.

Conservation for a Sustainable Society. Amory and Hunter Lovins, Dennis Meadows, and others explore the possibilities for building a sustainable society. 45 min. Griesinger Films. ISBN # 0961676272. 1993.

Baabu Banza: Nothing Goes to Waste. In Niger's capital city of Niamey, inventive and industrious citizens glean useful materials from garbage dumps, refashioning them into useful, marketable materials. 16 min. VHS #NN-3081, Films for the Humanities.

Garbage: The Movie. Churchill Media. Presents current solid waste problems and some solutions. Shows working landfills, incinerators, recycling plants, and composting yards. Laserdisc. Source: Emerging Technology Consultants.

Protecting Our Environment: Recycle. Outlines the process of recycling, discusses what materials are recyclable, and shows some of the process of breaking down and re-using materials. Also in this series: *Protecting Our Environment: Reduce*, and *Protecting Our Environment: Reuse*. Laserdisc. Source: Emerging Technology Consultants.

The Disposable Society. Americans generate 400,000 tons of garbage daily. The simplest solution to disposal for all this waste is to reduce our consumption of disposable materials. 26 min. VHS #NN-1709, Films for the Humanities.

Hazardous Waste: Who Bears the Cost?. Looks at Woburn, Massachusetts, with America's oldest toxic waste dumpsite, as a case study of a community affected by the presence of hazardous waste. 28 min. VHS, Umbrella Films.

The Growth of Towns and Cities. Considers urban landscapes as layers of development, and looks at the ways peoples' lives have been changed by technology. Discusses how industrialization led to urbanization, transportation and the development of suburbs, problems of urban living, and solutions to problems. 20 min. VHS #NN-3318, Films for the Humanities.

Urban Ecology. Inspects some of the problems of rapid urbanization in Abidjan, the Ivory Coast's capital city. Between its colonial legacy and its modern growth rate of 10% per year, increasingly serious conditions face residents. 24 min. VHS #NN-2344, Films for the Humanities.

Toward a Livable City. Looks at the development of Barcelona, Spain, from pre-Christian times through the Industrial Revolution, World War II, and modern growth. Effective planning and regulation have transformed Barcelona into a livable, even scenic, urban area. 28 min. VHS #VJ-2345, Richter Productions.

Conservation of the Southern Rainforest. Focuses on the development of controlled ecotourism as an economic alternative to existing, unsustainable forms of development in rainforest areas of developing nations. 58 min. VHS, Umbrella Films.

Restoring the Environment. Looks at ways technology is being used to correct the environmental problems it has created, including a mobile incinerator for destroying PCBs and environmental safeguards developed by an electroplating firm. 26 min. VHS #NN-1868, Films for the Humanities.

Wetlands and Pinelands. Looks at the New Jersey Pine Barrens and wetland ecosystems in Mexico and Belize, where environmental planning and recognizing the long-standing role of humans in the environment is demonstrating that it is possible to save both people and indigenous species. 28 min. VHS #VJ-2343, Richter Productions.

The Desert as Laboratory. Examines two desert ecosystems being used as research models to find ways to understand the human role in an arid environment and to control desertification. 28 min. VHS #VJ-2236, Richter Productions.

The Rebirth of Whitewood Creek. An award-winning documentary about reviving a stream once made barren by mine effluents, from mercury to raw sewage. Community, EPA, and the mining industry find a way to cooperate in bringing life back to this South Dakota Black Hills creek. 28 min. 16 mm, Cottonwood Productions.

Good Books

Forging International Agreements: The Role of Institutions in Environment and Development. Lee Kimbal, 1992. Washington, DC: World Resources Institute. ISBN # 0915825821. Highlights accomplishments of and challenges for international institutions, especially the UN, in forging environmental agreements and policies.

Material World. Peter Menzel, 1994. Sierra Club Books. A portrait of humanity at the end of the century. Average families from thirty countries share their lives.

Stuff: The secret lives of everyday things. John C. Ryan and Alan T. Durning, 1997, Northwest Environmental Watch (NEW), 1402 Third Avenue, Suite 1127, Seattle, WA 98101, (888) 643-9820, e-mail: nwwatch@igc.apc.org. The things we buy, consume, and use everyday are traced from their origins to the market, into our homes, and beyond.

Valuing the Earth: Economics, Ecology, and Ethics. Herman E. Daly and Kenneth N. Townsend, eds., 1993. Cambridge, Mass: MIT Press. ISBN # 0262540681. A collection of classic and recent essays approaching holistic thought about our ethical and intellectual approaches toward the environment.

Sources of Films, Computers Programs, Databases, and Networks

Film and Video Sources

Audubon Activist, the Audubon Society, 950 Third Avenue, New York, NY 10022, (212) 979-3000.
Bullfrog Films, Box 149, Oley, PA 19547, (800) 543-3764.
Coronet/MTI Film and Video, 108 Wilmot Road, Deerfield, IL 60015.
Films for the Humanities, Inc., P.O. Box 2053, Princeton, NJ 08543-2053.
Griesinger Films, 7300 Old Mill Road, Dept. IP, Gates Mills, OH 44040, (216) 423-1601.
National Film Board of Canada, 1251 Avenue of the Americas, 16th Floor, New York, NY 10020. (800) 542-2164 to preview videos.
Richter Productions, 330 West 42nd Street, New York, NY 10036, (212) 947-1395.
Scholastic Software, 730 Broadway, New York, NY 10003.
Emerging Technology Consultants, P.O. Box 120444, St. Paul, MN 55112, (612) 639-3973.

Umbrella Films, 60 Blake Road, Brookline, MA 02146, (617) 277-6639.
UNICEF, 331 East 38th Street, New York, NY 10016, (212) 686-5522.
University of California Extension Media Center, 2176 Shattuck Avenue, Berkeley, CA 94704.
University of Minnesota Film and Video, 1313 5th Street, S.E., Suite 108, Minneapolis, MN 55414.
University of Wisconsin, Bureau of Audiovisual Instruction, Box 2093, Madison WI 53701-2093, (608) 262-3902.
World Resources Institute, 1709 New York Avenue, NW, Washington, DC, 20006.

Sources of Computer Games and Simulations

Cambridge Development Laboratory, Inc., 214 Third Avenue, Waltham, MA 02514, (800) 637-0047.
Educorp, 7434 Trade Street, San Diego, CA 92121-2410, (800) 843-9497.
MacWarehouse Catalog, P.O. Box 3013, 1720 Oak Street, Lakewood, NH 08701-3013, (800) 225-6227.
World Game Institute, 3215 Race Street, Philadelphia, PA 19104, (215) 387-0220.
William C. Brown Publishers, 2460 Kerper Boulevard, Dubuque, IA 52001, (800) 336-5578.
ZPG Population Education Program, 1400 16th Street, NW, Suite 320, Washington, DC 20036. (202) 332-2200.

CD and On-line Databases

Educorp, 7434 Trade Street, San Diego, CA 92121-2410, (800) 843-9497.
World Resources Institute, 1709 New York Avenue, NW, Washington, DC 20006
Xiphias, 8758 Venice Boulevard, Los Angeles, CA 90343.
SilverPlatter Information, Inc., 1 Newton Executive Park, Newton Lower Falls, MA 02162.
Institute for Scientific Information, 3501 Market Street, Philadelphia, PA 19104.

How to Subscribe to Networks and Mailing Lists

BITNET: Subscribe through a BITNET account if it is available at your institution, or contact the BITNET Network Information Center, EDUCOM, 112 16th Street, NW, Suite 600, Washington, DC 20036, (202) 872-4200. Usually available free or for a small hourly fee.

Bulletin Boards: These are usually accessed by communications software and a modem or through an institutional network. Your software will determine the method of linking. For further information see *Ecolinking: Everyone's Guide to On-line Environmental Information,* by Don Rittner (Berkeley, CA: Peachpit Press 1993), chapter 7.

Internet: Because Internet is an international network designed and funded in the US for academic research, most users access it by establishing an account with an educational or research institution that is connected to the Internet (to subscribe contact the address given in list description). If you do not have access to such an institution, you can get on-line via DIAL n'CERF, a " gateway" network service based in California. Contact CERFnet, San Diego Supercomputer Center, P.O. Box 85608, San Diego, CA 92186; (800) 876-CERF; electronic mail address: help@cerf.net Costs vary with access method: network accounts usually free, external accounts usually charged only for telephone time.

Knowledge Index. Part of Dialog Information Services, the largest on-line bibliographic company in the United States. To subscribe call (800) 334-02564.

UNDERSTANDING OUR ENVIRONMENT

Special Note to Instructors

The authors would greatly appreciate your comments about the text. Is the presentation suitable for your students? Are there materials that the authors could add or delete or corrections they should make? If you have suggestions for how they could improve the text they would be very grateful. Please send comments to William P. Cunningham, College of Biology, University of Minnesota, St. Paul, MN 55108.

Note to Instructors about Critical Thinking in the Classroom

Since critical thinking involves questioning experts and the sources of information, these and subsequent activities can help students start thinking more critically. However, as instructors it is important for us to be open to, and supportive of, students' questions and not intimidated by student thinking. Similarly, it is important to *explicitly* model critical thinking in the classroom. One way to do this is by thinking out loud when students ask questions.

Study Aids

Most of the questions in the *Questions for Review* require recall of the chapter material and can help students remember details of the chapter through reinforcement of key ideas. If you emphasize that students are required to explain their reasoning, the questions can help students practice supporting their thoughts with evidence. The *Questions for Critical Thinking* ask for more application, comparison, and prediction and can be useful for the students to synthesize the information in the chapter and make meaningful connections. Again, the students need to support their reasoning for practice in providing evidence and facilitating the development of logical thinking.

Chapter Outline

Objectives
Deformed Frogs
What Is Environmental Science?
A Brief History of Conservation and Environmentalism
       Historic Roots of Nature Protection
       Pragmatic Resource Conservation
       Moral and Aesthetic Nature Preservation
       Modern Environmentalism
       Global Concerns
Current Conditions
       A Marvelous Planet
       Environmental Dilemmas
       Signs of Hope
North/South: A Divided World
       Rich and Poor Countries
       A Fair Share of Resources?
       North/South Division
       Political Economies
Human Development
       Developmental Discrepancies

In Depth: Getting to Know Our Neighbors
What Do You Think? Environmental Futures: Deciding What to Think

Objectives

After studying this chapter, students should be able to:

- define the term, environment, and identify some important environmental issues that we face today.
- discuss the history of conservation and the different attitudes toward nature revealed by utilitarian conservation and biocentric preservation.
- briefly describe some major environmental dilemmas and issues that shape our current environmental agenda.
- understand the connection between poverty and environmental degradation, as well as the division between the wealthy, industrialized countries and the poorer, developing countries of the world.
- recognize some of the reasons for feeling both optimistic and pessimistic about our environmental future.

Questions for Review

1. Define environment and environmental science.

2. List six environmental dilemmas that we now face and describe how each concerns us.

3. Describe the differences between the North/South or rich/poor or more-developed/less-developed nations. What do we mean by First, Second, and Third World?

4. Compare some indicators of quality of life between the richest and poorest nations.

5. Why should we be concerned about the plight of the poor? How do they affect us?

6. What benefit to us would there be in protecting the rights of indigenous people?

7. Give some reasons for pessimism and optimism about our environmental future and summarize how you feel personally about the major environmental problems that we face.

8. Do you think that environmental conditions are better now or worse than they were 20 or 100 or 1000 years ago? Why?

Questions for Critical Thinking

1. How could we determine whether the disappearance of frogs has some grand, global significance, or is merely a random, local event?

2. What are the fundamental differences between utilitarian conservation and altruistic preservation? Which do you favor? Why?

3. Do the issues discussed in this chapter as global environmentalism belong in an environmental *science* text? Why would anyone ask this question?

4. Some people argue that we can't afford to be generous, tolerant, fair, or patient. There isn't enough to go around as it is, they say. What questions would you ask such a person?

5. Others claim that we live in a world of bounty. They believe there would be plenty for all if we just shared equitably. What questions would you ask such a person?

6. Around 200 million children are forced into dangerous, degrading slave labor each year. Is it our business what goes on in other countries?

7. What would it take for human development to be really sustainable? What does sustainable mean to you?

8. Are there enough resources in the world for 8 or 10 billion people to live decent, secure, happy, fulfilling lives? What do those terms mean to you? Try to imagine what they mean to others in our global village.

9. What responsibilities do we have for future generations? What have they done for us? Why not use whatever resources we want right now?

10. Do you see any similarities between current conditions and those of the 14th century? Have we made any real progress or do things just stay the same?

Key Terms

acute poverty

altruistic preservation

cornucopian fallacy

environment

environmental science

environmentalism

First World

Fourth World

global environmentalism

human development index

neo-Malthusian

North/South division

Promethean environmentalism

Second World

sustainable development

technological optimists

Third World

utilitarian conservation

TOOLS FOR BUILDING A BETTER WORLD

Note to Instructors about Fostering Critical Thinking Skills

This chapter provides information that can form the basis for discussions throughout the class term and guidance for students in forming their own arguments and worldviews. It could be extremely effective to spend enough time on this chapter so that you can refer to its components throughout the rest of the term and hold the students accountable for the key ideas and techniques. The *What Do You Think?* box on page 32 is an excellent resource for a class activity. Most students have not thought about the basis of their opinions or values. A useful activity is to have the students reflect on their values and describe (as much as possible) their worldview. It is helpful to have the students identify the sources of their worldview (culture, schooling, parents, etc.) while they are reflecting. Evaluating the list (1-15) in the *What Do You Think?* box on page 32 could be a good activity to support the reflective thinking. The list could also be used in applying the concepts in this chapter by having the students "label" each statement with respect to the appropriate worldviews or values discussed in the text (e.g., ecofeminism, anthropocentric worldview, etc.).

The critical thinking component is another skill that many students need to develop. Critical thinking is apparent throughout the rest of the chapters in the text. As mentioned previously, the use of critical thinking can be very empowering for students. However, students have not had practice *thinking* and may need explicit help. The questions at the end of each chapter in *Questions for Critical Thinking* are especially useful for student practice. For practice in critical thinking it is also useful for students to evaluate conclusions based on insufficient evidence in contrast with those that are well supported. Choose a few examples from journals, books, or newspapers that are well supported and provide a contrast to poorly supported conclusions. It is helpful for the students to be exposed to well supported statements because they can use these as a model of how to support their own reasoning.

Chapter Outline

Objectives
People or Wildlife in South Africa?
Environmental Ethics and Philosophy
    Are There Universal Ethical Principles?
    Modernism and Postmodernism
    Values, Rights, and Obligations
        Do Other Animals Have Rights?
        Intrinsic and Instrumental Values
        Do Nonsentient Things Have Inherent Value?
Worldviews and Ethical Perspectives
    Domination
    Stewardship
    Biocentrism, Animal Rights, and Ecocentrism
    Ecofeminism
Environmental Justice
    Environmental Racism
    Dumping Across Borders
    Are "Green" Organizations Too White?
    Is Nature Fragile or Resilient?
Science as a Way of Knowing
    A Faustian Bargain?

What Do You Think? Worldviews and Values
Case Study: Squirrels or Science?

Objectives

After studying this chapter, students should be able to:

understand some principles of environmental ethics and philosophy.

compare and contrast how different ethical perspectives shape our view of nature and our role in it.

explain anthropocentrism, biocentrism, ecocentrism, utilitarianism, and ecofeminism, and what each says about human/nature relationships.

summarize the methods, applications, and limitations of the scientific method.

discuss the role of technology in *causing* environmental problems as well as helping us solve them.

apply the skills of critical thinking to what you read here and elsewhere.

Questions for Review

1. Define universalist, nihilist, relativist, utilitarian, postmodern, and ecofeminist ethics.

2. Explain how resource explorers and social justice advocates use these ethical positions to support their causes.

3. Describe the differences between moral agents, moral subjects, and those who qualify for moral considerability.

4. What are inherent and instrumental values? Who has them? Why?

5. Where is Mineral King Valley and why is it important in environmental history? What happened there?

6. Compare and contrast stewardship, anthropocentric, biocentric, ecocentric, and environmental justice worldviews. Which is closest to your own views?

7. Draw a diagram showing the scientific method and describe, in your own words, what it means.

8. Not every science is experimental. Explain how geologists or evolutionary biologists might test their hypotheses.

9. List and explain Richard Paul's ten questions for critical thinking.

10. Itemize six dispositions, tendencies, or attitudes necessary for critical thinking. Elaborate on how they help us think.

Questions for Critical Thinking

1. Review a topic in this chapter -ecofeminism or the question of nature's fragility or resiliency, for example- and arrange the arguments for or against this idea as a series of short statements. Determine whether each is a statement of fact or opinion.

2. How would you verify or disprove fact statements given in question 1? Do the opinions or conclusions reached in this argument *necessarily* follow from the facts given? What alternative proposals could be proposed?

3. Reflect on the preconceptions, values, beliefs, and contextual perspective that you bring to the discussion above. Does it coincide with those in the textbook? What different interpretation would your perspective impose on the argument?

4. Try to put yourself in the place of a person from a minority community, an underdeveloped nation, or a Third World country in discussing questions of environmental justice and environmental quality. What preconceptions, values, beliefs, and contextual perspective would you bring to the issue? What would you ask for from the majority society?

5. What is your environmental ethic? What experiences, cultural background, education, and religious beliefs help shape your worldview?

6. Try some role playing with a classmate, friend, or family member. Take the position of a universalist, biocentrist, ecocentrist, postmodernist, or ecofeminist and debate the merits of cutting trees in the National Forest. On what points would you agree and where would you disagree on this issue?

7. This chapter addresses many social issues and theories. Are these areas appropriate for an environmental science textbook? Why or why not? Try answering this question from the perspective of Gifford Pinchot, John Muir, the ecofeminist, or the person of color whom you identified in questions above. Would they agree?

Key Terms

anthropocentric	moral agents	universalists
appropriate technology	moral extensionism	utilitarians
biocentric	moral subjects	value
critical thinking	morals	
domination	neo-Luddites	
ecocentric	nihilists	
ecofeminism	NIMBY protests	
environmental ethics	postmodernism	
environmental justice	relativists	
environmental racism	science	
inherent value	scientific method	
instrumental value	stewardship	
LULUs	toxic colonialism	

Note to Instructors about the Concepts in Chapter 3

Many students are familiar with the concepts presented in this chapter. However, they probably do not have the skills to synthesize the information so that it is meaningful in the context of environmental science and their own lives. It would be useful to hold them accountable for *why* the information is important and *how* it relates to environmental science. For example, when dealing with atoms, molecules, and compounds, have a discussion of *why* an understanding of the atom is important in environmental science. It is important for you as the instructor to first decide why you think the students need to know the information so you can guide them, helping them make the content meaningful. The introduction of mercury poisoning and risks to human health is a good way to help the students find the content in this chapter meaningful.

Chapter Outline

Objectives
Pigibowin: Poisoning the Wabigoon-English Rivers
From Atoms to Cells
      Atoms, Molecules, and Compounds
      Organic Compounds
      Cells: The Fundamental Units of Life
Energy and Matter
      Energy Types and Qualities
      Conservation of Matter
      Thermodynamics and Energy Transfers
Energy for Life
      Solar Energy: Warmth and Light
      How Does Photosynthesis Capture Energy?
From Species to Ecosystems
      Population, Communities, and Ecosystems
      Food Chains, Food Webs, and Trophic Levels
      Ecological Pyramids
Material Cycles and Life Processes
      The Carbon Cycle
      The Nitrogen Cycle
      The Phosphorous Cycle
      The Sulfur Cycle
Summary
Questions for Review
Questions for Critical Thinking
Key Terms
Additional Information on the Internet

What Do You Think? Chaos or Stability in Ecosystems?
In Depth: A Water Planet

Objectives

After studying this chapter, students should be able to:

- describe matter, atoms, and molecules and give simple examples of the roles of four major kinds of organic compounds in living cells.
- define energy and explain the difference between kinetic and potential energy.
- understand the principles of conservation of matter and energy and appreciate how the laws of thermodynamics affect living systems.
- know how photosynthesis captures energy for life and how cellular respiration releases that energy to do useful work.
- define *species populations, communities,* and *ecosystems* and understand the ecological significance of these levels of organization.
- discuss food chains, food webs, and trophic levels in biological communities and explain why there are pyramids of energy, biomass, and numbers of individuals in the trophic levels of an ecosystem.
- recognize the unique properties of water and explain why the hydrologic cycle is important to us.
- compare the ways that carbon, nitrogen, sulfur, and phosphorous cycle within ecosystems.

Questions for Review

1. Define *atom* and *element*. Are these terms interchangeable?

2. Your body contains vast numbers of carbon atoms. How is it possible that some of these carbon atoms also may have been part of the body of a prehistoric creature?

3. In the biosphere, matter follows a circular pathway while energy follows a linear pathway. Explain.

4. The oceans store a vast amount of heat, but (except for climate moderation) this huge reservoir of energy is of little use to humans. Explain the difference between high-quality and low-quality energy.

5. Ecosystems require energy to function. Where does this energy come from? Where does it go? How does the flow of energy conform to the laws of thermodynamics?

6. Heat is released during metabolism. How might it be detrimental, especially in a large, complex organism?

7. Photosynthesis and cellular respiration are complementary processes. Explain how they exemplify the laws of conservation of matter and thermodynamics.

8. What do we mean by carbon-fixation or nitrogen-fixation? Why is it important to humans that carbon and nitrogen be "fixed"?

9. The population density of large carnivores is always very small compared to the population density of herbivores occupying the same ecosystem. Explain this in relation to the concept of an ecological pyramid.

10. A species is a specific kind of organism. What general characteristics do individuals of a particular species share? Why is it important for ecologists to differentiate among the various species in a biological community?

Questions for Critical Thinking

1. When we say that there is no "away" where we can throw things we don't want anymore, are we stating a premise of a conclusion? If you believe this is a premise, supply the appropriate conclusion. If you believe it is a conclusion, supply the appropriate premise. Does the argument change if this statement is a premise or a conclusion?

2. Suppose one of your classmates disagrees with the statement above, saying, "Of course there is an 'away.' It's anywhere out of *my* ecosystem." How would you answer?

3. A few years ago laundry detergents commonly contained phosphates for added cleaning power. Can you imagine any disadvantages to adding soluble phosphate to household products?

4. The first law of thermodynamics is sometimes summarized as "you can't get something for nothing." The second law is summarized as "you can't even break even." Explain what this means. Is it dangerous to oversimplify these important concepts?

5. The ecosystem concept revolutionized ecology by introducing holistic systems thinking as opposed to individualistic life history studies. Why was this a conceptual breakthrough?

6. Why is it important to recognize that ecosystems often are open and that boundaries may be fuzzy? Do these qualifications diminish the importance of the ecosystems study?

7. The holistic or systems approach to biology has sometimes been criticized as "black box" engineering. It allows us to make broad generalizations about what goes into or comes out of a system without knowing the precise details of how the system works. What do you think are the benefits and limitations of this approach?

8. Compare and contrast the views of F. E. Clements and H. A. Gleason concerning the concept of biological communities as superorganisms. How could these eminent biogeographers study the same communities and reach opposite interpretations? What evidence would be necessary to settle this question? Is lack of evidence the problem?

9. The properties of water are so unique and so essential for life as we know it that some people believe it proves our planet was intentionally designed for our existence. What would an environmental scientist say about this belief?

10. The DMS feedback control of global climate change is offered by some people as evidence for the Gaia hypothesis. Why might they take this position?

Key Terms

atomic number	detritivores
atoms	ecology
biological community	ecosystem
biomass	energy
carbon cycle	enzymes
carbon sinks	first law of thermodynamics
carnivores	food chain
cells	food web
cellular respiration	half-life
chemical energy	heat
compound	herbivores
conservation of matter	homeostasis
consumers	ions
decomposers	isotopes

joules

kinetic energy

matter

metabolism

molecules

nitrogen cycle

omnivores

organic compounds

pH

phosphorous cycle

photosynthesis

population

potential energy

producers

productivity

radioactive isotopes

scavengers

second law of thermodynamics

species

sulfur cycle

temperature

trophic level

BIOLOGICAL COMMUNITIES AND SPECIES INTERACTIONS

Note to Instructors about the Scientific Method, the Nature of Science, and Biodiversity

The What Do You Think? Understanding Competition (p. 79) is an excellent description of applying the scientific method. Similarly, the section on Resilience and Stability (p. 84) is an effective example of the nature of science. The section on Community Properties (pp. 82 - 86) is an up-to-date and well written explanation of diversity, complexity, and stability. Some students have misconceptions about these concepts so it would be useful to emphasize the concepts and how they are related. Some students also believe that increasing edges increases diversity (pp. 85 - 86). It is important to emphasize the detrimental effects of edges on biodiversity. A good, ten-minute introductory videotape for biodiversity is Diversity Endangered (Smithsonian Institution Traveling Exhibition Service, Washington, DC 20560; Telephone: 202-357-3168).

Chapter Outline

Objectives
Sea Otters, Kelp, and Sea Urchins: A Triangular Affair
Who Lives Where, and Why?
    Critical Factors and Tolerance Limits
    Natural Selection, Adaptation, and Evolution
    The Ecological Niche
Species Interactions and Community Dynamics
    Predation
    Keystone Species
    Competition
    Symbiosis
    Defensive Mechanisms
Community Properties
    Productivity
    Abundance and Diversity
    Complexity and Connectedness
    Resilience and Stability
    Community Structure
    Edges and Boundaries
Communities in Transition
    Ecological Succession
    Introduced Species and Community Change
Summary
Questions for Review
Questions for Critical Thinking
Key Terms
Additional Information on the Internet

Case Study: Where Have All the Songbirds Gone?
What Do You Think? Understanding Competition

Objectives

After studying this chapter, students should be able to:

- describe how environmental factors determine which species live in a given ecosystem and where or how they live.
- understand how random genetic variation and natural selection lead to evolution, adaptation, niche specialization, and partitioning of resources in biological communities.
- compare and contrast interspecific predation, competition, symbiosis, commensalism, and mutualism.
- discuss productivity, diversity, complexity, and structure of biological communities and how these characteristics might be connected to resilience and stability.
- explain how ecological succession results in ecosystem development and allows one species to replace another. You should also understand the difference between primary and secondary succession.
- give some examples of exotic species introduced into biological communities and describe the effects such introductions can have on indigenous species.

Questions for Review

1. Explain how tolerance limits to environmental factors determine distribution of a highly specialized species such as desert pupfish. Compare this to the distribution of a generalist species such as cowbirds or starlings.

2. Productivity, diversity, complexity, resilience, and structure are exhibited to some extent by all communities and ecosystems. Describe how these characteristics apply to the ecosystem in which you live.

3. Describe the general niche occupied by a bird of prey, such as a hawk or an owl. How can hawks and owls exist in the same ecosystem and not adversely affect each other?

4. Define keystone species and explain how they are important in community structure and function.

5. All organisms within a biological community interact with each other. The most intense interactions often occur between individuals of the same species. What concept discussed in this chapter can be used to explain this phenomenon?

6. Relationships between predators and prey play an important role in energy transfers that occur in ecosystems. They also influence the process of natural selection. Explain how predators affect the adaptations of their prey. This relationship also works in reverse. How do prey species affect the adaptations of their predators?

7. Competition for a limited quantity of resources occurs in all ecosystems. This competition can be interspecific or intraspecific. Explain some of the ways an organism might deal with these different types of competition.

8. Each year fires burn large tracts of forestland. Describe the process of succession that occurs after a forest fire destroys an existing biological community. Is the composition of the final successional community likely to be the same as that which existed before the fire? What factors might alter the final outcome of the successional process? Why may periodic fire be beneficial to a community?

9. Explain the concept of climax community. Why does the climax community often exhibit a higher level of stability than that found in other successional stages?

10. Discuss the dangers posed to existing community members when new species are introduced into ecosystems. What type of organisms would be most likely to survive and cause problems in a new habitat?

Questions for Critical Thinking

1. Ecologists debate whether biological communities have self-sustaining, self-regulating characteristics or are highly variable, accidental assemblages of individually acting species. What outlook or worldview might lead scientists to favor one or the other of these theories?

2. The concepts of natural selection and evolution are central to how most biologists understand and interpret the world, and yet the theory of evolution is contrary to the beliefs of many religious groups. Why do you think this theory is so important to science and so strongly opposed by others? What evidence would be required to convince opponents of evolution?

3. What is the difference between saying that a duck has webbed feet because it needs them to swim and saying that a duck is able to swim because it has webbed feet?

4. The concept of keystone species is controversial among ecologists because most organisms are highly interdependent. If each of the trophic levels is dependent on all the others, how can we say one is most important? Choose an ecosystem with which you are familiar and ask whether it has a keystone species or keystone set.

5. Some scientists look at the boundary between two biological communities and see a sharp dividing line. Others looking at the same boundary see a gradual transition with much intermixing of species and many interactions between communities. Why such different interpretations of the same landscape?

6. The absence of certain lichens is used as an indicator of air pollution in remote areas such as national parks. How can we be sure that air pollution is really responsible? What evidence would be convincing?

7. We tend to regard generalists or "weedy" species as less interesting and less valuable than rare and highly specialized endemic species. What values or assumptions underlie this attitude?

8. What part of this chapter do you think is most likely to be challenged or modified in the future by new evidence or new interpretations?

Key Terms

abundance	environmental indicators	pathogens
Batesian mimicry	equilibrium communities	pioneer species
climax community	evolution	plankton
coevolution	fire-climax communities	predator
commensalism	habitat	primary productivity
complexity	interspecific competition	primary succession
critical factor	intraspecific competition	productivity
disclimax communities	keystone species	resource partitioning
diversity	Muellerian mimicry	secondary succession
ecological development	mutualism	structure
ecological niche	natural selection	symbiosis
ecotone	parasites	territoriality
edge effect	patchiness	tolerance limits

BIOMES, LANDSCAPES, RESTORATION, AND MANAGEMENT

Note to Instructors about Biomes, Human Impact, and Aldo Leopold

Assigning reading from Aldo Leopold's *A Sand County Almanac* would be extremely effective in conjunction with the concepts in this chapter. The author draws heavily from much of Leopold's writings and it would be useful for students to read the book. The chapter is much more than a listing of the abiotic and biotic factors present in each biome. Instead, the biomes are presented in a way that human impact and restoration ecology are woven together to create an interesting and meaningful chapter.

Note to Instructors about Test Questions in Chapter 5

The test questions are in the order presented in the chapter and the students could memorize the order of the biomes rather than the distinguishing characteristics of each area. It may be useful to change the order of the questions when you design your exam.

Chapter Outline

Objectives
Integrity, Stability, and Beauty of the Land
Terrestrial Biomes
      Deserts
      Grasslands, Prairies, and Savannas
      Tundra
      Conifer Forests
      Broad-Leaved Deciduous and Evergreen Forests
      Tropical Moist Forests
      Tropical Seasonal Forests
Aquatic Ecosystems
      Freshwater and Saline Ecosystems
      Estuaries and Wetlands: Transitional Communities
      Shorelines and Barrier Islands
Human Disturbance
Landscape Ecology
      Patchiness and Heterogeneity
      Landscape Dynamics
Restoration Ecology
      Defining Some Terms
      Conflicting Views of Restoration
      Tools of Restoration
      Letting Nature Heal Itself
      Authenticity
      Back to What?
      Creating Artificial Ecosystems
Ecosystem Management

Case Study: Restoration of the Bermuda Cahow
Case Study: Yanesha Forestry in Peru

Objectives

After studying this chapter, students should be able to:

- recognize the characteristics of major aquatic and terrestrial biomes and understand the most important factors that determine the distribution of each type.
- describe ways in which humans disrupt or damage each of these ecosystem types.
- summarize the overall patterns of human disturbance of world biomes as well as some specific, important examples of losses obscured by broad aggregate categories.
- explain the principles and practices of landscape ecology and ecosystem management.
- evaluate the pros and cons of restoring, replacing, or substituting ecosystems and resources for those we have damaged.

Questions for Review

1. Who was Aldo Leopold and why is he considered important in the history of American conservation?

2. Throughout the central portion of North America is a large biome once dominated by grasses. Describe how physical conditions and other factors control this biome.

3. What is the taiga and where is it found? Why might logging in taiga be more disruptive than in southern coniferous forests?

4. Why are tropical moist forests often less suited for agriculture and human occupation than tropical deciduous forests?

5. Describe four different kinds of wetlands and explain why they are important sites of biodiversity and biological productivity.

6. Which major biomes have been most heavily disturbed by human activities?

7. Define a landscape. Describe the major ecological and cultural features of the landscape in which you live.

8. Define restoration, rehabilitation, remediation, reclamation, ecological re-creation, and mitigation. Give an example of each.

9. List and explain either the seven principles or the five goals of ecosystem management.

10. Explain some of the major criticisms of ecosystem management.

Questions for Critical Thinking

1. In which biome do you live? What physical and biological factors are most important in shaping your biological community? How do the present characteristics of your area differ from those 100 or 1000 years ago?

2. Could your biome be returned to something resembling its original condition? What tools (or principles) would you use to do so?

3. A beautiful stand of pine trees in a park in Connecticut was blown down by a windstorm and is now a fire hazard to nearby property as well as being an aesthetic mess. Some people argue that salvage loggers should clean out the area and replant pine trees. Others argue that it was a natural forest and should be left to natural forces. What do you think?

4. Historic records show that indigenous aboriginal people kept the forest described in question 3 as an open, park-like savanna by burning it regularly. Should prescribed fires be part of the restoration ecology plan?

5. Some environmentalists worry that the science of restoration ecology may give us the arrogant attitude that we can do anything we want now because we can repair the damage later. How would you respond to that concern?

6. What do you think Aldo Leopold meant by integrity, stability, and beauty of the land?

7. Disney World in Florida wants to expand onto a wetland. It has offered to buy and preserve a large nature preserve in a different area to make up for the wetland it is destroying. Is that reasonable? What conditions would make it reasonable or unreasonable?

8. Suppose further that the wetland being destroyed in question 7 and its replacement area both contain several endangered species (but different ones). How would you compare different species against each other? How many plant or insect species would one animal species be worth?

9. Explain why there might be differences in philosophy or worldview between preservationists and restorationists. Which approach do you prefer?

10. Authenticity is a contentious issue in restoration. Is it necessary, or even desirable, to try to create an exact replica of an original ecosystem? Could the changes that humans make be considered part of natural change?

Key Terms

barrier islands	fens	taiga
benthos	freshwater ecosystems	temperate rainforest
biomes	grasslands	thermocline
bogs	landscape ecology	timberline
boreal forest	marshes	tropical rainforests
cloud forests	mitigate	tropical seasonal forests
conifer	reclamation	tundra
coral reefs	re-creation	wetlands
deciduous	rehabilitation	
delta	remediation	
deserts	restoration	
ecosystem management	restoration ecology	
estuaries	swamps	

PART II
POPULATION, ECONOMICS, AND ENVIRONMENTAL HEALTH

POPULATION DYNAMICS

Note to Instructors about Wolves and Moose on Isle Royale

The relationship between wolves and moose on Isle Royale is an interesting case study in population dynamics and species interactions. This case offers an opportunity to discuss stochastic events, scientific uncertainty, and the ethics of intervention in natural systems because it is still not completely clear why the wolves decreased so drastically in numbers. Some questions for reflection include, but are not limited to: How disruptive is the process of studying the wolves? When should we intervene if the population seems headed for extinction? Would we be equally concerned if the animals in question were a less charismatic, endangered species?

Chapter Outline

Objectives
Wolves and Moose on Isle Royale
      Moose Population Growth and Decline
      Moose-Wolf Equilibrium?
      Wolves and Moose in Trouble
Dynamics of Population Growth
      Exponential Growth and Doubling Times
      Biotic Potential
      Population Oscillations and Irruptive Growth
      Growth to a Stable Population
      Chaotic and Catastrophic Population Dynamics
      Strategies of Population Growth
            Malthusian " Strategies"
            Logistic " Strategies"
Factors that Increase or Decrease Populations
      Natality, Fecundity, and Fertility
      Immigration
      Mortality and Survivorship
      Age Structure
      Emigration
Factors that Regulate Population Growth
      Density-Independent Factors
      Density-Dependent Factors
            Interspecific Interactions
            Intraspecific Interactions
            Stress and Crowding
Summary
Questions for Review
Questions for Critical Thinking
Key Terms
Additional Information on the Internet

What Do You Think? What Is Earth's Carrying Capacity for Humans

Objectives

After studying this chapter, students should be able to:

- appreciate the potential of exponential growth.
- draw a diagram of J and S curves and explain what they mean.
- explain who Thomas Malthus was and what he said about population growth.
- describe environmental resistance and discuss how it can lead to logistic or stable growth.
- define *fecundity, fertility, birth rates, life expectancy, death rates, and survivorship.*
- compare and contrast density-dependent and density-independent population processes.

Questions for Review

1. Why did moose populations grow so rapidly on Isle Royale in the 1920s?

2. What is the difference between exponential and arithmetic growth?

3. Given a growth rate of 3 percent per year, how long will it take for a population of 100,000 individuals to double? How long will it take to double when the population reaches 10 million?

4. What is environmental resistance? How does it affect populations?

5. What is the difference between fertility and fecundity?

6. Describe the four major types of survivorship patterns and explain what they show about the role of the species in an ecosystem.

7. What are the main interspecific population regulatory interactions? How do they work?

8. What are the suspected causes and effects of stress shock or stress-related disease?

Questions for Critical Thinking

1. Compare the advantages and disadvantages to a species that result from exponential or logistic growth. Why do you think moose have evolved to reproduce as rapidly as possible, while wolves appear to have intrinsic or social mechanisms to limit population growth?

2. We're not sure why wolf populations on Isle Royale declined in the 1990s. How would you design a study to examine the possible explanations offered in this chapter without compromising the wilderness nature of the park and its wildlife?

3. If wolves or moose die off in a national park due to natural causes, should we intervene or let nature take its course?

4. Are humans subject to environmental resistance in the same sense that other organisms are? How would you decide whether a particular factor that limits human population growth is ecological or social?

5. There obviously are vast differences in birth and death rates, survivorship, and life spans among species. There must be advantages and disadvantages in living longer or reproducing more quickly. Why hasn't evolution selected for the most advantageous combination of characteristics so that all organisms would be more or less alike?

6. Abiotic factors that influence population growth tend to be density independent, while biotic factors that regulate population growth tend to be density dependent. Explain.

7. Some people consider stress and crowding studies of laboratory animals highly applicable in understanding human behavior. Other people question the cross-species transferability of these results. What considerations would be important in interpreting these experiments?

8. What implications for human population control might we draw from our knowledge of basic biological population dynamics?

Key Terms

abiotic

arithmetic growth

biotic

biotic potential

carrying capacity

catastrophic system

chaotic systems

dieback

emigration

environmental resistance

exponential growth

fecundity

fertility

geometric growth

irruptive or Malthusian growth

J curve

life expectancy

life span

logistic growth

mortality

natality

overshoot

population crash

population explosion

population momentum

S curve

stress-related diseases

stress shock

survivorship

HUMAN POPULATIONS

Note to Instructors about Human Population Growth

In many ways, human population growth is the most important and most controversial topic in environmental science. The absence of any substantive discussion of population at the 1992 Rio Earth Summit along with the controversy around preparations of the 1994 Cairo Population Conference reflect some of the complexity and divisiveness of this issue. The cartoon in figure 7.15 expresses the view of many in developing nations about resource consumption levels in the richer countries of the world. Asking students to imagine themselves in the place of a person in the developing world facing questions about fertility control and ideal family size gives them an opportunity to practice the critical thinking skills of empathy and considering issues from more than one point of view. The concepts presented in *What Do you Think*? Looking for Bias in Graphs (p. 137) are very useful to empower students in interpreting graphs. Spending time on these skills is worthwhile, especially in light of critical thinking and evaluating information that is presented in an argument.

An excellent short videotape is Zero Population Growth's *World Population Growth*. The video illustrates the history of human population growth visually on a world map and is *very* effective in portraying the increase in population with the advent of sanitation and technology.

Chapter Outline

Objectives
The Saga of Easter Island
Population Growth
      Human Population History
Limits To Growth: Some Opposing Views
      Malthusian Checks on Population
      Malthus and Marx Today
      Can Technology Make the World More Habitable?
      Can More People Be Beneficial?
Human Demography
      How Many of Us Are There?
      Fertility and Birth Rates
      Mortality and Death Rates
      Population Growth Rates
      Life Span and Life Expectancy
      Living Longer: Demographic Implications
      Emigration and Immigration
Population Growth: Opposing Factors
      Pronatalist Pressures
      Birth Reduction Pressures
      Birth Dearth?
Demographic Transition
      Development and Population
      An Optimistic View
      A Pessimistic View
      A Social Justice View

What Do You Think? Looking for Bias in Graphs
Case Study: Family Planning in Thailand

Objectives

After studying this chapter, students should be able to:

- trace the history of human population growth.
- summarize Malthusian and Marxian theories of limits to growth as well as why technological optimists and supporters of social justice oppose these theories.
- explain the process of demographic transition and why it produces a temporary population surge.
- understand how changes in life expectancy, infant mortality, women's literacy, standards of living, and democracy affect population changes.
- evaluate pressures for and against family planning in traditional and modern societies.
- compare modern birth control methods and prepare a personal family planning agenda.

Questions for Review

1. At what point in history did the world population pass its *first* billion? What factors restricted population before that time, and what factors contributed to growth after that point?

2. How might growing populations be beneficial in solving development problems?

3. Why do some economists consider human resources more important than natural resources in determining the future of a country?

4. Where will most population growth occur in the next century? What conditions contribute to rapid population growth in some countries?

5. Define *crude birth rate, total fertility rate, crude death rate,* and *zero population growth.*

6. What is the difference between life expectancy and longevity?

7. What is a dependency ratio, and how might it affect the United States in the future?

8. What pressures or interests make people want to or not want to have babies?

9. Describe the conditions that lead to a demographic transition.

10. Describe the major choices in modern birth control.

Questions for Critical Thinking

1. What do you think is the optimum human population? The maximum human population? Are the numbers different? If so, why?

2. Some people argue that technology can provide solutions for environmental problems; others believe that a "technological fix" will make our problems worse. What personal experiences or worldviews do you think might underlie these positions?

3. Karl Marx called Thomas Malthus a "shameless sycophant of the ruling classes." Why would the landed gentry of the eighteenth century be concerned about population growth of the lower classes? Are there comparable class struggles today?

4. Try to imagine yourself in the position of a person your age in a Third World country. What family planning choices and pressures would you face? How would you choose among your options?

5. Some demographers claim that population growth has already begun to slow; others dispute this claim. How would you evaluate the competing claims of these two camps? Is this an issue of uncertain facts or differing beliefs? What sources of evidence would you accept as valid?

6. What role do race, ethnicity, and culture play in our immigration and population policies? How can we distinguish between prejudice and selfishness on one hand and valid concerns about limits to growth on the other?

Key Terms

birth control

crude birth rate

crude death rates

demographic transition

demography

dependency ratio

family planning

life expectancy

natural increase

neo-Malthusians

pronatalist pressures

social justice

total fertility rate

total growth rate

zero population growth (ZPG)

ECOLOGICAL ECONOMICS

Note to Instructors about Environmental Careers and Ecological Economics

The topics of environmental jobs and green businesses are introduced in this chapter but you have probably noticed the Environmental Profiles presented earlier (before and after chapter 3) and throughout the rest of the text (after chapter 8, for example). The authors based the content of these profiles on interviews with the people and on a publication by The Environmental Careers Organization, *Environmental Studies: 2000*. This publication provides an overview of undergraduate, interdisciplinary environmental programs and the careers of graduates from the programs. Many insights as to what employers are looking for when they hire someone are presented in the Environmental Careers Organization publication. When the authors of this text highlight critical thinking, communication, and other skills necessary for an environmental career in the Environmental Profiles it is based on that individual's experience, but also on what potential employers communicated in the publication. The take home message for students is to keep in mind the skills that individuals in the profiles highlight as important and work on refining them for success in the job market. Chapter 25 also highlights careers and green organizations.

Chapter Outline

Objectives
Creating Another Earth
      Origins of Our Economic Worldviews
Classical Economics
      Neoclassical Economics
      Ecological Economics
Resources, Capital, and Reserves
      Resource Types
      Economic Resource Categories
      Communal Property Resources
Population, Technology, and Scarcity
      Market Efficiencies and Technological Development
      Increasing Environmental Carrying Capacity
      Economic Models
      Why Not Conserve Resources?
Natural Resource Accounting
      Gross National Product
      Alternatives to GNP
      Measuring Nonmarket Values
      Cost/Benefit Ratios
      Intergenerational Justice and Discount Rates
      Internal and External Costs
Trade, Development, and Jobs
      International Trade
      International Development
      Green Business
      Jobs and the Environment

Sustainability: The Challenge
Summary
Questions for Review
Questions for Critical Thinking
Key Terms
Additional Information on the Internet

What Do You Think? Market-Based Incentives for Environmental Protection
Case Study: Microlending at the Grammeen Bank

Objectives

After studying this chapter, students should be able to:

- explain the difference between neoclassical and ecological economics and how each discipline views ecological processes and natural resources.
- distinguish between different types and categories of resources.
- understand how resource supply and demand affect price and technological progress.
- develop a position on limits to growth and economic carrying capacity of our environment
- discuss internal and external costs, market approaches to pollution control, and cost/benefit ratios.
- define GNP and explain some alternative ways to measure values of natural resources and real social progress.
- analyze the role of business and some possible strategies for achieving future sustainability.

Questions for Review

1. Define economics and distinguish between classical, neoclassical, and ecological economics.

2. Define resources and give some examples of renewable, nonrenewable, and intangible resources.

3. List four economic categories of resources and describe the differences among them.

4. Describe the relationship between supply and demand.

5. What causes diminishing returns in natural resource use? How does population growth affect this phenomenon?

6. Describe how cost/benefit ratios are determined and how they are used in natural resource management.

7. Explain how scarcity and technological progress can extend resource availability and extend the carrying capacity of the environment.

8. Describe how GNP is calculated and explain why this may fail to adequately measure human welfare and environmental quality. Discuss some alternative measures of national progress.

9. Why does the marketplace sometimes fail to optimally allocate natural resource values?

10. List some of the characteristics of a sustainable economic system.

Questions for Critical Thinking

1. If you could retroactively stabilize economic growth or population growth at some point in the past, when would you choose? What assumptions or values shape your choice?

2. When the ecologist warns that we are using up irreplaceable natural resources and the economist rejoins that ingenuity and enterprise will find substitutes for most resources, are they talking about the same things? What underlying premises and definitions shape their arguments?

3. How can intangible resources be infinite and exhaustible at the same time? Isn't this a contradiction in terms? Can you find other similar paradoxes in this chapter?

4. What is the difference between hypothetical and unconceived (or unknown-unknown) resources? How can we plan for resources that we haven't even thought of yet? Are there costs in assuming that there are no unknown-unknowns?

5. What would be the effect on the developing countries of the world if we were to change to a steady-state economic system? How could we achieve a just distribution of resource benefits while still protecting environmental quality and future resource use?

6. Resource use policies bring up questions of intergenerational justice. Suppose you were asked: "What has posterity ever done for me?" How would you answer?

7. If you were doing a cost/benefit study, how would you assign a value to the opportunity for good health or the existence of rare and endangered species in faraway places? Is there a danger or cost in simply saying some things are immeasurable and priceless and therefore off limits to discussion?

8. Why not conserve resources to the maximum extent possible? Discuss the costs and benefits of resource investment versus conservation.

9. Is it right for business to consider ethics and the welfare of future generations? Why or why not?

10. What does it really mean to say that sustainable development meets the needs of the present without compromising the ability of future generations to meet their own needs? Is this possible? What is meant here by needs?

Key Terms

capital

classical economics

communal resource management

cost/benefit analysis

demand

discount rates

ecological economics

external costs

gross national product (GNP)

intangible resources

internal costs

internalizing costs

known resources

marginal costs

market equilibrium

neoclassical economics

nonrenewable resources

pollution charges

price elasticity

proven resources

open access system

renewable resources

resource

steady-state economy

supply

sustainable development

tragedy of the commons

undiscovered resources

ENVIRONMENTAL HEALTH AND TOXICOLOGY

Note to Instructors about Facilitating Meaningful Learning and Relative Risks

In order to facilitate meaningful learning and connectedness, it is useful for students to apply concepts from previous chapters to examples presented later. For example, environmental racism and justice can be highlighted in the case of the Bhopal accident. Would the accident have happened in the United States or another more-developed country? Is this a case of toxic colonialism?

For many students a concern about the health effects of pollution are a major reason for an interest in the environment. It is valuable for students from affluent communities to understand that common infectious diseases remain a terrible threat for most people in the world. The concepts of relative risk and acceptable risks are also difficult for many students who tend to view everything as either black or white. As a society we tend to focus our attention and concerns on relatively low- and medium-risk problems while more systemic high-risk problems such as global climate change, species extinction, and habitat destruction are not rated as high in the public's perception of risks. It might be useful to ask the students to rate the risks based on their perceptions and discuss their results in the context of the EPA's priority list (p. 200, table 9.7). The example of Thalidomide treatment in Brazil might be a good lead into a discussion of risks assessment and dangers to future generations.

Chapter Outline

Objectives
Poisoning Bhopal
Types of Environmental Health Hazards
      Infectious Organisms
      Toxic Chemicals
      Natural and Synthetic Toxins
      Physical Agents, Trauma, and Stress
      Diet
Movement, Distribution, and Fate of Toxins
      Solubility
      Bioaccumulation and Biomagnification
      Persistence
      Chemical Interactions
Mechanisms for Minimizing Toxic Effects
      Metabolic Degradation and Excretion
      Repair Mechanisms
Measuring Toxicity
      Animal Testing
      Toxicity Ratings
      Acute Versus Chronic Doses and Effects
      Detection Limits
Risk Assessment and Acceptance
      Assessing Risk
      Accepting Risks
Establishing Public Policy
Summary

In Depth: Iringa Nutrition Program
What Do You Think? Electromagnetic Fields and Your Health

Objectives

After studying this chapter, students should be able to:

- define *health* and *disease* in terms of some major environmental factors that affect humans.
- identify some major infectious organisms and hazardous agents that cause environmental diseases.
- distinguish between toxic and hazardous chemicals and between chronic and acute exposures and responses.
- compare the relative toxicity of some natural and synthetic compounds as well as report on how such ratings are determined and what they mean.
- evaluate the major environmental risk we face and how risk assessment and risk acceptability are determined.

Questions for Review

1. What is the difference between toxic and hazardous? Give some examples of materials in each category.

2. What are some of the most serious infectious diseases in the world? How are they transmitted?

3. How do stress, diet, and life style affect environmental health? What diseases are most clearly related to these factors?

4. How do the physical and chemical characteristics of materials affect their movement, persistence, distribution, and fate in the environment?

5. Define LD50. Why is it more accurate than simply reporting toxic dose?

6. What is the difference between acute and chronic toxicity?

7. Define *carcinogenic*, *mutagenic*, *teratogenic*, and *neurotoxic*.

8. What are irritants, sensitizers, allergens, caustics, acids, and fibrotic agents?

9. How do organisms reduce or avoid the damaging effects of environmental hazards?

10. What are the relative risks of smoking, driving a car, and drinking water with the maximum permissible levels of trichloroethylene? Are these relatively equal risks?

Questions for Critical Thinking

1. What consequences (positive or negative) do you think might result from defining health as a state of complete physical, mental, and social well-being? Who might favor or oppose such a definition?

2. How would you feel or act if your child were dying of diarrhea? Why do we spend more money on heart or cancer research than on childhood illnesses?

3. Some people seem to have a poison paranoia about synthetic chemicals. Why do we tend to assume that natural chemicals are benign while industrial chemicals are evil?

4. Analyze the claim that we are exposed to thousands of times more natural carcinogens in our diet than industrial ones. Is this a good reason to ignore pollution?

5. Describe what is shown in figure 9.7. What does it mean to show 95 percent confidence intervals? Could you conclude from these data that it is safer to eat more fat rather than less?

6. What are the premises in the discussion of assessing risk? Could conflicting conclusions be drawn from the facts presented in this section? What is your perception of risk from your environment?

7. Table 9.6 equates activities such as smoking 1.4 cigarettes, having one chest X ray, and riding ten miles on a bicycle. How was this equation derived? Do you agree with it? Are there items on this list that require further clarification?

8. Who were the stakeholders in the saccharine controversy, and what were their interests or biases? Was Congress justified in refusing to ban saccharine? Should soft drink cans have a warning label similar to those on cigarettes?

9. Should pollution levels be set to protect the average person in the population or the most sensitive? Why not have zero exposure to all hazards?

10. What level of risk is acceptable to you? Are there some things for which you would accept more risk than others?

Key Terms

acute effects

allergens

antigens

asphyxiants

bioaccumulation

biomagnification

cancer

carcinogens

chronic effects

disease

fetal alcohol syndrome

hazardous

health

irritants

LD50

morbidity

mutagens

neurotoxins

respiratory fibrotic agents

risk

stress

teratogens

toxins

trauma

Note to Instructors about Food, Hunger, Nutrition, and Critical Thinking

The politics behind the recommendations of the new daily minimum dietary recommendation (food pyramid) is an interesting topic for discussion and can help reinforce the idea that we need to be able to think critically. What role did the meat and dairy industry play in establishing the four basic food groups 40 years ago? What health effects and environmental consequences might those recommendations have had? Despite ominous predictions 30 years ago of impending food crises and mass starvation, food production in most countries has kept up with or surpassed population growth. Will these trends continue? This is a good topic for discussion of setting policy in the absence of certainty.

The authors communicate that they had some qualms about whether the image in figure 10.19 is a fair representation of food aid by the richer nations. A good short writing assignment might be to ask students to create their own caption for this photograph or to write a short scenario describing what they think is happening. What is the woman thinking? What are the interests and motives of the white man? What happened after the photo was taken? What is the role of women in feeding families and how does that relate to aid?

Chapter Outline

Objectives
Famine in China
Human Nutrition
    Energy Needs
    Nutritional Needs
      Proteins
      Carbohydrates
      Lipids and Oils
      Minerals
      Vitamins
    Eating a Balanced Diet
World Food Resources
    Major Crops
    Meat and Milk
    Croplands
    Increasing Food Production
    Green Revolution
    New Food Sources
    Blue Revolution
Agricultural Economics
    Food Surpluses, Subsidies, and Agricultural Aid
    International Food Trade
World Hunger
    Famines
    Chronic Food Shortages
    How Many People Can the World Feed?

What Do You Think? Collapse of the Canadian Cod Fishery

Objectives

After studying this chapter, students should be able to:

- explain the major human nutritional requirements as well as sources for meeting those needs and the consequences of not doing so.
- describe the major crops on which humans depend and suggest some potential new crops for the future.
- sketch the sources of recent food supply increases and prospects for future growth of food production.
- differentiate between famine and chronic malnutrition and understand the sources and distribution of world hunger.
- analyze the role of cash crops and food trade policies in world hunger
- suggest some solutions to the problems of malnutrition and world hunger.

Questions for Review

1. How many people in the world are chronically undernourished and how many die each year from starvation and nutritionally related diseases?

2. How many calories does the average person need per day to maintain a healthy, active life?

3. What are proteins, vitamins, lipids, and minerals, and why do we need them in our diet?

4. What are the three major crops of the world? List some alternative crops that might help feed the world.

5. What do we mean by green and blue revolutions?

6. List some potential benefits and dilemmas associated with biotechnology and genetic engineering.

7. Describe some problems associated with fish farming and fish ranching.

8. Which countries receive the greatest total amounts and the highest per capita food aid? What does this distribution reveal about food aid programs?

9. What are cash crops and how do they affect local and international food supplies?

10. How are interfamily relationships important in food security?

Questions for Critical Thinking

1. Why has agricultural research paid so little attention to tropical crops like yams and cassava? How would you decide whether our priorities are fair or not?

2. What worldviews make people believe that there are already too many people to be fed or that technological progress may allow us to feed double or triple current populations? Which side of this argument do you support?

3. Suppose that a seafood company wants to start a fish farming operation in a lake near your home. What regulations or safeguards would you want to see imposed on its operation? How would you weigh the possible costs and benefits of this operation?

4. Why do we have agricultural surpluses in the United States and Canada? Delve more deeply into this issue than the simple fact that we grow more food than we eat. Think about some underlying social, political, economic, and environmental implications of surpluses.

5. Some critics claim that international food aid creates more problems than it solves. List some arguments for and against this proposition.

6. Should poor countries like Guatemala grow cash crops? What are some advantages and disadvantages of doing so?

7. Debate the claim that famines are caused more by human actions (or inactions) than by environmental forces. What is the critical element or evidence in this debate?

8. How many people do you believe the world could feed or should feed? What changes might be necessary to reach an ideal food per person ratio?

Key Terms

anemia

blue revolution

cash crops

chronic food shortages

famines

food aid

food security

gene banks

green revolution

hypothyroidism

kwashiorkor

malnourishment

marasmus

pellagra

undernourishment

vitamins

SOIL RESOURCES AND SUSTAINABLE AGRICULTURE

Note to Instructors about Sustainable Agriculture

Tracing the origins of the food served in college dining rooms and trying to find local sources for the same items might be a good project for students who want a hands-on learning experience. Many students these days are so highly urbanized that they have little knowledge of where their food comes from and how it is grown and prepared for market. During the dust bowl days of the 1930s, soil conservation was one of the most important and most popular causes of environmental concern in the United States. Modern students are so removed from the farm, however, that they may not appreciate the significance of this topic. The introduction to John Steinbeck's *The Grapes of Wrath* makes a powerful reading to give students a taste of what the dust bowl was like. The December 1995 issue (Vol. 188, No. 6) of *National Geographic* has an excellent article on sustainable agriculture (A Farming Revolution, pp. 61 - 89).

Chapter Outline

Objectives
Dust Bowl Days
What Is Soil?
      A Renewable Resource
      Soil Composition
      Soil Organisms
      Soil Profiles
      Soil Types
Ways We Use and Abuse Soil
      Land Resources
      Land Degradation
      Erosion: The Nature of the Problem
      Mechanisms of Erosion
      Erosion in the United States and Canada
      Erosion in Other Countries
Other Agricultural Resources
      Water
      Fertilizer
      Climate
      Energy
      Crop Diversity
Toward a Just and Sustainable Agriculture
      Soil Conservation
            Managing Topography
            Providing Ground Cover
            Using Reduced Tillage Systems
      Low-Input Sustainable Agriculture
      Public Policies to Encourage Fair and Ecologically Sound Farming Systems
Summary
Questions for Review

Questions for Critical Thinking
Key Terms
Additional Information on the Internet

Case Study: Organic Farming in Cuba
What Do You Think? Sustainability: What Does It Mean?

Objectives

After studying this chapter, students should be able to:

- describe soil composition and the role of soil particles, soil organisms, and soil chemistry in soil formation and productivity.
- understand soil types and soil profiles and what they mean for agriculture.
- differentiate between the causes and consequences of land degradation including soil erosion, nutrient depletion, waterlogging, salinization, and other abuses that decrease soil fertility and crop production.
- analyze the agricultural inputs needed for sustained food production and tell how these resources may limit human activities.
- evaluate the principles of just and sustainable agriculture.
- explain what each of us can do to ensure a safe, secure food supply.

Questions for Review

1. What is the composition of soil? What is humus? Why are soil organisms so important?

2. Describe the differences between light, moderate, severe, and extreme soil degradation.

3. What are four kinds of erosion? Is erosion ever beneficial? Why is it a problem?

4. What are some possible effects of over irrigation?

5. What can farmers do to increase agricultural production without increasing land use?

6. What is the estimated potential for increasing world food supply by increasing fertilizer use in low-production countries?

7. What is sustainable agriculture?

8. What is a perennial species? Why is coffee a good crop for rugged and hilly country?

9. What is genetic engineering, or biotechnology, and how might it help or hurt agriculture?

Questions for Critical Thinking

1. Should farmers be forced to use ecologically sound techniques that serve farmers' best interests in the long run, regardless of short-term consequences? How could we mitigate hardships brought about by such policies?

2. In a crisis, when small farms are in danger of being lost, should preserving the soil be the farmer's first priority?

3. Should we encourage (and subsidize) the family farm? What are the advantages and disadvantages (economic and ecological) of the small farm and the corporate farm?

4. How many people do you think the world could support? What do you think would be the ideal number?

5. Should we try to increase food production on existing farmland, or should we sacrifice other lands to increase farming areas?

6. Some rice paddies in Southeast Asia have been cultivated continuously for thousands of years without losing fertility. Could we, and should we, adapt these techniques to our own country?

7. Should we continue our current rate of pesticide use? What are the advantages and disadvantages of continuing such use?

Key Terms

bedrock

contour plowing

cover crops

gully erosion

humus

mulch

parent material

perennial species

reduced tillage systems

regenerative farming

rill erosion

salinization

sheet erosion

soil

soil horizons

streambank erosion

strip-farming

subsoil

sustainable agriculture

terracing

tied ridges

topsoil

waterlogging

zone of leaching

Note to Instructors about Reinforcing Concepts and Pest Control

The issues in this chapter can be used to serve as topics to reinforce concepts presented in earlier chapters. For example, a discussion of the "strategies" of pest species ties in with chapter 6 (Population Dynamics) and examining the risks of pesticide use is clearly associated with environmental toxicology (chapter 9) and sustainable agriculture (chapter 11). Since many students tend to compartmentalize information and do not make the necessary links between concepts it is important to *overtly emphasize* these relationships.

There is great public concern about pesticide residues in food and water. For many students, pesticide issues and threats to endangered species are the most important environmental issues. It is important for the public to achieve a better understanding of the risks and benefits associated with pesticide use so they can make informed decisions about their own behaviors. As mentioned previously (chapter 11), the December 1995 issue (Vol. 188, No. 6) of *National Geographic* has an excellent article on sustainable agriculture (A Farming Revolution, pp. 61 - 89) and has examples of IPM and behavioral changes in pesticide use.

Chapter Outline

Objectives
DDT and Fragile Eggshells
What are Pests and Pesticides?
A Brief History of Pest Control
      Early Pest Controls
      Synthetic Chemical Pesticides
Pesticide Uses and Types
      Pesticide Use in the United States and Canada
      Pesticide Types
Pesticide Benefits
      Disease Control
      Crop Protection
Pesticide Problems
      Effects on Nontarget Species
      Pesticide Resistance and Pest Resurgence
      Creation of New Pests
      Persistence and Mobility in the Environment
      Human Health Problems
Alternatives to Current Pesticide Uses
      Behavioral Changes
      Biological Controls
      Integrated Pest Management
Reducing Pesticide Exposure
      Regulating Pesticides
      Personal Safety
Summary

Case Study: Regenerative Agriculture in Iowa
What Do You Think? Environmental Estrogens

Objectives

After studying this chapter, students should be able to:

- define the major types of pesticides and describe the pests they are meant to control.
- outline the history of pest control, including the changes in pesticides that have occurred in the last half of this century.
- appreciate the benefits of pest control.
- relate some of the problems of pesticide use.
- explain some alternative methods of pest control.
- discuss pesticide regulation and the acceptability of small amounts of weak carcinogens in our diets.

Questions for Review

1. What is a pest and what are pesticides? What is the difference between a biocide, an herbicide, an insecticide, and a fungicide.

2. How much pesticide is used worldwide and in your country? In your country, which of the general categories of use and which type accounts for the greatest use? Has use been increasing or decreasing in recent years?

3. What is DDT and why was it considered a "magic bullet"? What are its benefits and disadvantages?

4. Describe fumigants, botanicals, chlorinated hydrocarbons, organophosphates, carbamates, and microbial pesticides.

5. Explain why pests often resurface or rebound after treatment with pesticides and how they become pesticide resistant. What is a pesticide treadmill and pesticide rain?

6. Identify three major categories of alternatives to synthetic pesticides and describe briefly how each one works.

7. How did Australia fight prickly pear cactus? How did Florida eradicate screw worms?

8. What is the Delaney Clause, and why is it controversial?

9. List nine things you could do to reduce pesticide use in your home.

10. List eight things you could do to reduce your dietary exposure to pesticides.

Questions for Critical Thinking

1. In retrospect, do you think Paul Muller should have received a Nobel Prize for discovering the insecticidal properties of DDT?

2. If you were a public health official in a country in which malaria, filariases, or onchoceriasis were rampant, would you spray DDT to eradicate vector organisms? Would you spray it in your own house?

3. Pesticide rain, pesticide treadmill, and Medfly war are all highly emotional terms. Why would some people choose to use or not to use these terms? Can you suggest alternative terms for the same phenomena that convey different values?

39

4. Many farm workers who suffer from pesticide poisoning are migrants or minorities. Is this evidence of environmental racism? What evidence would you look for to determine whether environmental justice is being served?

5. Suppose that a developing country believes that it needs a pesticide banned in the United States or Canada to feed or protect the health of its people. Are we right to refuse to sell that pesticide?

6. How much extra would you pay for organically-grown food? How would you define organic in this context?

7. If alternative pest control methods are so effective and so much safer, why aren't farmers and consumers adopting them more rapidly?

8. If you were a member of Congress, would you vote to repeal the Delaney Clause to the FFDCA? Why or why not?

9. What would you personally consider a "negligible" risk? Would you eat grapes if you knew they had a measurable amount of Propargite? How small would the amount have to be?

10. Why is California reluctant to admit that it might have a resident population of Medflies? How might its control program change if it were to do so?

Key Terms

biocide

biological controls

biological pests

Delaney Clause

economic thresholds

fungicides

herbicides

insecticides

integrated pest management (IPM)

pesticide

pesticide rain

pesticide treadmill

pest resurgence

Note to Instructors about Critical Thinking and the Endangered Species Act

The Case Study on Baby Seals (p. 280) is very good for small group discussion. This is a highly emotional subject and it illustrates different viewpoints in a very effective manner. Similarly, the What Do You Think on the Endangered Species Act (ESA) has high potential for class discussion. This reading reinforces critical thinking and evaluating what one reads. It may be useful to gather (or, even better, have the students gather) other articles based on the ESA and analyze them for bias and anecdotes. There are plenty of articles in popular magazines and requiring the students to present the analysis can be an effective way to help them improve their critical thinking skills.

Some students find this subject depressing and they can feel overwhelmed by the topic. Make sure that the recovery programs and other efforts are highlighted to try to avoid overly apathetic attitudes. As mentioned in the notes of chapter 4, a good, ten-minute introductory videotape for biodiversity is *Diversity Endangered* (Smithsonian Institution Traveling Exhibition Service, Washington, DC 20560; Telephone: 202-357-3168). An excellent book on biodiversity is *The Diversity of Life* by E. O. Wilson, 1992, W. W. Norton and Company. ISBN # 0-393-96457-4. This book is enjoyable and I encourage anyone who wants to learn more about biodiversity to read this book.

Chapter Outline

Objectives
Killing Lake Victoria
Biodiversity and the Species Concept
  What Is Biodiversity?
  What Are Species?
  How Many Species Are There?
How Do We Benefit from Biodiversity?
  Food
  Drugs and Medicines
  Ecological Benefits
  Aesthetic and Cultural Benefits
What Threatens Biodiversity?
  Natural Causes of Extinction
  Human-Caused Reductions in Biodiversity
    Habitat Destruction
    Hunting and Fishing
    Commercial Products and Live Specimens
    Predator and Pest Control
    Exotic Species Introductions
    Diseases
    Pollution
    Genetic Assimilation
Endangered Species Management and Biodiversity Protection
  Hunting and Fishing Laws
  The Endangered Species Act
  Recovery Plans

Case Study: Killing Baby Seals or Harvesting Furbearers?
What Do You Think? Economic Impacts of the Endangered Species Act

Objectives

After studying this chapter, students should be able to:

- define biodiversity and species.
- report on the total number and relative distribution of living species on the earth.
- summarize some of the benefits we derive from biodiversity.
- describe the ways humans cause biodiversity losses.
- evaluate the effectiveness of the Endangered Species Act and CITES in protecting endangered species.
- understand how gap analysis, ecosystem management, and captive breeding can contribute to preserving biological resources.
- propose ways we could protect endangered habitats and communities through large-scale, long range, comprehensive planning.

Questions for Review

1. What is the range of estimates of the total number of species on the earth? Why is the range so great?

2. What group of organisms has the largest number of species?

3. Define *extinction.* What is the natural rate of extinction in an undisturbed ecosystem?

4. What are rosy periwinkles and what products do we derive from them?

5. Describe some foods we obtain from wild plant species.

6. List three categories of damage to biological resources caused by humans.

7. What is the current rate of extinction and how does this compare to historic rates?

8. Compare the scope and effects of the Endangered Species Act and CITES.

9. Describe ten ways that humans directly or indirectly cause biological losses.

10. What is gap analysis, and how is it related to ecosystem management and design of nature preserves?

Questions for Critical Thinking

1. One reviewer said that this chapter is the most biased in this book. Do you agree? How much moral outrage is appropriate in an issue such as this? Does emotion interfere with rational analysis or effective communication? What is the proper balance between emotion and objectivity in a subject such as this?

2. Many ecologists would like to move away from protecting individual endangered species to concentrate on protecting whole communities or ecosystems. Others fear that the public will only respond to and support glamorous "flagship" species such as gorillas, tigers, or otters. If you were designing a conservation strategy, where would you put your emphasis?

3. Put yourself in the place of a Canadian fishing industry worker. If you continue to catch cod and haddock the species will quickly become economically extinct if not completely exterminated. On the other hand, there are few jobs in your village and the dole will barely keep you alive. What would you do?

4. Only a few hundred grizzly bears remain in the contiguous United States, but populations are healthy in Canada and Alaska. Should we spend millions of dollars for grizzly recovery and management programs in Yellowstone National Park and adjacent wilderness areas?

5. How could people have believed a century ago that nature is so vast and fertile that human actions could never have a lasting impact on wildlife populations? Are there similar examples of denial or misjudgment occurring now?

6. In the past, mass extinction has allowed for new growth, including the evolution of our own species. Should we assume that another mass extinction would be a bad thing? Could it possibly be beneficial to us? To the world?

7. Some captive breeding programs are so successful that they often produce surplus animals that cannot be released into the wild because no native habitat remains. Plans to euthanize surplus animals raise storms of protests from animal lovers. What would you do if you were in charge of the zoo?

8. Debate with a friend or classmate the ethics of keeping animals captive in a zoo. After exploring the subject from one side, debate the issue from the opposite perspective. What do you learn from this exercise?

9. The United States and Russia have the last known remaining stocks of the smallpox virus. Should they be destroyed? Will this diminish biological diversity?

Key Terms

biodiversity

endangered species

existence value

extinction

gap analysis

genetic assimilation

species recovery plan

threatened species

vulnerable species

14
LAND USE: FORESTS AND RANGELANDS

Note to Instructors about Land Use

This chapter has the potential of pulling together many issues from previous chapters. Biodiversity, human populations, sustainable agriculture, ecosystems, and biomes are referred to, and can help students understand why they need to know the basics to understand environmental issues. Your students might be interested to know that when Frank and Deborah Popper toured the western states to lecture about their ideas they met with such heated opposition and stirred up such violent emotions that they had to be escorted by an armed guard through some communities. This would be a good topic for role playing or case decision modeling. Students could represent the positions of Native Americans, ranchers, wildlife managers, small town business people, and other stakeholders in this controversy as they work out a management plan for the great plains. This would facilitate their understanding of the views and experiences for each group. An understanding of the different viewpoints can help students become better decision-makers and problem-solvers. What is a fair and just settlement for all the interests involved?

Chapter Outline

Objectives
The Buffalo Commons
World Land Uses
World Forests
      Forest Distribution
      Forest Products
      Forest Management
Tropical Forests
      Diminishing Forests
      Swidden Agriculture
      Logging and Land Invasions
      Forest Protection
      Debt-for-Nature Swaps
Temperate Forests
      Ancient Forests of the Pacific Northwest
      Wilderness and Wildlife Protection
      Harvest Methods
      Below-Cost and Salvage Sales
      Fire Management
Rangelands
      Range Management
      Overgrazing and Land Degradation
      Forage Conversion by Domestic Animals
      Harvesting Wild Animals
      Rangelands in the United States
          State of the Range
          Grazing Fees

Case Study: Forestry for the Seventh Generation
What Do You Think? Regulations and Property Rights

Objectives

After studying this chapter, students should be able to:

- discuss the major world land uses and ways human activities impact these areas.
- list some forest types and the products we derive from them.
- report on how and why tropical forests are being disrupted as well as how they might be better used.
- understand the major issues concerning forests in more highly developed countries such as the Untied States and Canada.
- be aware of the extent, location, and state of grazing lands around the world.
- describe how overgrazing causes desertification of rangelands.
- evaluate land ownership patterns and explain why land reform and recognition of indigenous rights are essential for social justice as well as for environmental protection.

Questions for Review

1. Which type of land use occupies the greatest land area?

2. List some products that we derive from forests.

3. What are the advantages and disadvantages of monoculture agroforestry?

4. Describe milpa (or swidden) agriculture. Why are these techniques better for fragile rainforest ecosystems than other types of agriculture?

5. What are some results of deforestation?

6. What are clear-cutting and below-cost timber sales, and why are they controversial?

7. How does overgrazing encourage undesirable forage species to flourish?

8. Why can grazing animals generate food on land that would otherwise be unusable?

9. What is the relationship between fair land distribution and appropriate land use?

10. Give some examples of recognition of indigenous land titles.

Questions for Critical Thinking

1. Some forest and rangeland would be suitable as cropland. Do you think it should be converted? Why or why not?

2. What could we do to reduce or redirect the demand for wood products?

3. Brazil needs cash to pay increasing foreign debts and to fund needed economic growth. Why shouldn't it harvest its forests and mineral resources to gain the foreign currency it wants and needs? If we want Brazil to save its forests, what can or should we do to encourage conservation?

4. Thousand of landless peasants are mining gold or cutting trees to create farms in officially protected Brazilian rainforests. What might the government do to stop these practices?

5. What lessons do you think milpa (or swidden) agriculture has to offer large-scale commercial farming?

6. The US government has kept timber sale prices and grazing leases low to maintain low prices of lumber and meat for consumers and to help support rural communities and traditional ways of life. How would you weigh those human interests against the ecological values of forests and rangelands?

7. Suppose that you live in an area of the High Plains that is proposed for return to native prairie or that you are a logger in the Pacific Northwest whose job is threatened by a diminishing supply of old-growth timber. How would you feel about the changes discussed in this chapter?

8. Native Americans often were cheated out of their land or paid ridiculously low prices for it in the past. Present owners, however, may not have been a part of earlier land deals and may have invested a great deal subsequently to improve the land. What would be a fair and reasonable settlement now of these competing land claims?

9. There is considerable uncertainty about the extent of desertification of grazing lands or destruction of tropical rainforests. Put yourself in the place of a decision-maker evaluating this data. What evidence would you want to see or how would you appraise conflicting evidence?

Key Terms

clear-cut

closed canopy

debt-for-nature swaps

desertification

ecosystem restoration

feral

forest management

fuelwood

industrial timber

land reform

milpa agriculture

mixed perennial polyculture

monoculture agroforestry

open canopy

open range

pasture

selective cutting

swidden agriculture

woodland

Note to Instructors about Class Activities

The Case Study (p. 323) in this chapter would be especially useful to start a discussion on the ethical considerations of emotions and empathy in park management. Ethical consideration #2 is an especially good question to get students thinking. This would be an excellent small group discussion activity. The *What Do You Think?* (p. 328) is a great exercise for students to continue developing their critical thinking skills. Having the students work independently and then come together in small groups to discuss their answers to the questions and added questions would be effective.

Chapter Outline

Objectives
Ecotourism on the Roof of the World
Parks and Nature Preserves
       Park Origins and History
       North American Parks
           Existing Systems
           Park Problems
           Wildlife
           New Directions
           New Parks
       World Parks and Preserves
           Protecting Natural Heritage
           Size and Design of Nature Preserves
           Conservation and Economic Development
           Indigenous Communities and Biosphere Reserves
Wilderness Areas
Wildlife Refuges
       Refuge Management
       International Wildlife Preserves
Wetlands, Floodplains, and Coastal Regions
       Wetland Values
       Wetland Destruction
       Floods and Flood Control
       Beaches, Barrier Islands, and Estuaries
Summary
Questions for Review
Questions for Critical Thinking
Key Terms
Additional Information on the Internet

Case Study: Donkeys in the Virgin Islands
What Do You Think? Nature Preservation: How Much is Enough?
In Depth: Zimbabwe's CAMPFIRE Program

Objectives

After studying this chapter, students should be able to:

- understand the origins and current problems of national parks in America and other countries.
- recount some of the current problems in national parks in the United States and elsewhere in the world.
- evaluate the tension between conservation and economic development and how the Man and Biosphere program and "debt-for-nature" swaps address this tension.
- explain the need for, and problems with, wildlife refuges and wilderness areas in the United States.
- demonstrate why wetlands are valuable ecologically and culturally and why they are currently threatened worldwide.
- report on current management policies and problems concerning floodplains, coastlines, and barrier islands.

Questions for Review

1. Why is Yosemite called the first park to preserve wilderness while Yellowstone is the first national park?
2. List some problems and threats from within and outside our national parks.
3. Why is the number of elk in Yellowstone and the Grand Tetons a controversial issue?
4. Describe the IUCN categories of protected areas and the amount of human impact or intervention allowed in each. Can you name some parks or preserves in each category?
5. Which biomes or landscape types are best represented among world protected areas and which are least represented?
6. List the three main points in the IUCN World Conservation Strategy and six steps in the action plan to meet these goals.
7. Draw a diagram of an ideal MAB reserve. What activities would be allowed in each zone?
8. What is the legal definition of wilderness in the United States?
9. What role did Teddy Roosevelt and his cousin Franklin play in establishing wildlife refuges?
10. Describe some ecological values of wetlands and how they are threatened by human activities.

Questions for Critical Thinking

1. Is "contrived" naturalness a desirable feature in parks and nature preserves? How much human intervention do you think is acceptable in trying to make nature more beautiful, safe, comfortable, or attractive to human visitors? Think of some specific examples that you would or would not accept.
2. Suppose you were superintendent of Yellowstone National Park. How would you determine the carrying capacity of the park for elk? How would you weigh having more elk or more ground squirrels? If there are too many elk, how would you thin the herd?
3. Suppose that as park manager you know that building tourist facilities brings in needed funds to protect nature at the same time that more tourists destroy the natural values you want to protect. How do you balance competing interests?
4. Why do you suppose that dry tropical forests and tundra are well represented in nature preserves, whereas grasslands are rarely protected? Consider social, cultural, and economic as well as biogeographical reasons in your answer.
5. Suppose that preserving healthy populations of grizzly bears and wolves requires that we set aside some large fraction of Yellowstone Park as a zone into which no humans will ever again be

allowed to enter for any reason. Would you support protecting bears even if no one ever sees them or could even be sure that they still existed?

6. Suppose that you had trespassed into the bear sanctuary and were attacked by a bear. Should the rangers shoot the bear or let it eat you?

7. Are there any conditions under which you would permit oil drilling in the Arctic National Wildlife Refuge?

8. People have built homes and businesses on flood plains, beaches, or barrier islands under the assumption that the government will protect them from floods and storms. Can we now tell them that we can't or won't protect them?

9. Is a zoning ordinance that says you can't use your land in ecologically damaging ways an unfair intrusion into private property rights?

Key Terms

biogeographical area

biosphere reserves

corridors

ecotourism

floodplains

Man and Biosphere (MAB) program

natural landscaping

poachers

wetland

wilderness

wildlife refuges

world conservation strategy

PART IV
PHYSICAL RESOURCES

THE EARTH AND ITS CRUSTAL RESOURCES

Note To Instructors about Making Geology and Mineral Resources Meaningful in this Course.

The discussion of geology and mineral resources is important in an environmental science course as is exemplified in *Encounters with the Archdruid,* by John McPhee (Farrar, Strauss and Giroux, 1971). Interestingly, among our greatest fears about resource scarcity twenty years ago were threats about impending shortages of strategic minerals. These fears have faded as new sources have been discovered, recycling programs have flourished, and substitute materials and more efficient ways of making things have been developed. A link between resource economics and economic mineralogy is meaningful due to difficult resource questions. Students may have a hard time visualizing the link of geology and mineral sources with environmental issues. Your reinforcement of the linkages can help them synthesize the information in a meaningful way. The controversial topic of a reform of the 1872 mining act is one way to tie mineral resource issues in with current environmental issues (*What Do You Think*" p. 350). Although the massive profits made by some mining companies on public lands seems outrageous, many individuals and communities in the west would be badly hurt by a sudden change in the current law. Finding a solution that eliminates harmful practices without penalizing innocent parties is difficult in this case as it is in so many such disputes.

Chapter Outline

Objectives
The Night the Earth Moved
A Dynamic Planet
      A Layered Sphere
      Tectonic Processes and Shifting Continents
The Rock Cycle
      Rocks and Minerals
      Rock Types and How They Are Formed
            Igneous Rocks
            Weathering and Sedimentation
            Metamorphic Rocks
Economic Mineralogy
      Metals
      Nonmetal Mineral Resources
      Strategic Minerals
Environmental Effects of Resource Extraction
      Mining
      Processing
Conserving Mineral Resources
      Recycling
      Steel and Iron Recycling: Minimills
      Substituting New Materials for Old
Geologic Hazards
      Earthquakes
      Volcanoes
      Floods

Landslides
Summary
Questions for Review
Questions for Critical Thinking
Key Terms
Additional Information on the Internet

What Do You Think? Reforming an Antiquated Mining Law
Case Study: Mining a Tropical Paradise

Objectives

After studying this chapter, students should be able to:

- understand some basic geologic principles, including how tectonic plate movements affect conditions for life on earth.
- explain how the three major rock types are formed and how the rock cycle works.
- summarize economic mineralogy and strategic minerals.
- discuss the environmental effects of mining and mineral processing.
- recognize the geologic hazards of earthquakes, volcanoes, and tsunamis.

Questions for Review

1. Describe the layered structure of the earth.
2. What heats the earth and keeps the core molten?
3. What are tectonic plates, and why are they important to us?
4. Why are there so many volcanoes and earthquakes along the "ring of fire" that rims the Pacific Ocean?
5. Describe the rock cycle and name the three main rock types that it produces.
6. Distinguish between gravitational, chemical, and biogenic sedimentation. Give an example of each.
7. Give some examples of strategic minerals. Where are the largest supplies of these minerals located?
8. Give some examples of nonmetal mineral resources and describe how they are used.
9. What are some of the advantages of recycling minerals?
10. Describe some ways we recycle metals and other mineral resources.
11. What are some environmental hazards associated with mineral extraction?
12. Describe some of the leading geologic hazards and their effects.

Questions for Critical Thinking

1. Look at the walls, floors, appliances, interior, and exterior of the building around you. How many earth materials were used in their construction?
2. What is the geologic history of our town or county?
3. Is your local bedrock igneous, metamorphic, or sedimentary? If you don't know, who might be able to tell you?
4. What would life be like without the global mineral trade network? Can you think of advantages as well as disadvantages?

5. Suppose a large mining company is developing ore reserves in the small, underdeveloped country where you live. How will revenues be divided fairly between the foreign company and local residents?

6. How could we minimize the destruction caused by geologic hazards? Should people be discouraged from building in volcanic or earthquake-prone areas?

7. What might be the climatic effects of having all the continents clustered together in one giant supercontinent?

8. How would your life be affected if your country were to run out of strategic minerals?

9. What effect do you think our need for strategic minerals has had on our foreign policy toward South Africa and the Soviet Union?

10. How could our government encourage more recycling and more efficient use of minerals?

11. What is the potential for geologic hazards where you live?

12. What can you do to protect yourself from geologic hazards?

Key Terms

core

crust

flood

heap-leach extraction

igneous rocks

landslide

magma

mantle

metamorphic rock

mineral

rock cycle

sedimentary rock

sedimentation

strategic minerals

tectonic plates

tsunami

weathering

AIR, CLIMATE, AND WEATHER

Note to Instructors about Weather, Climate and Global Climate Change

Global climate change is regarded by many scientists as the greatest potential threat to our environment and to life as we know it. The details of weather and climatology are important in order to better understand the implications of global climate change. If predictions of global climate change are correct, we may experience greatly increased incidence of extreme weather conditions such as storms, drought, heat or unusual cold. Some people argue that this increase has already begun to occur. Probably more people around the world are threatened by severe weather conditions than any environmental factor other than infectious organisms. An example of oscillating weather patterns with continent wide or even global consequences is the El Niño-Southern Oscillation (ENSO) about which we have been hearing more and more in recent years. An unusually prolonged El Niño event from 1991-1995 and an especially strong ENSO that formed in 1997 have led to fears that a major shift in weather patterns may already have occurred. The global aspects of environmental science and the importance of understanding global systems are illustrated well by our realization that what happens to the subtropical Indonesian low-pressure system impacts anchovy fishermen in Peru, corn farmers in Iowa, and perhaps even pastoralists in the sub-Saharan Sahel. Understanding how weather systems work and what weather patterns mean have great practical importance to students and are easily demonstrated by going outdoors (or having the students observe the outdoors).

Chapter Outline

Objectives
Hurricane!
Composition and Structure of the Atmosphere
      Past and Present Composition
The Great Weather Engine
      Solar Radiation Heats the Atmosphere
      A Layered Envelope
      Convection Currents and Latent Heat
Weather
      Energy Balance in the Atmosphere
      Convection Cells and Prevailing Winds
      Jet Streams
      Frontal Weather
      Cyclonic Storms
      Seasonal Winds
      Weather Modification
Climate
      Climatic Catastrophes
      Driving Forces and Patterns in Climatic Change
      El Niño/Southern Oscillations
      Human-Caused Global Climate Change
            Greenhouse Gases
            Aerosol Effects
      Climate Changes in This Century
      Effects of Climate Change

What Do You Think? Reasoned Judgments and Scientific Uncertainty

Objectives

After studying this chapter, students should be able to:

- summarize the structure and composition of the atmosphere.
- understand how solar energy warms the atmosphere and creates circulation patterns.
- explain how the jet streams, prevailing winds, and frontal systems determine local weather.
- evaluate previous climatic catastrophes and the driving forces thought to bring about climatic change.
- debate the hypothesis that human actions may bring about global climate change.

Questions for Review

1. What are the main constituents of air? What are their sources?
2. Name and describe the four layers of air in the atmosphere.
3. What is the greenhouse effect?
4. Describe the atmospheric heating and cooling cycle.
5. What are jet streams? How do they influence weather patterns?
6. Why does air pressure tend to be low near the equator and high at the poles?
7. Describe the Coriolis effect. What causes it?
8. What is the difference between weather and climate?
9. What are some theories explaining major climatic changes?
10. Would changes in Earth's orbit affect climate? How?

Questions for Critical Thinking

1. What questions would you ask a climate modeler about the assumptions, compromises, and limitations of mathematical models?
2. Should humans try to control the weather? What would be the positive effects? What would be the dangers?
3. Can we avoid great climatic changes, such as another ice age or a greenhouse effect? Will we have the gumption to change our ways?
4. Has there been a major change recently in the weather where you live? Can you propose any reasons for such changes?
5. What forces determine the climate in your locality? Are they the same for neighboring states?
6. What was the weather like when your parents were young? Do you believe the stories they tell you? Why or why not?

7. Have you ever experienced a tornado or hurricane? What was it like? What omens or warnings told you it was coming?

8. From which direction does bad weather come in your region? Why?

9. What would you do to adapt to a permanent drought? What effects would it have on your life?

10. What should we do about coastal cities threatened by rising oceans -rebuild, enclose in dikes, or just move?

11. Would you favor building nuclear power plants to reduce CO_2 emissions?

Key Terms

aerosols

albedo

climate

cold front

convection currents

Coriolis effect

front

hurricanes

ionosphere

jet streams

mesosphere

Milankovitch cycles

monsoon

stratosphere

thermosphere

tornadoes

troposphere

warm front

weather

Note to Instructors about Air Pollution

This chapter ties in well with chapter 17 and can serve to help the students apply some of their knowledge from previous readings. It can be difficult to foster enthusiasm about air pollution because the topic is not as charismatic as other environmental problems such as loss of biodiversity. Therefore, it is important to reinforce the connection of air pollution with other environmental issues, and to help the students see the applicability of air pollution to their own lives. This lack of enthusiasm is ironic since global climate change and stratospheric ozone depletion continue to be two of the most important environmental risks that we face. In fact, stratospheric ozone depletion has become of greater practical importance to most students in North America.. Increased UV irradiation has become something to consider for those who will be outdoors in Northern Europe, Canada, and the Northern United States.

Chapter Outline

Objectives
Killer Smog
The Air Around Us
Natural Sources of Air Pollution
Human-Caused Air Pollution
      Primary and Secondary Pollutants
      Conventional or "Criteria" Pollutants
            Sulfur Compounds
            Nitrogen Compounds
            Carbon Oxides
            Metals and Halogens
            Particulate Material
            Volatile Organic Compounds
            Photochemical Oxidants
      Unconventional Pollutants
      Indoor Air Pollution
Climate, Topography, and Atmospheric Processes
      Inversions
      Dust Domes and Heat Islands
      Long-Range Transport
      Stratospheric Ozone
Effects of Air Pollution
      Human Health
      Plant Pathology
      Acid Deposition
            pH and Atmospheric Acidity
            Aquatic Effects
            Forest Damage
            Buildings and Monuments
            Visibility Reduction

What Do You Think? Radon in Indoor Air

Objectives

After studying this chapter, students should be able to:

- describe the major categories and sources of air pollution.
- distinguish between conventional or "criteria" pollutants and unconventional types as well as explain why each is important.
- analyze the origins and dangers of some indoor air pollutants.
- relate why atmospheric temperature inversions occur and how they affect air quality.
- evaluate the dangers of stratospheric ozone depletion and radon in indoor air.
- understand how air pollution damages human health, vegetation, and building materials.
- compare different approaches to air pollution control and report on clean air legislation.
- judge how air quality around the world has improved or degraded in recent years and suggest what we might do about problem areas.

Questions for Review

1. What is the difference between bronchitis and emphysema? What causes these diseases?
2. What are the most important causes of human illness and death from air pollution?
3. What is acid deposition? What causes it?
4. What have been the effects of acid deposition on aquatic and terrestrial ecosystems?
5. How do electrostatic precipitators, baghouse filters, flue gas scrubbers, and catalytic converters work?
6. What is the difference between primary and secondary standards in air quality?
7. What is the difference between ambient standards and emission limits?
8. What are some of the major toxic air pollutants, and what are their sources?
9. Describe the health effects and suggested actions for each of the levels of the pollution standards index (PSI).

10. Which of the conventional pollutants has decreased most in the recent past and which has decreased least?

Questions for Critical Thinking

1.   How would you rank the risks of air pollution-related disease with other risks you face?

2.   What might be done to improve indoor air quality? Should the government mandate such changes?

3.   Why do you suppose that air pollution is so much worse in Eastern Europe than in the West?

4.   Suppose air pollution causes a billion dollars in crop losses each year but controlling the pollution would also cost a billion dollars. Should we insist on controls?

5.   In 1984 David Stockman, The Director of the Office of Management and Budget for President Reagan, said that it would cost $1000 per fish to control acid precipitation in the Adirondack lakes and that it would be cheaper to buy fish for anglers than to put scrubbers on power plants in Ohio. Suppose that was true. Does it justify continued pollution?

6.   What will the ban on fluorocarbon production do to your life? Will it be worth it to save the ozone layer?

7.   Is it possible to have zero emissions of pollutants? What does zero mean in this case?

8.   If there are thresholds for pollution effects (at least as far as we know now), is it reasonable or wise to depend on environmental processes to disperse, assimilate, or inactivate waste products?

9.   Catalytic converters on automobiles definitely improve air quality, but up to one-fourth of car owners disable the converters on their cars by using leaded gasoline. What should we do about this?

10. Do you think that we should continue to use ambient air-quality standards or change to absolute emission standards for all pollutants?

Key Terms

acid precipitation

aerosol

aesthetic degradation

ambient air

bronchitis

carbon monoxide

chlorofluorocarbons

conventional or criteria pollutants

cyclone collectors

dry alkali injection

electrostatic precipitators

emission standards

emphysema

filters

fugitive emissions

inflammatory response

nitrogen oxides

ozone

particulate material

photochemical oxidants

primary pollutants

primary standards

radon

secondary pollutants

secondary standards

sulfur dioxide

synergistic effects

temperature inversion

unconventional or noncriteria pollutants

volatile organic compounds

WATER USE AND MANAGEMENT

Note to Instructors about Water Resources and Politics

Water may be one of the critically limiting resources in the future. It already is in some places now. The introductory piece regarding international resource wars over water rights would be a good starting point for class discussions or student papers. Dilemmas such as this with no clear right or wrong give students a chance to explore different perspectives and think creatively about possible solutions. They also allow the students to expand their experiences since water shortages are not as critical here in North America as they are in the Middle East. Another potential starting point for a paper or class discussions could be made by referring back to the poignant photo in figure 14.26. The issue of land use and native peoples raises water rights as well as land use questions. Asking students to research the issue further and to write a short reflective essay from the position of George Gillette might give them a different perspective on this issue. What is at stake for the native people? What are the trade-offs between society's need for water and power and traditional use of resources? By the way, the Fort Berthold Tribe has essentially disappeared since giving up their land. On a more positive note, the case study of Bali (p. 422 - 423) is an example of positive cooperation and politics that work over a long term. It might be refreshing for students to write about or discuss positive examples. Further references to this case can also be found in the bibliography.

Chapter Outline

Objectives
Would You Fight for Water?
Water Resources
       The Hydrologic Cycle
       Rainfall and Topography
       Desert Belts
       Balancing the Water Budget
Major Water Compartments
       Oceans
       Glaciers, Ice, and Snow
       Groundwater
       Rivers and Streams
       Lakes and Ponds
       Wetlands
       The Atmosphere
Water Availability and Use
       Water Supplies
       Drought Cycles
       Types of Water Use
       Quantities of Water Used
       Use by Sector
Freshwater Shortages
       A Scarce Resource
       Depleting Groundwater
Increasing Water Supplies
       Seeding Clouds and Towing Icebergs

Case Study: The Endangered Landscape of Bali

What Do You Think? Three Gorges Dam

Objectives

After studying this chapter, students should be able to:

- summarize how the hydrologic cycle delivers fresh water to terrestrial ecosystems and how the cycle balances over time.
- contrast the volume and residence time of water in the earth's major compartments.
- describe the important ways we use water and distinguish between withdrawals, consumption, and degradation.
- appreciate the causes and consequences of water shortages around the world and what they mean in people's lives in water-poor countries.
- debate the merits of proposals to increase water supplies and manage demand.
- apply some water conservation methods in your own life.

Questions for Review

1. What is the difference between withdrawal, consumption, and degradation of water?

2. How does water use by sector differ between rich and poor countries?

3. What is subsidence? What are its results?

4. Describe some problems associated with dam building and water diversion projects.

5. Describe the path a molecule of water might follow through the hydrologic cycle from the ocean to land and back again.

6. Define *evaporation, sublimation, condensation, precipitation,* and *infiltration.* How do they work?

7. How do mountains affect rainfall distribution? Does this affect your part of the country?

8. What are the major water reservoirs of the world?

9. How much water is fresh (as opposed to saline) and where is it?

10. Define aquifer. How does water get into an aquifer?

Questions for Critical Thinking

1. What changes might occur in the hydrologic cycle if our climate were to warm or cool significantly?

2. Why does it take so long for the deep ocean waters to circulate through the hydrologic cycle? What happens to substances that contaminate deep ocean water or deep aquifers in the ground?

3. Where would you most like to spend your vacations? Does availability of water play a role in your choice? Why?

4. Why do we use so much water? Do we need all that we use?

5. Are there ways you could use less water in your personal life? Would that make any difference in the long run?

6. Should we use up underground water supplies now or save them for some future time?

7. How much should the United States invest to provide clean water to people in less-developed countries?

8. How should we compare the values of free-flowing rivers and natural ecosystems with the benefits of flood control, water diversion projects, hydroelectric power, and dammed reservoirs?

9. Would it be feasible to change from flush toilets and using water as a medium for waste disposal to some other system? What might be the best way to accomplish this?

10. How does water differ from other natural liquids? How do the properties of water make the hydrologic cycle, and life, possible? (You may need to review chapter 2 to answer this question.)

Key Terms

aquifer

artesian

condensation

condensation nuclei

consumption

degradation

desalinization

dew point

discharge

evaporation

groundwater

infiltration

rain shadow

recharge zones

relative humidity

residence time

runoff

saltwater intrusion

saturation point

sinkholes

stable runoff

sublimation

subsidence

water table

withdrawal

zone of aeration

zone of saturation

Note to Instructors about Water Pollution and Other Environmental Issues

Again, this chapter ties in with previous readings and is an excellent opportunity for you to connect water pollution and use issues with land use, human health, population growth, and a multitude of other topics. The key is to help the students see connectivity and learn the complex interrelationships that lead to environmental problems and the solutions to those problems. Water pollution can be an overwhelming problem and you may be experiencing some burnout by your students. It is critical that the positive stories and examples are told, and solutions are emphasized. The special edition of *National Geographic* in November 1993 focused on water and, although it is a few years old, it is timely in its presentation of the problems and the solutions. The photographs are powerful and the content is also excellent. To update the information from the 1993 issue there are more resources in the bibliography.

Chapter Outline

Objectives
Black Sea in Crisis
What is Water Pollution?
Types and Effects of Water Pollution
      Infectious Agents
      Oxygen-Demanding Wastes
      Plant Nutrients and Cultural Eutrophication
      Toxic Inorganic Materials
          Heavy Metals
          Nonmetallic Salts
          Acids and Bases
      Organic Chemicals
      Sediment
      Thermal Pollution and Thermal Shocks
Water Quality Today
      Surface Waters in the United States and Canada
          Areas of Progress
          Remaining Problems
      Surface Waters in Other Countries
      Groundwater and Drinking Water Supplies
      Ocean Pollution
Water Pollution Control
      Source Reduction
      Nonpoint Sources and Land Management
      Human Waste Disposal
          Natural Processes
          Municipal Sewage Systems
          Low-Cost Waste Treatment
Water Legislation
      The Clean Water Act

What Do You Think? Assessing Progress in Water Quality

In Depth: Water Remediation

Objectives

After studying this chapter, students should be able to:

- define *water pollution* and describe the sources and effects of some major types.
- appreciate why access to sewage treatment and clean water are important to people in developing countries.
- discuss the status of water quality in developed and developing countries.
- delve into groundwater problems and suggest ways to protect this precious resource.
- fathom the causes and consequences of ocean pollution.
- weigh the advantages and disadvantages of different human waste disposal techniques.
- judge the impact of water pollution legislation and differentiate between best available and best practical technology.

Questions for Review

1. Define water pollution.

2. List eight major categories of water pollutants and give an example for each category.

3. Describe ten major sources of water pollution in the United States. What pollution problems are associated with each source?

4. Name some waterborne diseases. How do they spread?

5. What is eutrophication? What causes it?

6. What are the origins and effects of siltation?

7. Describe primary, secondary, and tertiary processes for sewage treatment. What is the quality of the effluent from each of these processes?

8. Why do combined storm and sanitary sewers cause water quality problems? Why does separating them also cause problems?

9. What pollutants are regulated by the Clean Water Act? What goals does this act set for abatement technology?

10. What is the difference between best practical control technology and best available technology? Which do you think should be required? Why does the Clean Water Act start with BPT?

Questions for Critical Thinking

1. How precise do you suppose the estimate is that 2 billion people lack access to clean water? What differences would it make if the estimate is off by 10 percent or 50 percent?

2. How would you define *adequate* sanitation? Think of some situations in which people might have different definitions for this term.

3. Do you think that water pollution is worse now than it was in the past? What considerations go into a judgment like this? How do your personal experiences influence your opinion?

4. What additional information would you need to make a judgment about whether conditions are getting better or worse? How would you weigh different sources, types, and effects of water pollution?

5. Try to imagine yourself in a developing country with a severe shortage of clean water. What would you miss most if *your* water supply were to suddenly diminish?

6. What is the practical difference between best available, economically achievable technology and best practicable control technology? Why do environmentalists and industry fight over these terms?

7. Proponents of deep-well injection of hazardous wastes argue that it will probably never be economically feasible to pump water out of aquifers more than one kilometer below the surface. Therefore, they say, we might as well use those aquifers for hazardous waste storage. Do you agree? Why or why not?

8. Under what conditions might sediment in water of cultural eutrophication be beneficial? How should we balance positive and negative effects?

9. Suppose that part of the silt in a river is natural and part is human-caused. Is one pollution but the other not?

10. Suppose that you own a lake but it is very polluted. An engineer offers options for various levels of cleanup. As you increase water quality you also increase costs greatly. How clean would you want the water to be -fishable, swimmable, drinkable -and how much would you be willing to pay to achieve your goal? Make up your own numbers. The point is to examine your priorities and values.

Key Terms

atmospheric deposition

best available, economically achievable technology (BAT)

best practicable control technology (BPT)

biochemical oxygen demand (BOD)

coliform bacteria

cultural eutrophication

dissolved oxygen (DO) content

effluent sewage

eutrophic

nonpoint sources

oligotrophic

oxygen sag

point sources

primary treatment

red tides

secondary treatment

tertiary treatment

thermal plume

CONVENTIONAL ENERGY

Note to Instructors about Nuclear Energy

Many of your students are concerned about nuclear safety and may have even participated in protests against nuclear power. Unfortunately, although they may have participated in active protests, many students have almost no understanding of the technology. On the other hand, there are some students who have no familiarity with Chernobyl. It may be helpful to survey your students to find out their knowledge level of this topic. Revelations about Soviet dumping of old reactors and nuclear waste in the Arctic Ocean are an alarming point for most students as are the details of Chernobyl. It is therefore important for them, as critical thinkers, to educate themselves on this topic so they can be more effective and empowered in their actions. It is interesting to speculate whether history would have been different if we had designed nuclear power generators initially for maximum safety rather than simply enlarging the reactors designed for nuclear submarines.

Chapter Outline

Objectives
The Night the Lights Went Out in New York City
    A Brief Energy History
    Current Energy Sources
    Per Capita Consumption
How Energy Is Used
Coal
    Coal Resources and Reserves
    Mining
    Air Pollution
Oil
    Oil Resources and Reserves
    Oil Imports and Domestic Supplies
    Oil Shale and Tar Sands
Natural Gas
    Natural Gas Resources and Reserves
    Unconventional Gas Sources
Nuclear Power
    How Do Nuclear Reactors Work?
    Kinds of Reactors in Use
    Alternative Reactor Designs
    Breeder Reactors
Radioactive Waste Management
    Ocean Dumping of Radioactive Wastes
    Land Disposal of Nuclear Wastes
    Decommissioning Old Nuclear Plants
Changing Fortunes of Nuclear Power
Nuclear Fusion
Summary
Questions for Review

Questions for Critical Thinking
Key Terms
Additional Information on the Internet

Case Study: Oil Versus Wildlife
What Do You Think? Chernobyl: Could It Happen Here?

Objectives

After studying this chapter, students should be able to:

- summarize our current energy sources and explain briefly how energy use has changed through history.
- compare our energy consumption with that of other people in the world.
- itemize the ways we use energy.
- analyze the resources and reserves of fossil fuels in the world.
- evaluate the costs and benefits from using coal, oil, and natural gas.
- understand how nuclear reactors work, why they are dangerous, and how they might be made safer.
- discuss our options for radioactive waste storage and disposal.
- summarize public opinion about nuclear power and how you feel about this controversial energy source.

Questions for Review

1. What is energy? What is power?

2. What are the major sources of commercial energy worldwide and in the United States? Why is data usually presented in terms of commercial energy?

3. How is energy used in the United States?

4. How does our energy use compare with that of people in other countries?

5. How much coal, oil, and natural gas are in proven reserves worldwide? Where are those reserves located?

6. What are the most important health and environmental consequences of our use of fossil fuels?

7. Describe how a nuclear reactor works and why they are dangerous.

8. What are the four most common reactor designs? How do they differ from each other?

9. What are the advantages and disadvantages of the breeder reactor?

10. Describe methods proposed for storing and disposing of nuclear wastes.

Questions for Critical Thinking

1. We have discussed a number of different energy sources and energy technologies in this chapter. Each has advantages and disadvantages. If you were an energy policy analyst, how would you compare such different problems as the risk of a nuclear accident versus air pollution effects from burning coal?

2. If your local utility company were going to build a new power plant in your community, what kind would you prefer?

3. The nuclear industry is placing ads in popular magazines and newspapers claiming that nuclear power is environmentally friendly since it doesn't contribute to the greenhouse effect. How do you respond to that claim?

4. Our energy policy effectively treats some strip-mine lands as national sacrifice areas since we know that they will never be restored to their original state when mining is finished. How do we decide who wins and who loses in this transaction?

5. Storing nuclear wastes in dry casks outside nuclear power plants is highly controversial. Opponents claim that the casks will inevitably leak. Proponents claim they can be designed to be safe. What evidence would you consider adequate or necessary to choose between these two positions?

6. Since the environmental impact of a nuclear power plant accident cannot be limited to national boundaries (as in the case of Chernobyl), should there be international regulations for power plants? Who would define these regulations? How could they be enforced?

7. Although we have wasted vast amounts of energy resources in the process of industrialization and development, some would say that it was a necessary investment to get to a point at which we can use energy more efficiently and sustainably, do you agree? Might we have followed a different path?

8. The policy of the United States has always been to make energy as cheap and freely available as possible. Most European countries charge three to four times as much for gasoline as we do. Think about the ramifications of our energy policy. Why is it so different from that in Europe? Who benefits and who or what loses in these different approaches? How have our policies shaped our lives? What does existing policy tell you about how our government works?

Key Terms

black lung disease

breeder reactor

chain reaction

control rods

energy

fossil fuel

fuel assembly

high-level waste repository

inertial confinement

magnetic confinement

methane hydrate

monitored, retrievable storage

nuclear fission

nuclear fusion

oil shale

power

secondary recovery techniques

unconventional oil

work

Note to Instructors about Sustainable Energy and Personal Energy Use

Sustainable energy tends to be a very popular topic with students. Perhaps it is because they find the new technologies appealing and encouraging. It is advisable to combine the information in this chapter with chapter 21 so that students are aware of the alternatives to fossil and nuclear energy. As is the case with most environmental issues, issues of energy are closely related to issues such as human health, global climate change, environmental justice, and biodiversity. The James Bay Project would be an excellent case study to research further. This case involves political issues, economic factors, biodiversity, and energy issues. A useful activity for the students would be to document their personal energy use and share it with other members of the class (in a nonthreatening environment, of course). This would help increase students' awareness of their own use and perhaps help them reduce their dependence on energy. The *In Depth* (p. 494) is an excellent way to begin this activity.

Chapter Outline

Objectives
A Photovoltaic Village in Java
Conservation
       Utilization Efficiencies
       Energy Conversion Efficiencies
       Negawatt Programs
       Cogeneration
Tapping Solar Energy
       A Vast Resource
       Passive Solar Heat
       Active Solar Heat
High-Temperature Solar Energy
       Solar Cookers
       Promoting Renewable Energy
       Photovoltaic Solar Energy
       Storing Electric Energy
Energy from Biomass
       Burning Biomass
       Fuelwood Crisis in Less-Developed Countries
       Dung and Methane as Fuels
       Alcohol from Biomass
       Crop Residues, Energy Crops, and Peat
Energy from the Earth's Forces
       Hydropower
       Wind Energy
       Geothermal Energy
       Tidal and Wave Energy
       Ocean Thermal Electric Conversion
Research in Renewables
Summary

Questions for Review
Questions for Critical Thinking
Key Terms
Additional Information on the Internet

In Depth: Personal Energy Efficiency
What Do You Think? Living Off the Grid
Case Study: James Bay Hydropower
What Can You Do? Some Things You Can Do To Save Energy

Objectives

After studying this chapter, students should be able to:

- appreciate the opportunities for energy conservation available to us.
- understand how active and passive systems capture solar energy and how photovoltaic collectors generate electricity.
- comprehend why fuelwood supplies are a crisis in less-developed countries.
- evaluate the use of dung, crop residues, energy crops, and peat as potential energy sources.
- explain how hydropower, wind, and geothermal energy contribute to our power supply.
- describe how tidal and wave energy and ocean thermal gradients can be used to generate electrical energy.
- compare and contrast different options for storing electrical energy from intermittent or remote sources.

Questions for Review

1. What is cogeneration and how does it save energy?
2. Explain the principle of net energy yield. Give some examples.
3. What is the difference between active and passive solar energy?
4. How do photovoltaic cells work?
5. Describe the advantages and disadvantages of multiple-bladed, two-bladed, and Darius windmills.
6. Describe some problems with wood burning in both industrialized nations and Third World nations.
7. How is methane made?
8. What are some advantages and disadvantages of large hydroelectric dams?
9. What are some examples of biomass fuel other than wood?
10. Describe how tidal power and ocean thermal electric conversion work.

Questions for Critical Thinking

1. What alternative energy sources are most useful in your region and climate?
2. What can you do to conserve energy where you live? In your personal habits? In your home, dormitory, or workplace?
3. What massive heat storage materials can you think of that could be attractively incorporated into a home?
4. Do you think building wind farms in remote places, parks, or scenic wilderness areas would be damaging or unsightly?

5. If you were a government energy administrator or planner, how would you distribute energy research funds?

6. What are the advantages and disadvantages of being disconnected from central utility power?

7. Can you think of environmental consequences associated with tidal or geothermal energy? If so, how can they be mitigated?

8. You are offered a home solar energy system that costs $10,000 but saves you $1000 a year. Will you take it at this rate? If the cost were higher and the payoff time longer, what is the threshold at which you would not buy the system?

Key Terms

active solar systems

cogeneration

energy efficiency

eutectic chemicals

gasohol

geothermal energy

low-head hydropower

micro-hydro generators

net energy yield

ocean thermal electric conversion (OTEC)

passive heat absorption

photovoltaic cells

run-of-the-river flow

tidal station

wind farms

SOLID, TOXIC, AND HAZARDOUS WASTE

Note to Instructors about Garbage

Garbage is probably not the most important topic in environmental science, but it is one that is accessible to students and that has great practical applications. All of us create garbage and all of us can do more to reduce our wasteful ways. Having students do a personal inventory of how much solid waste they generate in a week is a good way to illustrate the extent of this problem. Most students are surprised to learn how much waste they make. This exercise provides an opportunity to discuss the wastefulness of our materialistic lifestyles. At the same time it's important to point out the dangers of becoming so involved with recycling that we ignore other more important issues. Changing the institutions and conditions that encourage (or require) us to live wastefully is probably more important in the long run than to spend our time and energy collecting recyclable materials for which there is little market demand.

There is a Bill Moyer's videotape on international dumping of toxic wastes that is an excellent presentation of this topic. It opens with photographs of the *Khian Sea,* the boat loaded with toxic ash from Philadelphia that sailed around the world looking for a place to dump its toxic load. In one episode, a crew member actually eats a handful of ash to prove that it's not dangerous. Students tend to remember that scene. The videotape also has images of waste recycling programs in Taiwan and China operating under appalling conditions. Perhaps more than anything we can say, these images illustrate our connection with environmental conditions elsewhere. If you did not use the test questions that relate to environmental justice from chapter 2 they would be applicable for this chapter.

Chapter Outline

Objectives
What a Long, Strange Journey It Has Been
Solid Waste
      The Waste Stream
Waste Disposal Methods
      Open Dumps
      Ocean Dumping
      Landfills
      Exporting Waste
      Incineration and Resource Recovery
            Types of Incinerators
            Incinerator Cost and Safety
Shrinking the Waste Stream
      Recycling
            Benefits of Recycling
            Creating Incentives for Recycling
      Composting
      Energy from Waste
      Reuse
      Producing Less Waste
Hazardous and Toxic Waste
      What Is Hazardous Waste?
      Hazardous Waste Disposal

Objectives

After studying this chapter, students should be able to:

- identify the major components of the waste stream and describe how wastes have been -and are being- disposed of in North America and around the world.
- explain how incinerators work, as well as the advantages and disadvantages they offer.
- summarize the benefits, problems, and potential of recycling and reusing wastes.
- analyze some alternatives for reducing the waste we generate.
- understand what hazardous and toxic wastes are and how we dispose of them.
- evaluate the options for hazardous waste management.
- outline some ways we can destroy or permanently store hazardous wastes.

Questions for Review

1. What are solid wastes and hazardous wastes? What is the difference?

2. How much solid and hazardous waste do we produce each year in the United States? How do we dispose of the waste?

3. Why are landfill sites becoming limited around most major urban centers in the United States? What steps are being taken to solve this problem?

4. Describe some concerns about waste incineration.

5. List some benefits and drawbacks of recycling wastes. What are the major types of materials recycled from municipal waste and how are they used?

6. What is composting, and how does it fit into solid waste disposal?

7. Describe some ways that we can reduce the waste stream to avoid or reduce disposal problems.

8. List ten toxic substances in your home and how you would dispose of them.

9. What are brownfields and why do cities want to redevelop them?

10. What societal problems are associated with waste disposal? Why do people object to waste handling in their neighborhoods?

Questions for Critical Thinking

1. A toxic waste disposal site has been proposed for the Pine Ridge Indian Reservation in South Dakota. Many tribal members oppose this plan, but some favor it because of the jobs and income it will bring to an area with 70 percent unemployment. If local people choose immediate survival over long-term health, do we have a right to object or intervene?

2. There is often a tension between getting your personal life in order and working for larger structural changes in society. Evaluate the trade-offs between spending time and energy sorting recyclables at home as compared to working in the public arena on a bill to ban excess packaging.

3. Should industry officials be held responsible for dumping chemicals that were legal when they did it, but are now known to be extremely dangerous? At what point can we argue that they *should* have known about the hazards involved?

4. Look at the discussion of recycling or incineration presented in this chapter. List the premises (implicit or explicit) that underlie the presentation as well as the conclusions (stated or unstated) that seem to be drawn from them. Do the conclusions necessarily follow from these premises?

5. Suppose that your brother or sister has decided to buy a house next to a toxic waste dump because it is selling for $20,000 below market value. What do you say to him or her?

6. Is there an overall conceptual framework or point of view in this chapter? If you were presenting a discussion of solid or hazardous waste to your class, what would be your conceptual framework?

7. Is there a fundamental difference between incinerating municipal, medical, or toxic waste in your neighborhood but not others? Why or why not?

8. The Netherlands incinerates much of its toxic waste out at sea in a shipborne incinerator. Would you support this as a way to dispose of our wastes as well? What are the critical considerations for or against this approach?

Key Terms

biodegradable plastics

bioremediation

brownfields

energy recovery

hazardous waste

landfills

mass burn

permanent retrievable storage

photodegradable plastics

recycling

refuse-derived fuel

secure landfills

superfund

waste stream

URBANIZATION AND SUSTAINABLE CITIES

Note to Instructors about Developing Countries, Rural or Urban Housing, and Capstone Experiences

Few North American students have experienced or can fathom the noise, congestion, air pollution, substandard housing, dirt, air pollution, poverty, and environmental degradation experienced by poor people in megacities such as Cairo, Bombay, Delhi, Jakarta, or Mexico City. In less than a century we have gone from a situation in which most people in the world lived on farms or in rural villages to the point at which a majority now live in urban areas. The growth of enormous cities in developing countries has serious environmental implications that, once again, are related to, and stem from other environmental problems. New towns and gardens can be an inspiration for students who will probably be in the market for their own living space in the relatively near future. Some of these issues may not be as important to the traditional student now, but their choices of home ownership and rural/urban/suburban location have important environmental implications. Since the proportion of nontraditional students has been rising on most campuses, this is an excellent opportunity to allow an older student to discuss his/her experiences, choices, and dilemmas in finding more permanent housing than student apartments or dormitories.

This chapter can be used as a type of capstone if you are using the book in a linear fashion. Urban design and land use planning incorporate environmental science and ecological principles, population and human health issues, and the use of biological and physical resources. Having students design a land use planning blueprint or plans for revitalizing a nearby urban area can serve as both an excellent learning (for the students) and evaluation tool (for you).

Chapter Outline

Objectives
Pneumonic Plague in Surat
Urbanization
       What Is a City?
       World Urbanization
Causes of Urban Growth
       Immigration Push Factors
       Immigration Pull Factors
       Government Policies
Current Urban Problems
       The Developing World
          Traffic and Congestion
          Air Pollution
          Sewer Systems and Water Pollution
          Housing
       The Developed World
          Urban Problems
          Urban Renewal
Noise
Transportation and City Growth
City Planning
       Garden Cities and New Towns

What Do You Think? People for Community Recovery
Case Study: Curitiba: An Environmental Showcase

Objectives

After studying this chapter, students should be able to:

- distinguish between a rural village, a city, and a megacity.
- recognize the push and pull factors that lead to urban growth.
- appreciate the growth rate of giant metropolitan urban areas such as Mexico City, as well as the problems this growth engenders.
- picture the living conditions for ordinary citizens in the megacities of the developing world.
- understand the causes and consequences of noise and crowding in cities.
- critique options for suburban design.
- see the connection between sustainable economic development, social justice, and the solution of urban problems.

Questions for Review

1. What is the difference between a city and a village and between rural and urban?

2. How many people now live in cities, and how many live in rural areas worldwide?

3. What changes in urbanization are predicted to occur in the next fifty years, and where will that change occur?

4. Identify the ten largest cities in the world. Has the list changed in the past fifty years? Why?

5. When did the United States pass the point at which more people live in cities than in the country? When will the rest of the world reach this point?

6. Describe the current conditions in a typical megacity of the developing world. What forces contribute to its growth?

7. Describe the difference between slums and shantytowns.

8. Why are urban areas in US cities decaying?

9. How has transportation affected the development of cities? What have been the benefits and disadvantages of freeways?

10. Describe some ways that American cities and suburbs could be redesigned to be more ecologically sound, socially just, and culturally amenable.

Questions for Critical Thinking

1. Picture yourself living in a rural village or a Third World city. What aspects of life there would you enjoy? What would be the most difficult for you to accept?

2. Are there fundamental differences between the lives of homeless people in First World and Third World cities? Where would you rather be?

3. A city could be considered an ecosystem. Using what you learned in chapters 2 and 3, describe the structure and function of a city in ecological terms.

4. Extrapolating from laboratory animals to humans is always a difficult task. How would you interpret the results of laboratory experiments on stress and crowding in terms of human behavior?

5. Weigh the costs and benefits of automobiles on modern American life. Would we have been better off if the internal combustion engine had never been invented?

6. Boulder, Colorado, has been a leader in controlling urban growth. One consequence is that housing costs have skyrocketed and poor people have been driven out. If you lived in Boulder, would you vote for additional population limits? What do you think is an optimum city size?

7. Ten proposals are presented in this chapter for suburban redesign. Which of them would be appropriate or useful for your community? Try drawing up a plan for the ideal design of your neighborhood.

8. How much do you think the richer countries are responsible for conditions in the developing countries? How much have people there brought on themselves? What role should, or could, we play in remedying their problems?

Key Terms

city

conservation development

core region

garden cities

megacity

new towns

pull factors

push factors

rural area

shantytowns

slums

squatter towns

technopolis

urban area

urban renewal

urbanization

village

WHAT THEN SHALL WE DO?

Note to Instructors about Environmental Careers and Critical Thinking Skills

Many times in the course of a semester or quarter, the last chapter of a text is rushed because of a lack of time. This chapter deserves more because it has excellent tips and positive aspects that are important to an environmental studies/science student. The paper/plastic bag dilemma on page 567 is excellent and timely. So many times students ask whether paper or plastic is better. The answer requires solutions that depend on the circumstances at hand. On page 564 there are good tips for students and their future careers. As was mentioned in chapter 3's notes, the Environmental Profiles that were inserted throughout the text are excellent resources for students. It may be useful to spend an entire class on environmental careers. There are references in the bibliography that can help both you and your students. Many times people have a narrow view of an environmental career. Using this chapter is a perfect opportunity to communicate the fact that environmental jobs can be in the Arts, Sciences, Law, Politics, etc.

The critical thinking that students have been practicing throughout the term is reinforced with the *What Do You Think?* box on page 574. You can involve the students in self reflection by having them think back to their critical thinking in the beginning of the term (see chapter 2 notes) and contrast their level of thinking now. It can be very empowering for students to begin to recognize their skills in evaluating the world around them.

Chapter Outline

Objectives
Environmental Justice for Ogoniland
Environmental Education
       Environmental Literacy
       Environmental Careers
Individual Accountability
       How Much Is Enough?
       Shopping for Green Products
       Blue Angels and Green Seals
       Limits of Green Consumerism
       Paying Attention to What's Important
Collective Actions
       Student Environmental Groups
       Mainline Environmental Organizations
       Broadening the Environmental Agenda
       Deep or Shallow Environmentalism?
       Radical Environmental Groups
       Antienvironmental Backlash
Global Issues
       Public Opinions and Environmental Protection
       Sustainable Development
       International Nongovernmental Organizations
Green Government and Politics
       Green Politics
       Green Plans

Case Study: Citizens Against Toxic Waste
What Do You Think? Evaluating Extremist Claims

Objectives

After studying this chapter, students should be able to:

- be aware of the goals and opportunities in environmental education and environmental careers.
- recognize opportunities for making a difference through the goods and services we choose as well as the limits of green consumerism.
- compare the differences between radical and mainline environmental groups and the tactics they employ to bring about social change.
- summarize some practical suggestions for how to reduce consumption, organize an environmental campaign, communicate effectively with the media, and write to elected officials.
- appreciate the need for sustainable development and explain how nongovernmental groups work toward this goal.
- evaluate how green politics and governments function nationally and internationally to help protect the earth.
- formulate your own philosophy and action plan for what you can and should do to create a better world and a sustainable environment.

Questions for Review

1. Summarize the goals of environmental education.

2. What are deep and shallow ecology? Why do progressives object to being called shallow ecologists?

3. List some things you can do to reduce resource consumption.

4. Discuss some of the limits to green consumerism and how you can spot fraudulent or meaningless green marketing claims.

5. Review the trade-offs between paper and plastic bags. Which is better in your view?

6. List ten key issues in organizing an environmental campaign or using media to influence public opinion.

7. What are the ten largest, oldest mainline environmental organizations in the United States?

8. Describe and evaluate the tactics used by radical environmental groups. Do you subscribe to monkey wrenching?

9. Describe the goals and tactics of the antienvironmental wise use groups. In what ways are their claims extremist?

10. List the four key values of the Green Party.

11. Explain how the legislative, judicial, and administrative branches of government work to protect the environment.

12. In a few words, summarize the main concept in each of the principles presented in Table 25.7.

Questions for Critical Thinking

1. How would it change your life if all the principles of the Earth Charter were really taken seriously?

2. Do you agree with the principles presented in Table 25.7? Why or why not?

3. Put yourself in the place of someone who might object to one or more of these principles. What would they find challenging or objectionable?

4. The wise use movement appeals to people who fear that their livelihood and way of life are threatened by those who want to "lock up" resources in parks and nature preserves. What would you say to convince them that their loss is worthwhile?

5. People in many cultures traditionally regard wild nature as disagreeable and dangerous. How would you approach environmental education if you were assigned to such a country?

6. Do you support the conservative, mainstream approach to conservation followed by the mainline environmental groups, or do you prefer the more challenging, innovative approaches of more radical groups? What are the advantages and disadvantages of each?

7. Extremists on both sides of the environmental debate sometimes use violence against property—and sometimes against people—to advance their agendas. Would you ever condone taking the law into your own hands for an environmental cause? Under what circumstances and what limits might you do so?

8. Do you agree that sustainable development has the potential to simultaneously reduce poverty *and* protect the environment? What responsibility do those of us in rich nations bear toward the rest of the world?

9. Choose one of the ambiguous dilemmas presented in this chapter such as whether it is better to use paper or plastic bags. What additional information would you need to choose between alternatives? How should competing claims or considerations be weighted in an issue such as this?

10. The Talmud say, "If not now, when?" How might this apply to environmental science?

Key Terms

deep ecology

direct action

environmental impact statement (EIS)

environmental literacy

green plans

green political parties

life-cycle analysis

monkey wrenching

nongovernmental organizations (NGOs)

postmaterialist values

precycling

shallow ecology

social ecology

Wise Use Movement

CHAPTER 1
UNDERSTANDING OUR ENVIRONMENT

1. The example of deformed frogs illustrates the

    A. ability of scientists to completely understand the components of an environmental problem.

    B. natural cycle of amphibian population abnormalities in wetland systems.

    C. complex and interrelated nature of environmental problems.

    D. lack of governmental support for amphibian research.

2. Skeptics argue that frog abnormalities

    A. are found only in indicator species and therefore do not show harm to humans.

    B. do not normally cycle through populations.

    C. are a warning that human activities are disrupting nature.

    D. always existed and are now found because we are now looking for them.

3. Amphibian populations worldwide seem to be

    A. declining slowly.

    B. naturally cycling through population fluctuations.

    C. staying about the same.

    D. declining quickly.

4. The word "environment" comes from a French word that means to do with

    A. surroundings.   B. nature.   C. wildlife.   D. home.   E. life.

5. Environmental science is _____.

    A. a narrowly defined set of physical, life, and social sciences.

    B. the best way to interpret the environment.

    C. a way to see the world in scientific terms.

    D. a systematic, orderly way to learn about our environment.

    E. a special set of problem-solving skills.

6. Most environmental problems result from

    A. excessive pollution problems.   C. technological development problems.

    B. complex, interrelated problems.   D. urban degradation problems.

7. The word "environment" as used in environmental science includes

    A. our culture.   B the biosphere.   C. our political system.   D. All of these.

8. The fundamental basis of environmental science as a discipline is the

    A. history of the use of natural resources.   C. human impact on the Earth.

    B. diversity of life on Earth.   D. pollution on the Earth.

9. In explaining your choice of an environmental science major in college to your roommate you would probably emphasize the fact that environmental science is a(n)

   A. applied interdisciplinary field with an emphasis on solving problems.

   B. well established field that has been in existence for a long time.

   C. theoretical discipline that will help solve the problems created by human impact.

   D. relatively new field that will identify remedies to environmental issues.

10. The ability to use critical-thinking and problem-solving skills in dealing with environmental issues was suggested as one of your goals in studying environmental science. This is probably because

   A. it was outlined by the Wisconsin National Environmental Education Advancement Project.

   B. it is a good goal in attempting to understand and identify remedies to environmental problems.

   C. environmental issues are complex and require these skills for effective problem solving.

   D. environmental issues are massive and require these skills to keep from getting overwhelmed.

11. One major difference affecting the scope of environmental issues of the past and present is the

   A. current ability to alter the natural world through technology.

   B. relatively new emergence of environmentalists.

   C. historical ignorance of the interconnected nature of environmental issues.

   D. development of new fields such as environmental science.

12. In the fourth century b.c. the philosopher Plato wrote of the erosion and deforestation that _____ Greece.

   A. would one day plague   C. were caused by the teeming population in

   B. were prevalent in countries outside of   D. had stripped the fine soils and forests of

13. The first people to introduce ideas about saving the environment to Europe were mainly

   A. European colonial botanists and zoologists.

   B. indigenous tribes of central Africa.

   C. European peasant farmers.

   D. industrial leaders of the nineteenth century.

14. The history of conservation and environmentalism is

   A. a relatively modern movement.   C. largely unrecorded.

   B. a twentieth century phenomenon.   D. traceable well back into human history.

15. Mauritius, an island in the Indian Ocean, is a model for balancing nature and human needs because in the eighteenth century a French governor

   A. declared the island a nature sanctuary.

   B. ordered sensitive areas such as steep slopes to be preserved in forests.

   C. bought the island as a private sanctuary for the government of France.

   D. supported an extensive environmental education campaign.

16. Pragmatic conservationists, including Gifford Pinchot and Theodore Roosevelt, supported forest conservation in order to protect

   A. wildlife habitat.

   B. untouched, unvisited wilderness areas.

   C. wood, jobs, and recreation for people.

   D. resources such as wood for future generations.

17. Utilitarian conservationists tend to believe that resources should be saved because they are important

    A. as a home for wildlife.
    B. to our understanding of the biosphere.
    C. and utilized by all living things.
    D. in the conservation of aesthetic values.
    E. for a strong economic system.

18. The approach that reflects the philosophy that there is waste in neglecting the development and use of certain natural resources (such as dead trees in old growth forests) would best be described as

    A. moral and aesthetic preservation.
    B. pragmatic resource conservation.
    C. global environmental citizenship.
    D. a cornucopian worldview.

19. Biocentric preservationists, first led by John Muir, advocate saving natural areas for their

    A. beauty and wildlife habitat.
    B. wood and mineral resources for the future.
    C. hunting and fishing value.
    D. tourism and recreation potential.

20. Biocentrism or altruistic preservation is a philosophy that supports the belief that

    A. the biosphere is a central resource for humans.
    B. humans must manage resources for maximum productivity.
    C. preservation of wildlife is needed for human survival.
    D. all living things have an equal footing in the biosphere.

21. The National Park Service reflects a _____ approach while the Forest Service reflects a _____ approach.

    A. moral and aesthetic preservationist, pragmatic resource conservationist
    B. global environmentalist, cornucopian
    C. pragmatic resource conservationist, moral and aesthetic preservationist
    D. cornucopian, global environmentalist

22. Environmentalism stemming from the publication of Rachel Carson's *Silent Spring* differed from earlier conservation perspectives by

    A. focusing on human population growth.
    B. emphasizing international problems.
    C. placing more emphasis on pollution problems.
    D. encouraging energy efficiency.

23. An emphasis on pollution problems

    A. is a relatively new concern.
    B. was recognized in the eleventh century.
    C. was the main agenda of the 1960s and 1970s.
    D. is the key argument for technological optimism.

24. Modern environmentalism, in part led by David Brower and Barry Commoner, is becoming well established in the United States. One of the main reasons for this is probably the _____ in the modern movement.

    A. emphasis on technological remedies
    B. interconnected nature of our global village
    C. combination of activism and research
    D. emphasis on impending doom

25. The end of the twentieth century has added _____ to environmental thinking.

    A. global concerns
    B. water supply and pollution problems
    C. urban problems
    D. human population growth

26. The "global village" refers to the fact that the world's

    A. size is getting smaller.
    B. technology is getting simpler.
    C. population is increasingly interdependent.
    D. population is becoming larger.

27. Although many people in the United States are extremely afraid of cancer, the main cause of death in the world is

    A. heart disease.

    C. violence and accidents.

    B. chronic and acute lung diseases.

    D. infectious diseases aggravated by malnutrition.

28. Using the analogy of the world as a village of 1000 people, what would probably impress you the most if you visited this village?

    A. The disparity among the villagers' quality of life.

    B. The amount of pollution in the better parts of town.

    C. The rapid increase in the number of children.

    D. The high number of people who live in the village.

29. The world's population is now nearly

    A. 60 million.   B. 2 billion.   C. 6 billion.   D. 100 billion.

30. Most of the world's population growth will occur in

    A. developed countries.

    C. eastern block countries.

    B. developing countries.

    D. the northern hemisphere.

31. In the future it is likely that more conflicts will arise because of

    A. racial antagonisms.

    C. natural resource degradation.

    B. nuclear weapons.

    D. religious conflicts.

32. Supplies of fossil fuels are

    A. continually expanding in nature.

    C. being renewed as fast as we use them.

    B. being steadily depleted.

    D. almost entirely depleted.

33. The US, with about 4.5 percent of the world's population consumes _____ of all oil.

    A. 13 percent   B. 26 percent   C. 50 percent   D. 75 percent

34. Global warming, deforestation, and toxic pollution are all problems that

    A. might be solved if we understood them better.

    B. we can do nothing about because they are much too large.

    C. will ultimately solve themselves.

    D. are too complex to solve.

35. Evidence of progress in dealing with population problems is best illustrated by

    A. a growing population of people in the developing and developed world.

    B. a declining average number of children born to each woman.

    C. current evidence of a globally stable population growth.

    D. the decreasing population growth rate in the United States.

36. The world's poorest people _____ environmental degradation.

    A. cause the most

    D. cause and suffer from

    B. are unaffected by

    E. don't really care about

    C. are ignorant of

37. About _____ of the world lives in acute poverty.

    A. .2 percent   B. 2 percent   C. 20 percent   D. 25 percent

38. The world's two most populated countries are
   A. United States and Russia.   C. China and India.
   B. China and Brazil.   D. Mexico and India.

39. The best title for the vertical axis on the graph below is
   A. Life expectancy.   C. Average dietary protein intake per day.
   B. Female literacy.   D. Infant mortality.

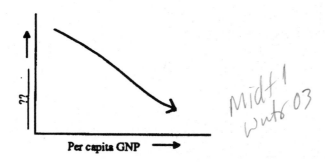

Per capita GNP ⟶

40. The world's ten poorest countries in 1993 all had an annual per capita Gross National Product of less than
   A. US $200.   B. US $500.   C. US $2000.   D. US $5000.

41. If everybody in the world used resources at the rate that people in the United States do,
   A. people would be healthier and happier.
   B. our current resources would run out quickly.
   C. war would be eliminated because basic needs would be met.
   D. economies would prosper.

42. Western Europe, North America, Japan, Australia, and New Zealand combined make up _____ of the world's population, but consume _____ of the world's resources.
   A. less than 25 percent, more than half   C. about 50 percent, more than half
   B. more than 50 percent, more than half   D. less than 25 percent, almost 100 percent

43. Massive consumption of resources results in
   A. better economic conditions.
   B. a decrease in the disparity between rich and poor.
   C. an increased urban population.
   D. a corresponding high production of waste.

44. Poverty is usually passed on from one generation to the next through
   A. the lack of available opportunities.   C. genetic conditions.
   B. improper care of natural resources.   D. the lack of motivation to change.

45. In general, as per capita GNP rises both _____ and _____ increases.
   A. infant mortality, life expectancy
   B. average dietary protein intake, rate of infectious diseases
   C. infant mortality, female literacy
   D. average dietary protein intake, female literacy

46. The North/South division refers to generalized differences in

   A. climate.   C. culture.

   B. wealth and development.   D. environmental quality.

47. The term Third World originally meant

   A. poor.   B. powerless.   C. less advanced.   D. unaligned.

48. Which curve on the graph below best represents air pollution trends in cities for a wealthy country like the US?

   A. a   B. b   C. c   D. d

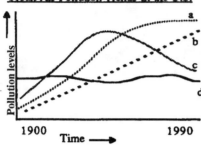

Urban Air Pollution Trends in the U.S.

49. A country's Human Development Index (HDI) is based primarily on such factors as

   A. average life expectancy and annual income per capita.

   B. population structure and average life expectancy.

   C. dominant religion and population structure.

   D. annual income per capita and dominant religion.

50. One of the drawbacks of using the Human Development Index (HDI) is that it

   A. fails to indicate current conditions because it is only reported every other year.

   B. fails to indicate issues such as gender inequities.

   C. fluctuates annually.

   D. stays relatively the same for most countries of the world.

51. In the past twenty years the gap between the richest and poorest of the world has

   A. increased.   B. decreased.   C. more than doubled.   D. stayed the same.

52. Proponents of sustainable development argue that

   A. all development has environmental costs.

   B. development is less important than the environment.

   C. development can proceed with minimal costs to the environment.

   D. the environment is less important than development.

53. Sustainable development, ideally, improves living conditions

   A. for decades into the future.   C. for the entire current political administration.

   B. as long as resources last.   D. for generations in the future.

54. Sustainable development differs from traditional economic development in that it emphasizes economic development in the

   A. short term.   B. long term.   C. present.   D. past.

55. Indigenous people are valuable to us today for their

    A. ability to live in universal harmony with nature.   C. exotic and picturesque religious beliefs.

    B. thorough and unique understanding of their ecosystem.   D. culture that forbids harm to animals.

56. Places in the world where indigenous people live tend to have

    A. terrible environmental conditions.   C. high biodiversity.

    B. little or no biodiversity.   D. little natural resources.

57. Aldo Leopold was a proponent of using fear and warnings of impending doom because he

    A. was aware of environmental degradation even in his time.

    B. felt it was the most effective way to communicate the threat of disasters.

    C. saw a scarcity of resources and high competition for those resources.

    D. None of these is a reflection of Leopold's philosophy.

58. Technological optimists believe that technology will

    A. solve population and environmental problems.

    B. eliminate human unhappiness.

    C. restore the earth's biodiversity.

    D. return us to nomadic pastoralism.

59. Which of the following best describes a cornucopian worldview?

    A. The assumption that nothing is wrong and there is no reason to change anything.

    B. Our world is a place where there is too much competition for limited resources.

    C. Expectation of the worst case scenario with no hope to avoid problems.

    D. Problems are faced realistically, but with hope for creating new solutions.

60. What would probably happen if we dwell on environmental problems and failures?

    A. People would start acting responsibly because they don't want any more environmental problems.

    B. People would finally understand the serious nature of the environmental problems that are currently facing us.

    C. People would get overwhelmed with the problems and expect them, instead of focusing on creating solutions.

    D. People would invest more resources (time, money, etc.) in finding a technological solution to the problem.

61. Critical thinking is important to learn in environmental science because

    A. sound thinking is an automatic result of the scientific method.

    B. disagreements are common in society but beliefs do not influence conclusions of the scientific method.

    C. you would not encounter it in daily life making it necessary to learn for this discipline.

    D. environmental issues are complex and evidence is incomplete, making decisions difficult.

CHAPTER 2
TOOLS FOR BUILDING A BETTER WORLD

1. President Nelson Mandela is hesitant to support the argument of the former occupants of lands in South African National Parks because

    A. they are ruthless poachers and trespassers.

    B. establishing a national park requires removal of all local people.

    C. there is no way that they could live in harmony with the wildlife in the area.

    D. ecotourism and big game safaris are a source of cash for the country.

2. The case study of South African wildlife refuges and indigenous people is important because it illustrates the

    A. ethical considerations that are an inherent part of complex environmental issues.

    B. large amount of land preserved in South Africa.

    C. conflict that usually occurs between people and animals when resources are scarce.

    D. political orientation of President Nelson Mandela.

3. The branch of philosophy concerned with the distinction between right and wrong and the ultimate worth of actions or things is

    A. values.   B. ethics.   C. morals.   D. attitudes.

4. Universalists such as Plato assert that

    A. moral principles are always relative to a particular person, situation, or society.

    B. an action is right if it holds the greatest good for the greatest number of people.

    C. there are fundamental principles of ethics that are eternal and unchanging.

    D. moral principles are social constructs.

5. The early conservationists (Pinchot and others) were inspired by the contentions of the empirical and intellectual form of

    A. Universalists.   B. Postmodernists.   C. Relativists.   D. Utilitarians.

6. Yesterday you told your friend that you didn't need to worry about recycling or decreasing your consumption of resources because you feel overwhelmed by environmental problems and survival is the ultimate reason for being. She responded that your philosophical view was in accordance with the

    A. Nihilists.   B. Utilitarians.   C. Relativists.   D. Postmodernists.

7. John Muir argued that nature deserves to exist for its own sake, regardless of its usefulness to humans. If he believed that this is not contextual and is valid, regardless of the interests, attitudes, or preferences of humans, it could be stated that Muir was a

    A. Postmodernist.   B. Utilitarian.   C. Relativist.   D. Universalist.

8. You were discussing the South Africa Case Study with your classmate and he stated that protecting wildlife needed to take precedence over human life *if* the wildlife was in danger of going extinct. He further supported his position by saying that the *context* of the situation is very important to him. Your classmate's viewpoint is consistent with the

    A. Relativists.   B. Utilitarians.   C. Universalists.   D. Postmodernists.

9. Postmodernism is more similar to _____ than to _____ because of the belief that our relation with nature, for example, is a social construction rather than an ethical absolute.

    A. constructionism, utilitarianism   C. relativism, universalism

    B. universalism, relativism   D. instrumentalism, constructionism

10. Moral agents _____ while moral subjects _____.

    A. have rights, are not responsible for doing what is right

    B. are responsible for doing what is right, have rights

    C. are not responsible for doing what is right, have rights

    D. have rights, are responsible for doing what is right

11. Could a person change from being a moral subject to a moral agent?

    A. Yes, if they mature in adulthood.   C. No, they would not be able to make the transition.

    B. Yes, if they have children.   D. No, as a person matures they can no longer be a moral agent.

12. Most pet owners would probably _____ with Rene Descartes' view of animals as _____.

    A. disagree, automa   C. disagree, moral subjects

    B. agree, automa   D. agree, moral subjects

13. The Mineral King Valley court case is important environmental history because it was a case that argued for the

    A. inherent value of trees, rocks, and wildlife.

    B. instrumental value of trees, rocks, and wildlife.

    C. status of moral agents for trees, rocks, and wildlife.

    D. sustainable development of the area.

14. The early conservationists (Pinchot and others) would argue that forests have _____ value.

    A. inherent   B. individual   C. instrumental   D. increasing

15. Admonitions from the Bible have often been used to

    A. condemn exploitation of nature.   C. argue that we are just another animal species.

    B. urge conservation for future generations. D. justify exploitation of nature.

16. Using the role model of St. Francis of Assisi in the Judeo-Christian culture would reflect an attitude of

    A. stewardship.   B. anthropocentrism.   C. biocentrism.   D. ecofeminism.

17. The question of whether humans are just another animal species or are destined to rule nature is important because

    A. our answer to this question tells us who are our friends and enemies.

    B. one opinion is for the environment, the other against it.

    C. our opinions determine our policies.

    D. our answer determines how long we'll survive.

18. Another word for "steward" is

    A. caretaker   B. organizer   C. participant   D. consumer

19. The idea of stewardship is that we have a/the _____ the environment.

    A. privilege of using   C. technology to shape

    B. duty to care for   D. opportunity to degrade

20. Anthropocentric means _____.

    A. focused on people   C. selfish

    B. disinterested in nature   D. morally upright

21. Unlike most other ethics, an ecocentric philosophy grants rights and value to

    A. plants.   C. inanimate things (e.g. rocks and water).

    B. all animal species.   D. minority peoples.

22. In the words ecocentric, biocentric, and anthropocentric, the root "centric" means _____.

    A. recognition of   B. exclusion of   C. centered on   D. acting like

23. Ecocentric is to _____ as stewardship is to _____.

    A. ecofeminism, dominion   C. anthropocentric, biocentric

    B. dominion, ecofeminism   D. biocentric, anthropocentric

24. You are surprised that an animal rights activist and an ecologist are having a major disagreement. The animal rights activist is opposing the extermination of an introduced species which is outcompeting species normally found in an area. The ecologist argues that the ecosystem is adversely affected and will be destroyed if the introduced species is not removed. You thought that animal rights activists and ecologists had the same basic ethical perspective but after some research you now realize that the animal rights activist is probably a(n) _____ while the ecologists is a(n) _____.

    A. ecocentric, biocentric   C. anthropocentric, biocentric

    B. biocentric, ecocentric   D. biocentric, anthropocentric

25. Ecofeminists assert that

    A. women make better ecologists than men because they are able to see relationships.

    B. women and nature have been oppressed in many of the same ways.

    C. nature has historically suffered from sexism.

    D. nature is essentially female.

26. Which of the following is not an important characteristic of ecofeminism?

    A. hierarchical organization   B. pluralism   C. kinship values   D. reciprocity

27. In ecofeminism the Hindu god Shiva is a useful image because it represents _____ and can therefore serve as a model in transforming the distinction between nature and culture.

    A. the power of nature   C. the evil of human activity

    B. the integration of creation and destruction   D. nature's resistance to disruption

28. Environmental justice can be seen as

    A. the power to make laws for a just society.

    B. an issue that is of special interest to the global community.

    C. both a local and an international issue.

    D. a local issue central to the middle class citizens in the United States.

29. That racial and ethnic minorities face unusually high exposure to environmental hazards is a central argument to

    A. sustainable development.   C. environmental justice.

    B. economic development.   D. urban renewal.

30. The term "toxic colonialism" has been used in describing

    A. lax environmental regulations for toxic wastes.

    B. the exportation of toxic wastes to poor communities.

    C. rulings that toxins must not be exported to rich nations.

    D. high level of toxic waste production by rich countries.

31. Using the example that the discrepancy between the exposure of middle class African Americans and middle class whites to environmental hazards is even greater than the difference between poor African Americans and whites is effective in supporting the contention that _____, rather than _____ is the strongest determinant of exposure to environmental hazards.

    A. race, income   B. class, race   C. class, income   D. income, race

32. Your Native American friend explains that she lives in a community that has an uncontrolled toxic waste site. Unfortunately you are not surprised because _____ the people with her ethnic background live in communities with locally unwanted land uses.

    A. about a quarter of   C. nearly half of

    B. over three-quarters of   D. almost all

33. Lead poisoning in children is an example that exemplifies the problem of _____ for minority children.

    A. environmental racism   C. inadequate nutrition

    B. poverty   D. sanitary conditions

34. Maquiladoras are

    A. treaties that regulate international shipping of toxins.

    B. regulations for the cleanup of industrial facilities along the US/Mexico border.

    C. birth defects in towns along the US/Mexico border.

    D. assembly plants located along the US/Mexico border.

35. Currently in the United States and Canada the average environmental activist is

    A. a victim of environmental racism.   C. wealthy and elite.

    B. well educated, white, and middle-class.   D. someone living near a pollution source.

36. The agendas of many environmental organizations focus on wilderness, resource management, and outdoor recreation. Critics contend that these issues are

    A. not communicated well enough to make positive improvements.

    B. not in line with the concerns of all people, especially those struggling to make a living.

    C. too broad and need to be focused in order to make real progress in solving problems.

    D. based on too many different philosophies and do not reflect the concerns of all people.

37. Environmental organizations in the United States and Canada will probably emphasize _____ in the near future as the environmental justice movement becomes a more integral component of environmentalism.

    A. urban issues   C. environmental laws

    B. global issues   D. extinction

38. NIMBY protests often result in

    A. the reduction of waste generation.

    B. the invention of new ways to process waste.

    C. putting waste in rich, powerful communities.

    D. putting waste in poor, powerless areas.

39. The remains of Mayan temples are a good example of the _____ nature.

    A. resiliency of   C. systems connection with

    B. fragility of   D. domination of

40. Our idea of wilderness as a fearsome place has become less fearful as

    A. we have come to live more in nature.   C. we have moved from cities to suburbs

    B. we have become farmers and gardeners.   D. civilization and urbanization have grown.

41. Humans have historically viewed nature as fierce and forceful. However, that view has changed in recent years due in part to an increase in

    A. human population.

    B. technological power that can disrupt natural systems.

    C. domestic animal use by humans.

    D. knowledge of the power of natural systems.

42. Why do astronomers view Mt. Graham as an especially advantageous site for research?

    A. It is an area of wilderness and inaccessible to vandalism.

    B. The area is not used for anything else and is therefore available as a site for building telescopes.

    C. The air is clear, it is dark at night, and the area is accessible.

    D. Telescopes have been built and there are plans for building more telescopes.

43. Ideally, scientific methods

    A. are correct most of the time.   C. tell us what we expected to find.

    B. use new technology.   D. are neutral and unbiased.

44. The best definition of a hypothesis is a(n)

    A. proof of a proposed theory.   C. proposed explanation based on observation.

    B. theory based on experiments.   D. argument based on acute intuition.

45. Generally, distinguished scientists

    A. always agree if they really are expert scientists.

    B. may have different interpretations of the same evidence.

    C. never disagree once a theory is established.

    D. believe each other and support each other in their work.

46. Proof in science is always

    A. firmly established. C. beyond question.

    B. an impossible goal. D. open to question or new evidence.

47. Although your sister is not a scientist, she says that she uses scientific techniques in her everyday life. You don't believe her but she insists it is true. Which of the following examples could she use to best persuade you?

    A. When she cooks she measures ingredients and puts them together to form something else (i.e., a cake).

    B. When she drives in her car she hypothesizes about things (i.e., when the red light will turn green).

    C. She put some tomatoes in the sun and some in the shade to see if the sun causes them to ripen faster.

    D. She buys a brand of toothpaste based on statistical data (four out of five dentists recommend it).

48. Why might you disagree with someone if they said that astronomers are not really scientists because they do not use "controls" in their experiments?

A. I would not disagree with them because scientific techniques require a hypothesis, an experiment with controls, and interpretations of the results.

B. Since science proves theories and astronomers have theories, they must be scientists.

C. I would not disagree with them because having controls in a scientific experiment is a way of ensuring that they are only testing one variable at a time.

D. Hypotheses can be tested indirectly with historic evidence or model systems.

49. Perhaps one of the reasons Neo-Luddites feel the way they do is because

A. technology allows us to make mistakes on a larger and quicker scale.

B. there is an increase in wealth that is associated with the industrial revolution.

C. technology allows us to fix our mistakes and remediate environmental problems.

D. progress has led to an increased standard of living that may spread to all members of society.

50. Appropriate technology promotes

A. the fact that science and technology cause problems rather than solutions.

B. techniques and knowledge suitable for a particular place and culture.

C. industrialization using the model of Western thinking.

D. an abandonment of modern life for a low technological-based society.

51. The point of critical thinking is to learn to

A. weigh evidence and draw your own conclusions.

B. distrust all opinions other than your own.

C. trust only your own experimental results.

D. learn to accept the views of real authorities.

52. In the following statement, use the letter to identify the premise:

(A) "Because the sun is bright"

(B) "it must be warm out;"

(C) "therefore I will go out to play Frisbee."

A. A   B. B   C. C   D. both A and B

53. The first step in critical thinking is to

A. decide whether conclusions follow premises.

B. decide if premises are true.

C. identify premises and conclusions.

D. identify whether premises are facts or values.

54. Critical thinking is based on formal logic, but *differs* from formal logic in that it

A. helps us decide whether conclusions follow premises.

B. includes contextual skills, attitudes, and dispositions.

C. includes the identification of premises and conclusions.

D. helps us identify whether premises are facts or values.

55. In reading a claim that Ozone Depletion is not an actual environmental problem, a critical thinker would

    A. ignore the claim because it does not align with their opinions.

    B. feel relieved because Ozone Depletion was such an overwhelming problem.

    C. look for evidence that is in line with their past experience.

    D. look for evidence of the reliability of the source.

56. Being cognizant of our own worldview is useful because worldviews

    A. help us solve environmental problems by approaching them in a logical manner.

    B. direct what we see and how we interpret what is happening around us.

    C. show us that science and technology can be used to enhance people's lives.

    D. help us understand why other people think the way they do.

57. While the following list of factors all influence our worldview, which one is "deeper" and more influential?

    A. Personal experiences.   C. The kind of education we have had.

    B. The amount of education we have had.   D. Our culture.

CHAPTER 3
MATTER, ENERGY, AND LIFE

1. Blurred vision, slurred speech, coordination loss, depression, and confusion are all symptoms native Ojibwa people experienced due to high levels of _____ in their diet.

   A. lead   B. dioxins   C. chlorine   D. mercury

2. Why is it especially difficult for some people if authorities advise people to limit their fish intake due to local surface water contamination?

   A. They are unaccustomed to other diets and have gastrointestinal problems if they change their diet.

   B. They rely on local fish as a source of protein in their diet because they cannot afford store-bought food.

   C. They view fishing as a source of recreation and cannot afford other recreational activities.

   D. They will no longer be able to use the water for drinking since the fish will die due to the contamination.

3. Ecologists study

   A. living things and their genetic makeup.

   B. genetic patterns and the chemistry in them.

   C. the physical world and its processes.

   D. relationships between organisms and their environment.

4. How are matter and mass related?

   A. Mass is a component of matter.   C. Neither matter nor mass take up space.

   B. Matter is a component of mass.   D. Both matter and mass take up space.

5. Water vapor, water, and ice are examples of

   A. types of matter.   C. transfers of energy into matter.

   B. phases of matter.   D. forms of energy.

6. The smallest particle that exhibits the characteristics of a chemical element is known as a(n)

   A. molecule.   B. microorganism.   C. atom.   D. phase of matter.   E. isotope.

7. The relationship among atoms, elements, and compounds is most like the relationship among

   A. grains of sugar, sugar, and sweetened iced tea.   C. grains of sand, rocks, and continents.

   B. bricks, sidewalks, and paved roads.   D. pond, lake, and ocean.

8. A compound is to a(n) _____ as a word is to a _____.

   A. element, phrase   C. isotope, sentence

   B. atom, letter   D. molecule, punctuation mark

9. In chemical terms water (H_2O) would best be described as a(n)

   A. element.   B. atom.   C. ion.   D. compound.

10. Which of the following is not a molecule?

   A. C   B. O_2 C. H_2O D. DNA

11. Which of the following statements changes the statement: "Most, but not all, living organisms are made up of organic compounds." into a true statement?

 A. All living organisms are made up of organic compounds.

 B. Most, but not all, living organisms are made up of inorganic compounds.

 C. All living organisms are made up of inorganic compounds.

 D. Most, but not all, living organisms are made up of organic elements.

12. The distinction between an organic compound and an inorganic compound is that organic compounds contain

 A. oxygen.   B. water.   C. carbon.   D. nitrogen.   E. All of these.

13. A fat or oil is to a _____ as an enzyme is to a _____.

 A. nucleic acid, lipid   C. protein, nucleic acid

 B. lipid, protein   D. carbohydrate, protein

14. Nucleic acid is to _____ as lipid is to _____.

 A. cellular membrane structure, energy storage

 B. cellulose structure, genetic storage

 C. energy storage, cellulose structure

 D. genetic storage, cellular membrane structure

15. Deoxyribonucleic acid (DNA) contains billions of atoms and is very large. It would be considered a(n)

 A. element.   B. molecule.   C. compound.   D. mega-atom.

16. A cell is

 A. the smallest molecule exhibiting organic characteristics.   C. a building block for DNA.

 B. the smallest unit in which life processes go on.   D. made up of DNA.

17. A(n) _____ is like a screwdriver that you use to build something because it _____.

 A. enzyme, does not get consumed as it is used

 B. molecule, organizes pieces together to form something different

 C. lipid, provides the structure and form of the piece you are building

 D. sugar, provides the energy to put something together

18. Metabolism is a collective term for thousands of

 A. organic compounds in a cell.   C. molecular reactions in a compound.

 B. enzymatic reactions necessary for life.   D. cells in an organism.

19. Energy is the ability to

 A. move objects.   C. both A and B are true.

 B. transfer heat from one object to another.   D. become heated.

20. Which of the following is a form of energy?

 A. electricity   D. food

 B. heat   E. All of these are forms of energy.

 C. light

21. Potential energy is _____ energy.

 A. electrical   B. motion   C. stored   D. heat   E. latent

22. The motion of a rock rolling downhill is known as _____ energy.

    A. kinetic   B. latent   C. potential   D. electrical   E. mechanical

23. The total kinetic energy of atoms in a mass or body is known as its

    A. potential energy.   D. cumulative energy.

    B. latent energy.   E. temperature.

    C. heat.

24. Metabolism can be seen as the process of converting

    A. energy into matter.   C. kinetic energy into potential energy.

    B. potential energy into kinetic energy.   D. atoms into compounds.

25. An object's heat content depends upon its

    A. mass and temperature.   C. mass and potential energy.

    B. temperature and potential energy.   D. potential energy and matter.

26. The ocean has a high heat but a relatively low average temperature. How can this be true?

    A. The average rate of energy flow from one object to another is high, but there is low kinetic energy.

    B. The average speed of particles is relatively high but there is a low average rate of energy flow.

    C. There is high kinetic energy but there are few molecules per unit volume.

    D. The average speed of molecules is relatively slow but there is much mass with many moving particles.

    E. It is not true.

27. Which of the following has the highest quality energy?

    A. a warm brick   B. a flame   C. a flowing stream   D. a rock rolling downhill E. hot air

28. The law of conservation of matter tells us that matter

    A. can never be reused.   C. is used over and over again.

    B. can be destroyed.   D. can be conserved by some adaptive strategies.

29. What implication(s) does the law of conservation of matter have for humans?

    A. We cannot create energy because it is neither created or destroyed.

    B. As matter is recycled it loses some of its integrity so we need to be careful when we dispose of goods.

    C. Natural resources are unlimited because they are used and reused by living organisms.

    D. Disposable goods are not going "away" when we throw them out.

    E. All of these are implications of the law of conservation of matter.

30. If an ecosystem exchanges both matter and energy with its surroundings, it would be referred to as a(n) _____ system.

    A. closed   B. open   C. dynamic   D. isolated

31. The first law of thermodynamics and the law of conservation of matter are similar in that

    A. under normal circumstances neither energy or matter is created nor destroyed.

    B. both energy and matter are recycled through biological systems.

    C. both energy and matter flow in a one-way path through biological systems.

    D. The first law of thermodynamics and the law of conservation of matter are not similar.

32. The second law of thermodynamics states that as energy moves through different forms and systems it gradually

    A. becomes more concentrated.   C. disappears and is lost.

    B. dissipates and becomes unavailable.   D. accumulates in the form of electricity.

33. As energy is used and transformed it gradually becomes _____ quality and _____ concentrated.

    A. higher, more   B. lower, more   C. higher, less   D. lower, less

34. What implication(s) does the second law of thermodynamics have for biological systems?

    A. Systems cannot create energy because it is neither created nor destroyed.

    B. With each transformation less available energy is available to do work so older systems have less energy.

    C. A constant supply of energy is necessary for maintenance of biological systems.

    D. Energy is unlimited because it is used and reused by living organisms.

    E. None of these is an implication of the second law of thermodynamics.

35. Photosynthesis is the process of converting _____ into _____ energy.

    A. chemical bond energy, kinetic   C. sunlight, chemical bond

    B. solar energy, kinetic   D. solar electrical energy, heat

36. On the spectrum of solar energy wavelengths shown below, visible light falls near the letter

    A. a.   B. b.   C. c.   D. d.

The Electromagnetic Spectrum

37. On the spectrum of solar energy wavelengths shown above, the wavelengths that plants use for photosynthesis is closest to which letter?

    A. a   B. b   C. c   D. d

38. About _____ percent of the solar energy that falls on plants is captured for photosynthesis.

    A. 100   B. 60 - 70   C. 40 - 50   D. 10 - 20   E. 1 - 2

39. Photosynthesis produces sugars from

    A. water, carbon dioxide, and energy.   C. oxygen, carbon dioxide, and water.

    B. water, other sugars, and oxygen.   D. carbon dioxide, enzymes, and energy.

40. The process of photosynthesis and cellular respiration are similar in that they both

    A. capture energy in the form of sugar.

    B. occur in all living organisms.

    C. store energy in ATP, an energy currency for the cell.

    D. Photosynthesis and cellular respiration are not similar, they are exact opposite processes.

41. The process of cellular respiration

   A. helps primary producers store energy accumulated by chloroplasts.

   B. releases energy from chemical bonds of molecules such as glucose.

   C. eliminates the need for enzymes in metabolism.

   D. does not occur in primary producers.

43. With respect to _____, every ecosystem is open.

   A. species   B. populations   C. matter cycling   D. energy flow

44. Although there are exceptions, in general, a species includes all organisms that are similar enough to

   A. produce fertile offspring in nature.   C. look alike.

   B. fill the same niche.   D. occupy the same community.

45. All members of a species that live in the same area at the same time make up a/an

   A. species.   B. ecosystem.   C. community.   D. population.

46. A biological community consists of all

   A. populations living and interacting in an area.   C. living things on Earth.

   B. members of a species living in the same area.   D. populations of a given species.

47. An ecosystem consists of

   A. a physical environment within which a biological community lives.

   B. the species with which a biological community interacts.

   C. a biological community and its physical environment.

   D. the primary producers within a biological community.

48. The systems approach is important in ecology because it emphasizes

   A. the relationships in the interrelated processes of an ecosystem.

   B. the energy source that all living organisms depend upon.

   C. that many living things function independently of their surroundings.

   D. the closed nature of ecosystems.

49. Homeostasis refers to

   A. a state in which conditions do not change.

   B. a reduction in energy during transformation.

   C. speeding up of chemical reactions at high temperatures.

   D. a dynamic balance in living systems.

50. Many ecologists think of ecosystems and even the Earth as a superorganism because its systems appear to be

   A. unregulated.   C. completely unpredictable.

   B. self-regulating and self-stabilizing.   D. unchangeable.

51. Gaia is a name many ecologists use to describe

   A. ecosystems that function successfully on Earth.

   B. the Earth as transformed by human action.

   C. the Earth as a living, self-regulating being.

   D. the Earth and the moon as a part of the solar system.

52. In viewing ecosystems and biological communities, F. E. Clements' views were very influential in the early days of ecology. Clements viewed the relationships in biological communities as _____ while his contemporary, H. A. Gleason, viewed biological communities as _____.

   A. self-maintaining, chance associations
   C. deterministic, chance associations

   B. chance associations, deterministic
   D. chance associations, self-maintaining

53. Productivity in an ecosystem has to do with

   A. the efficiency of its primary producers.

   B. the number of different species living in the ecosystem.

   C. its longevity.

   D. its rate of producing biomass.

54. How can a highly productive ecosystem (high total productivity) have a low net productivity?

   A. The rate of photosynthesis is low.
   C. The rate of decomposition is high.

   B. The rate of secondary productivity is high.
   D. The rate of decomposition is low.

55. Biomass includes all

   A. biological material.
   C. things that are living at a given time.

   B. living and nonliving things.
   D. matter produced by primary producers.

56. A simple linked feeding series such as corn-chicken-human is known as a(n)

   A. energy cycle.   B. food web.   C. carbon cycle.   D. food chain.

57. The length and complexity of a food web in the Arctic would be _____ when compared to one in the tropical rainforest.

   A. short and less complex
   D. long and more complex

   B. short and more complex
   E. about the same

   C. long and less complex

58. Living things that carry out photosynthesis are known as

   A. consumers.   B. producers.   C. decomposers.   D. primary consumers.

59. Producers rely on _____ to release chemical energy and consumers rely on _____ to release chemical energy.

   A. cellular respiration, photosynthesis
   C. photosynthesis, cellular respiration

   B. cellular respiration, cellular respiration
   D. photosynthesis, photosynthesis

60. Primary consumers are also known as

   A. carnivores.   B. scavengers.   C. decomposers.   D. herbivores.

61. Omnivores eat mainly

   A. plants.
   C. plants and animals.

   B. animals.
   D. dead plants and animals.

62. The organisms at the "a" level of the food pyramid below are

    A. primary producers.   C. herbivores.

    B. primary consumers.   D. carnivores.

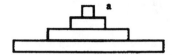

63. In the biomass pyramid above the bottom level represents

    A. carnivores.   C. primary producers.

    B. primary consumers.   D. decomposers.

64. Energy enters a system as sunlight and a producer is able to produce 10 kilograms of tissue. If eaten, the producer would produce about _____ kilograms of consumer tissue that would provide about _____ kilograms of tissue for a secondary consumer.

    A. 100, 10   B. 10, 1   C. 100, 1   D. 1, 0.1   E. 10, 0.1

65. Detritivores, scavengers, and decomposers are all similar in that they

    A. are primarily microorganisms.   C. are primary producers.

    B. consume nonliving organic matter.   D. are among the Earth's least useful organisms.

66. Which of the following does not cycle repeatedly through the Earth's ecosystems?

    A. water   B. nitrogen   C. matter   D. carbon   E. energy

67. Living vegetation and the ocean are known as "carbon sinks" because they

    A. are made of carbon.   B. create carbon.   C. destroy carbon.   D. store carbon.

68. Nitrogen is an essential component of

    A. amino acids and proteins.   C. sugars, the product of photosynthesis.

    B. organic molecules.   D. the hydrologic cycle.

69. Nitrogen gas (N_2), the most abundant form of nitrogen on Earth, is

    A. also the easiest for plants to use.   C. outside of the global nitrogen cycle.

    B. the easiest form for both animals and plants to use.   D. inaccessible to most plants.

70. Phosphorus cycles through the Earth's ecosystems

    A. extremely quickly.   C. only when activated by human activity.

    B. very slowly.   D. very rarely.

71. Human activities such as _____ release large quantities of sulfur

    A. the burning of fossil fuels   C. using synthetic fertilizers

    B. the burning of wood   D. using detergents

1. Which of the following statements best describes the biological community of the giant kelp forests when otters are removed?

   A. Abalone, lobsters, and crabs can finally recover from otter predation and increase in number.

   B. Sea urchins increase in number and destroy the kelp forests resulting in few species.

   C. Fish and other species increase in number because there are more sea urchins to feed on.

   D. The kelp forests are destroyed because of the increased competition among the abalone, lobsters, and crabs.

2. Some commercial shellfishers are opposed to the reintroduction of sea otters in an area. They claim that

   A. sea otters compete with them for abalone, lobsters, and crabs.

   B. sea urchins would increase in number and destroy the kelp forests resulting in few commercial species.

   C. fish and other species increase in number when sea otters are not present in the ecosystem.

   D. sea otters destroy their nets and traps.

3. Tolerance limits are _____ that limit a species' survival.

   A. temperature ranges   C. any environmental conditions

   B. population sizes   D. salinity levels

4. There is/are usually _____ tolerance limit(s) responsible for limiting the number and location of a species. However, there are some organisms that have _____ that limit(s) their distribution.

   A. one, a specific critical factor   C. one, other environmental conditions

   B. many, a specific critical factor   D. many, other environmental conditions

5. A species can withstand a wide range of pH as an adult but the juveniles can only withstand a narrow range of pH. The abiotic factor, pH, would best be described as a

   A. stress factor   B. intolerance factor   C. tolerance limit   D. critical factor

6. Which of the following fish species would be the best indicator of clean, well-oxygenated water?

   A. carp   B. largemouth bass   C. catfish   D. rainbow trout

7. Populations are most critically limited by

   A. available food.   C. suitable shelter from the elements.

   B. available water.   D. any of these, depending on the system.

8. Indicator species, such as lichens, generally have a _____ tolerance range for a _____.

   A. narrow, critical factor   C. broad, critical factor

   B. narrow, number of physical factors   D. broad, number of critical factors

9. A species can withstand a narrow range of temperature. Above 100°F there are no species present. In the range from 97°F–100°F and 90°F–94°F there are a few species present. Below 90°F there are no species present. What would you label the range of temperature from 90°F to 94°F for this particular species?

   A. zone of intolerance   C. tolerance limit range

   B. zone of physiological stress   D. optimal range

10. Using the same example from the question above, for this particular species what would you label the range of temperature from 95°F to 96°F?

    A. zone of intolerance   C. tolerance limit range

    B. zone of physiological stress   D. optimal range

11. What is the difference in the adaptation of a sled dog's (such as a Husky) thick coat of hair to help it withstand the cold temperatures of Arctic winters and a dog that adapts to cold temperatures in the fall by growing a thickened coat? The adaptation of the sled dog best describes adaptation at the _____ level while the dog exposed to seasonal colder temperatures has _____.

    A. regional, natural selection at the individual level

    B. individual, physiological modifications at the population level

    C. population, physiological modifications at the individual level

    D. species, natural selection at the population` level

12. Evolution occurs as a result of

    A. the discovery of a desirable characteristic in a population.

    B. an individual's physiological modification.

    C. environmental change that forces modification in a resident species.

    D. better survival or reproduction rates by individuals with a particular characteristic.

13. When industrial pollution darkened the trees around urban areas how did the European peppered moth change coloration?

    A. Darker moths adapted to the different coloration and dominated the population.

    B. Lighter moths were more visible and eaten by predators and the darker moths were able to reproduce.

    C. Lighter moths adapted to the different coloration and gradually became darker.

    D. Darker moths adapted to the changing environment because they were less visible to predators.

14. In the example of the European peppered moth where did the darker moths come from?

    A. They were already present in the population as a result of genetic variation.

    B. They evolved as a result of the selective pressure of predation.

    C. They adapted to the change in the tree coloration and gradually became darker.

    D. They were present in a different region and migrated to the urban areas where the trees were darker.

15. Which of the following is a physiological modification used to adapt to environmental conditions?

    A. Young saguaro seedlings sprouting under mesquites.

    B. Leaves becoming thick and leathery on a plant growing in a dry, hot climate.

    C. Locoweed growing only where selenium is present in soil.

    D. Desert pupfish learning to deposit eggs where temperatures are optimal.

16. Natural selection gradually makes a species

    A. more intelligent.   C. more adapted to its environment.

    B. physically bigger.   D. more aggressive.

17. Regular lawn mowing selects for short-headed rather than tall-headed dandelions because

    A. short flowers can reproduce.   C. tall flowers spread their seeds farther.

    B. tall flowers cannot reproduce.   D. short flowers spread their seeds farther.

18. Your friend stated that natural selection would occur at the individual level while evolution and adaptation would occur at the population level. How would you respond to your friend?

   A. I would agree because individuals cannot change their genetic makeup.

   B. I would agree because individuals can adapt to their environment.

   C. I would disagree because populations cannot change their genetic makeup.

   D. I would disagree because populations can adapt to their environment.

19. In the process known as convergent evolution, environmental conditions lead

   A. a species to adapt especially quickly.

   B. a species to resist the changes of random mutation.

   C. unrelated species to live together.

   D. unrelated species to look like each other.

20. Cheetahs can run extremely fast because

   A. they need to run extremely fast in order to catch their prey.

   B. an ancestor that was able to run fast had an advantage and passed those genes on to its offspring.

   C. over time they gradually built up speed as they adapted to faster and faster prey species.

   D. All of these are reasons cheetahs can run extremely fast.

21. The word "niche" refers to an organism's _____ while its habitat refers to _____.

   A. environmental surroundings, its cumulative tolerance limits

   B. cumulative tolerance limits, its environmental surroundings

   C. role and relationships in its community, its environmental surroundings

   D. life cycle within its population, its role and relationships in its community

22. A generalist is a species that

   A. occupies a large habitat range.

   B. occupies a variety of ecological niches.

   C. can reproduce under highly variable conditions.

   D. All of these are characteristics of a generalist species.

23. Humans can best be described as

   A. occupying a narrow niche.

   C. generalists.

   B. an example of convergent evolution.

   D. outside the rules of natural selection.

24. Most organisms' niches are controlled by

   A. genetic determinants.

   C. behavior learned from others in their social groups.

   B. lessons learned from parents.

   D. luck.

25. Resource partitioning leads species to

   A. feed at different times.

   C. develop different physiological adaptations.

   B. migrate to other regions.

   D. All of these would be a result of resource partitioning.

26. Resource partitioning tends to lead to a high degree of _____ in species.

   A. specialization   B. evolution   C. convergent evolution   D. generalization

27. Certain night-active moths and day-active birds are specialized nectar feeders. How do these species coexist if they are using the same resource for food?

    A. Since they both use the nectar eventually one of the two species will need to move to a new area.

    B. They do not compete for the nectar because they feed at different times of the day.

    C. There is enough nectar to supply both the birds and the moths with their feeding needs.

    D. Eventually the niche breadth will increase and there will be less competition.

28. Which of the following is not considered a predator?

    A. a grasshopper   B. a lion   C. an intestinal tapeworm   D. a dandelion

29. How does the loss of large predators such as wolves and owls in the United States relate to songbird population decline?

    A. Nest parasites such as the brown-headed cowbirds are no longer eaten by the wolves and owls.

    B. The loss of owls does not relate to the songbird population decline because owls are songbird predators.

    C. Songbird predators such as raccoons and opossums are no longer eaten by the wolves and owls.

    D. None of these - the decline of songbirds in the US is due mainly to deforestation in developing countries.

30. Predation could influence evolution when

    A. prey species develop defensive characteristics.

    B. individual predators adapt and become more efficient in catching their prey.

    C. individual prey adapt and become more efficient in eluding predators.

    D. a population of predators develop defensive characteristics.

31. A keystone species is a species whose presence

    A. is the main reason a community exists.

    B. provides food for all other species in a community.

    C. is an indicator of environmental health.

    D. influences the population size of many other species in its community.

    E. is always at the top of the trophic levels as a top predator.

32. A Titmouse and a Chickadee are living in the same territory and are using some of the same resources. The *best* way to classify this interaction is as

    A. mutualism.   C. interspecific competition.

    B. intraspecific competition.   D. symbiosis.

33. Intraspecific competition is competition _____ for resources.

    A. between predators and prey   C. between different species

    B. among both plants and animals   D. between members of a single species

34. A common strategy for successful interspecific competition is

    A. eating prey before they are "ready" (ripe) for other species.

    B. spreading seeds or offspring far and fast.

    C. producing substances that are toxic to competitors.

    D. All of these are strategies for successful interspecific competition.

35. An especially effective strategy for reducing intraspecific competition is

    A. different ecological niches for juveniles and adults.

    B. rapid reproduction.

    C. eating prey before they are "ready" (ripe) for other species.

    D. resource partitioning.

36. Territoriality is an important form of _____ for many animal species.

    A. symbiotic behavior   C. intraspecific competition

    B. interspecific competition   D. commensalism

37. In some species, young individuals float freely as plankton while mature members are fixed on the seafloor. This is a good strategy because

    A. different phases do not compete for food.   C. fixed adults are more likely to survive.

    B. plankton are more likely to survive.   D. predators cannot catch plankton.

38. Symbiosis means

    A. a relationship in which both species benefit.   C. commensalism.

    B. a parasitic relationship.   D. living together.

39. In a commensal relationship,

    A. one species benefits while the other neither suffers nor benefits.

    B. one species benefits while the other suffers.

    C. two species live together but both suffer.

    D. two species live together and neither benefits nor suffers.

40. In the partnership of a lichen, the fungus provides _____ and the relationship is best described as _____.

    A. most of the photosynthesis, symbiosis

    B. poisons that deter predation, commensalism

    C. structure and moisture-holding ability, mutualism

    D. very little to the algal partner, parasitism

41. The tall, narrow, buttressed trunks of tropical rainforest trees are evidence of intense

    A. parasitism.   B. interspecific competition.   C. commensalism.   D. resiliency.

42. Epiphytes growing on tropical trees exemplify

    A. mutualism.   B. predation.   C. parasitism.   D. commensalism.

43. A viceroy butterfly that closely resembles the bad tasting monarch is an example of _____ and the example of beetles which look like stinging wasps is an example of _____ mimicry.

    A. Batesian mimicry, Batesian mimicry   C. Muellerian mimicry, Muellerian mimicry

    B. Batesian mimicry, Muellerian mimicry   D. Muellerian mimicry, Batesian mimicry

44. A biological community's productivity is a measure of

    A. its number of species.

    B. the number of individuals in the community.

    C. available solar energy that can be converted to biomass.

    D. the amount of biomass produced in the community.

45. In the graph of primary productivity shown below the greatest variety of niches and of species is probably in ecosystem __.

    A. a   B. b   C. c   D. d

Gross Primary Productivity of Major World Ecosystems

ecosystem type: a, b, c, d, e

1,000 kcal/m/year (0, 4, 8, 12, 16, 20)

46. "Abundance" describes the total number of _____ while "diversity" describes the number of _____.

    A. species in a community, individual organisms in a community

    B. organisms in a community, species in a community

    C. individuals in a niche, niches available to a given species

    D. species in a bioregion, trophic levels in a community

47. In a biological community where diversity is great, such as a tropical rainforest, the abundance of any one species is likely to be

    A. great.   C. widely variable from year to year.

    B. small.   D. the same from year to year.

48. As a rule, near the Earth's north and south poles,

    A. diversity is great, while abundance is low.   C. neither abundance nor diversity is great.

    B. abundance is great, as is diversity.   D. abundance is great, but diversity is low.

49. Complexity in an ecological community has to do with the number of

    A. species in the population.   C. genetic variations within a species.

    B. species at each trophic level.   D. primary producers available.

50. A community with many primary producers, a few herbivores, and only one carnivore, has

    A. little complexity.   C. a great deal of complexity.

    B. little diversity.   D. low productivity.

51. A community that changes very little over time is said to have great

    A. renewal ability.   B. complexity.   C. diversity.   D. constancy.

52. The spatial arrangement of individuals and communities is known as

    A. diversity.   B. structure.   C. trophic levels.   D. niche specialization.

53. A species with intense intraspecific competition for nesting space or sunlight would probably be arranged after which pattern below?

   A. a   B. b   C. c   D. Any one of these.

Population Distributions

   a   b   c

54. A communal species, such as fish or wolves, would be arranged like pattern _____ above.

   A. a   B. b   C. c   D. None of these.

55. In ecological communities, patchiness reflects the fact that

   A. species have a hard time living together.

   B. intraspecific competition is intense and leads to sparse numbers of certain species.

   C. complexity and diversity are both low.

   D. local conditions vary, leading to differing community compositions.

56. The tropical rainforest canopy is an excellent example of _____ community distribution or structure.

   A. vertical   B. horizontal   C. patchy   D. diverse

57. In the Upper Peninsula of Michigan an area was clear-cut for logging. Trees at the edge of the clearing and 200 meters into the forest died within a few months after the logging began. What is the best explanation for the death of the trees?

   A. The trees at the edge of the forest were more prone to disease.

   B. Abiotic edge effects such as increased herbivory negatively affected the trees.

   C. Increased sunlight, wind, and temperature negatively affected the trees.

   D. The roots of all of the trees were damaged.

58. A "closed community" has a

   A. narrow ecotone.   C. wide ecotone.

   B. gradual transition zone.   D. very small area.

59. Primary succession occurs when a community develops _____ while secondary succession occurs when one _____.

   A. into a climax community, species replaces another

   B. and replaces another, ecosystem becomes stable

   C. on unoccupied ground, biological community replaces another

   D. and then fails, niche changes

60. Which of the following are pioneer species?

    A. wood warblers   B. dandelions   C. starlings   D. lichens

61. As ecological development proceeds, a biological community

    A. gradually stagnates.

    B. becomes more diverse.

    C. goes through repeated secondary successional stages.

    D. goes through repeated primary succession stages.

62. A climax community is one that

    A. is relatively stable and long-lasting.   C. contains oaks or White Spruce.

    B. lasts forever.   D. is impervious to disruption.

63. Some communities, such as some grasslands, may never really reach a climax stage because

    A. ecological succession works too slowly.

    B. there is no optimum community for these environments.

    C. they are adapted to periodic interruption.

    D. their environmental conditions are too unstable.

64. Introduced species often cause trouble because they

    A. are larger than native species.   C. are unusually efficient predators.

    B. disrupt pre-existing niches.   D. All of these are correct.

65. Which of the following migrations is likely to cause the extinction of a native species?

    A. Migration of a member of a species of island birds to a large continent.

    B. Migration of a pack of wolves to a nearby valley.

    C. The introduction of a predator onto an island originally free from predators.

    D. A seasonal move of large grazers that travel north in the summer and south in the winter.

CHAPTER 5
BIOMES, LANDSCAPES, RESTORATION, AND MANAGEMENT

1. A biome is described by

    A. a specified bioregion.

    B. broadly similar environmental conditions.

    C. a watershed divide, generally.

    D. geographic location.

2. Biomes are broad regions of the world with similar

    A. temperature and landforms.

    B. topography and climate.

    C. precipitation and temperature.

    D. latitude and altitude.

3. On the graph of precipitation and temperature below, desert biomes would fall in the area marked by the letter

    A. a.   B. b.   C. c.   D. d.

4. On the graph of precipitation and temperature below, temperate forest biomes would fall in the area marked by the letter

    A. a.   B. b.   C. c.   D. d.

5. Scotty has just beamed you into a biome that has relatively stable temperatures and abundant rainfall. Along with your laser gun, your compass, and rain poncho, you have a graph of precipitation and temperature similar to the one below. Which letter marks the area you are in?

    A. a   B. b   C. c   D. d

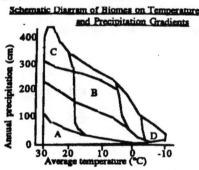

6. On the graph of precipitation and temperature above, the area marked A has a

    A. wide precipitation range and narrow temperature range.

    B. narrow precipitation and temperature range.

    C. wide precipitation and temperature range.

    D. wide temperature range and narrow precipitation range.

7. On the graph of precipitation and temperature above, the area marked D has a

    A. wide precipitation range and narrow temperature range.

    B. narrow precipitation and temperature range.

    C. wide precipitation and temperature range.

    D. wide temperature range and narrow precipitation range.

8. Plants have adapted to live in desert conditions by

    A. storing water in stems or roots.

    B. reducing water loss with thick epidermal layers.

    C. shedding leaves in the driest seasons.

    D. All of these are adaptations of plants living in desert conditions.

9. Deserts are characterized by

    A. an absence of vegetation.

    B. sand dunes, which cause plants to grow only with difficulty.

    C. low levels of measurable precipitation.

    D. their location at 30° latitude.

10. Most of the world's grasslands are found

    A. in North America.

    B. on relatively dry continental interiors.

    C. on the moist edges of continents.

    D. in narrow strips on the edges of mountains.

11. Grassland conditions make tree growth

    A. impossible.

    B. possible only during summer.

    C. possible mainly in corridors along streams.

    D. possible only for tiny, desert tree species.

12. Tundra biomes occur

    A. at high latitudes, where temperatures are low.

    B. where rainfall is too great for tree growth.

    C. at high latitudes and altitudes, where the growing season is short.

    D. almost exclusively on Antarctica.

13. You are led blindfolded by your "friends" into a wilderness environment and left to fend for yourself for the summer. Luckily you have your jacket because it looks like there may be a frost during the night and the mosquitoes are abundant. As you look around, you are relieved because you recognize some of the plants. There are some mosses, lichens, small shrubs, sedges, and grasses. However, you are annoyed because your shoes are wet and it looks like the soil all around you is waterlogged. Where are you?

    A. tropical rainforest

    B. temperate rainforest

    C. wetland

    D. tundra

14. The word "conifer" distinguishes plants that are

    A. needle-bearing.

    B. cone-bearing.

    C. evergreen.

    D. cone-shaped.

15. Having needle-shaped leaves benefits plants because needles

    A. reduce water loss and endure cold winters.

    B. are more efficient at photosynthesis because they are dark green.

    C. evaporate water more efficiently.

    D. don't rot in the excessive rainfall that characterizes coniferous forests.

16. You are in an area that has many lakes and bogs. There are also plants that indicate an acid soil. As you look around, the deciduous trees you see are birches, aspens, and maples. What forest are you in?

    A. temperate rainforest

    B. boreal forest

    C. tropical rainforest

    D. southern pine forest

17. Boreal forests are generally

    A. cold and dry, with extensive barren areas. C. dry because water is frozen most of the year.

    B. warm and humid, with large rivers.   D. cool and moist, with many streams and wetlands.

18. Taiga water and soils are often acidic because of

    A. acid rain.   C. salts exposed by erosion.

    B. moss and conifer needles.   D. It is not clear why they are acidic.

19. You are on the wet western coast and as you look around you see lots of mosses, lichens and ferns covering the tree branches. Condensation from fog on the leaves is a major form of precipitation. Where are you?

    A. temperate rainforest   C. tropical rainforest

    B. boreal forest   D. southern pine forest

20. Deciduous forests

    A. are adapted to extremely cold climates.   C. have trees that shed their leaves seasonally.

    B. have trees that bear seeds in cones.   D. are not useful commercially.

21. Many people in the United States make annual trips in the spring to see annual flowers that grow and flower before they are shaded by canopy. Where are these people going?

    A. deserts after winter rain showers C. tropical rainforests

    B. prairies or grasslands   D. temperate deciduous forests

22. Cloud forests are found in _____ areas in tropical regions.

    A. hot coastal   C. cool plains

    B. cool mountainous   D. low elevation

23. You are on a secret mission to save the world from ultimate disaster. Part of your assignment is to travel to a boreal forest and talk with the leader of an indigenous tribe. You have been kidnapped and as you wake you find yourself sweating in a moist forest but you don't see many streams or wetlands. You are amazed by the tremendous amount of biodiversity including an abundance of biting mosquitoes. Have you inadvertently gotten closer to your goal of finding a boreal forest?

    A. Yes

    B. No - the description is that of a tropical seasonal forest.

    C. No - the description is that of a temperate deciduous forest.

    D. No - the description is that of a tropical rainforest.

24. Humid tropical forests have extraordinary biological diversity

    A. because of the very fertile tropical soils.

    B. because rainfall dissolves soil nutrients and makes them available to plants.

    C. despite the poor, weathered soils.

    D. despite a complete absence of nutrients in the environment.

25. Tropical moist forests have high species diversity because

    A. they have highly developed, diverse niche opportunities and habitats.

    B. they are larger than any other biome type.

    C. due to heat and humidity, evolution has gone on faster there than in colder regions.

    D. there has been little history of human settlement in contrast to Europe.

26. Tropical seasonal forests are specially adapted to tolerate

    A. annual cycles of extreme heat and extreme cold.

    B. years of drought followed by years of rain.

    C. annual cycles of severe drought and heavy rain.

    D. extreme drought and cold at the same time.

27. Freshwater ecosystems are like dryland ecosystems except that

    A. they lack oxygen.   C. all primary production occurs outside the system.

    B. they lack carbon dioxide.   D. their surrounding medium is not air.

28. The diagram below shows what phenomenon in aquatic ecosystems?

    A. nutrient inputs from upstream and uphill   C. nutrient cycling

    B. vertical stratification   D. internal convective currents

29. What environmental factor does not change between "a" and "d" in the diagram below?

    A. light penetration   D. oxygen content

    B. temperature   E. All of these change between "a" and "d" in the diagram.

    C. nutrient availability

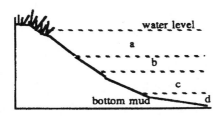

30. Oxygen levels are lowest in what section of the diagram above?

    A. a   B. b   C. c   D. d

31. The thermocline is the layer in a lake at which

    A. pollutants are trapped and held.   C. the warm upper zone meets the cold lower zone.

    B. seasonal lake mixing occurs.   D. nutrient levels are the lowest.

32. Estuaries are noted by biologists because they have

    A. unusual biological diversity and abundance.

    B. unusually poor productivity and diversity.

    C. few but highly specialized biological niches.

    D. an ability to withstand the beating of violent sea waves and storms.

33. Wetlands are biomes that

    A. are wet all year round.   C. have fresh, not salty, water.

    B. are wet at least some of the year.   D. receive more rainfall than other ecosystems.

34. Which type of wetland is noted for producing peat?

    A. swamps   B. marshes   C. bogs and fens   D. estuaries

35. Human settlement on sandy beaches is a problem chiefly because _____ often results.

    A. wetland drainage   C. overpopulation

    B. erosion   D. offshore marine pollution

36. Barrier islands are formed of

    A. wind- and wave-deposited sand.   C. silt and mud left by estuaries.

    B. volcanic debris.   D. coral deposits.

37. Coral reefs form in

    A. deep, warm, tropical seas.

    B. cold polar seas.

    C. warm, clear, tropical seas.

    D. deep, cold oceans off of continental shelves.

38. Mediterranean climate areas are characterized by

    A. constant light rainfall and cool temperatures.

    B. warm, dry summers and cool, wet winters.

    C. extreme winter-summer temperature changes.

    D. warm, wet summers and cool, dry winters.

39. A biome absent from North America is the

    A. temperate deciduous forest.   C. desert.

    B. alpine tundra.   D. tropical rainforest.

40. You are in an area that is relatively hot. You bend down and notice that there are tracks in the soil that are very old. Since you know that this area is easily destroyed by human activity and the harsh climate slows recovery from human damage you conclude that this biome is

    A. a tropical seasonal forest.   C. tundra.

    B. a desert.   D. a grassland.

41. Vast temperate deciduous forests still stand in eastern Siberia,

    A. but these are being harvested very rapidly.

    B. and these are still untouched by human activity.

    C. and they now form a great biome park/preserve.

    D. and they are spreading to neighboring regions.

42. The biome types that have lost the greatest percentage of their original (before human impact) area are

    A. temperate conifer forests and arctic tundra.   C. temperate forests and grasslands.

    B. tropical rainforests and cloud forests.   D. tropical and temperate forests.

43. The biome type that, if damaged, is slow to heal and is summer feeding and breeding grounds for caribou and grizzly bears is the

    A. temperate grasslands.   C. boreal forests.

    B. bog or fen.   D. arctic tundra.

44. In contrast with the _____, the soil of the _____ is more nutrient-rich and this type of biome has fewer insects, parasites, and fungal diseases. Therefore, in many places, these areas are highly endangered.

A. temperate grasslands, tropical seasonal forest

C. tundra, boreal forests

B. tropical rainforest, tropical seasonal forest

D. tropical seasonal forest, tropical rainforest

45. The biome types that are the least disturbed by humans are

A. temperate conifer forests and arctic tundra.

C. temperate forests and grasslands.

B. tropical rainforests and cloud forests.

D. tropical and temperate forests.

46. Landscapes are typically larger than a _____ and smaller than a _____.

A. biome, ecosystem

C. ecosystem, biome

B. habitat, ecosystem

D. habitat, biome

47. Landscape ecology includes many perspectives that, at least in part, more traditional ecology has held in the past. However, the main distinction between landscape ecology and traditional ecology is the inclusion of

A. humans in the system.

B. a systems perspective.

C. a philosophy of the dynamic nature of the ecosystem.

D. modern technological tools.

48. Efforts to repair or reconstruct ecosystems are known as

A. land stewardship.

C. landscape ecology.

B. conservation reserve programs.

D. restoration ecology.

49. Restoration ecology is similar, at least in part, to stewardship and management. However, the main distinction that sets restoration ecology apart from stewardship and management is

A. that humans are a part of the system.

B. direct human intervention for a predetermined end.

C. a philosophy that nature will heal without intervention.

D. the use of modern technological tools such as geographic information systems.

50. The word "mitigation" has come to mean to

A. let nature heal itself.

B. partially restore an ecosystem.

C. restore or create an ecosystem in exchange for a similar damaged one.

D. create a new type of ecosystem in place of an old one.

51. A preservationist is more likely to have a _____ worldview while a restorationist probably has a _____ worldview.

A. biocentric, ecocentric

C. anthropocentric, biocentric

B. biocentric, anthropocentric

D. ecocentric, biocentric

52. What was the most important factor in restoring the Curtis Prairie at the University of Wisconsin, Madison?

A. removal of alien intruders

C. allowing domestic livestock to disperse seeds

B. reintroduction of native bison

D. periodic fires

53. How did the hurricane in Bermuda relate to the restoration of the Bermuda Cahow?

    A. The majority of non-native trees were destroyed while the reintroduced native species were not damaged.

    B. Reintroduced native trees were damaged and after years of restoration efforts, the Cahow was not nesting.

    C. Reintroduced native trees were damaged and the Cahow nesting populations were decimated.

    D. The reintroduced native species were not destroyed, but the Cahow stopped nesting after the storm.

54. The wildlife that lives between former East Berlin and West Berlin is an example of

    A. the fact that once it is damaged by human activity, nature is rarely able to heal itself.

    B. the regenerative power of nature.

    C. the decline of biodiversity as a result of edge effects.

    D. living museum of prewar ecosystems.

55. The principal purpose of Arcata, California's, marsh and wildlife sanctuary is to

    A. re-establish populations of rare cranes.

    B. provide an educational resource for school students.

    C. filter the city's sewage.

    D. store drinking water for urban use.

56. Which of the following perspectives is *not* a difference between ecosystem management and traditional policies of the past?

    A. Humans cannot be separated from nature.

    B. Scientific knowledge is provisional and as more knowledge is gained, policies change.

    C. Scientific knowledge is the basis for management since science is free from bias.

    D. Ecosystem management requires a high level of routine monitoring.

57. In criticizing ecosystem management, one of your classmates says that it is arrogant for us to think that we can manage nature. You respond that you think she probably has a(n)

    A. biocentric worldview.

    B. anthropocentric worldview.

    C. expansionist worldview.

    D. anthropomorphic worldview.

CHAPTER 6
POPULATION DYNAMICS

1. Wolf and moose populations on Isle Royale present a good example of populations in
    A. auto-regulation by breeding behavior.   C. a catastrophic crash too severe for recovery.
    B. complete stability.   D. dynamic equilibrium.

2. After wolves arrived on Isle Royale the moose population
    A. stabilized.   C. exploded.
    B. suffered a catastrophic dieback.   D. suffered genetic depletion.

3. What is currently happening to the Isle Royale wolf and moose populations?
    A. Both the wolves and the moose numbers are continuing to increase in an arithmetic growth curve.
    B. The wolves are experiencing a population crash.
    C. The wolves are experiencing an increase in population numbers.
    D. Both the wolves and the moose are experiencing a population crash.

4. In nature, most populations are
    A. in a dynamic state of equilibrium.   C. increasing most of the time.
    B. stable most of the time.   D. always undergoing fluctuations.

5. Environmental resistance is to sigmoid curve (S-shaped curve) as bloom is to
    A. temperature changes.   C. exponential growth.
    B. arithmetic growth.   D. carrying capacity.

6. In cases of geometric growth rates, a population _____ each year.
    A. increases by adding the same number of individuals
    B. is multiplied by a constant number
    C. is multiplied by a constant percentage of itself
    D. is squared, or multiplied by itself

7. Which of the following sequences is an example of arithmetic growth rate?
    A. 2, 4, 8, 16   C. 1, 3, 5, 7
    B. 1, 2, 4, 8   D. 3, 6, 12, 24

8. Which of the following sequences is an example of geometric growth rate?
    A. 2, 4, 8, 16   C. 1, 3, 5, 7
    B. 1, 2, 4, 8   D. 3, 6, 12, 24

9. A population growing at 1 percent per year should double in about ___ years.
    A. 30   B. 70   C. 10   D. 2

10. Which of the following curves represents exponential growth?

    A. a   B. b   C. c   D. d

11. Which of the following curves represents arithmetic growth?

    A. a   B. b   C. c   D. d

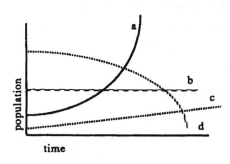

12. The doubling time for curve "a" above is

    A. constant.   C. unpredictable.

    B. constantly changing.   D. constantly increasing.

13. An organism's biotic potential is the maximum number of offspring

    A. that it can produce.   C. its habitat can support.

    B. that survive to adulthood.   D. it produces at one time.

14. A population explosion is usually followed by

    A. continuous high population levels.

    B. a gradual decrease as food supplies dwindle.

    C. a tremendous flowering of genetic diversity.

    D. a population crash.

15. A dieback, or population crash, often occurs after a species _____ its environmental carrying capacity.

    A. meets   C. overshoots

    B. undershoots   D. oscillates around

16. As shown in the graph below, after 1970 Peruvian anchovies underwent a(n)

    A. normal shift in the population's dynamic equilibrium.   C. population crash.

    B. population explosion.   D. introduction of natural predators.

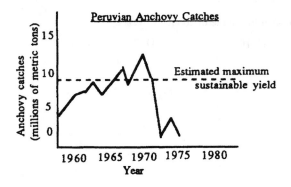

17. The effects of the Peruvian Fishery would be considered one factor of the _____ in the Anchovy population.

    A. butterfly effect   C. irruptive growth pattern

    B. environmental resistance   D. biotic potential

18. Since we only have data for twenty years it is impossible to make definite conclusions about Peruvian anchovies based on the graph above. However, based on this limited data which of the following statements best describes the pattern of the population dynamics in the graph?

    A. The pattern may be due to a chaotic or catastrophic species.

    B. This pattern may be indicative of logistic growth.

    C. The pattern may reflect a species which has a long life span and matures slowly.

    D. This pattern may reflect the introduction of natural predators.

19. Which of the following types of population growth patterns would best represent a group of elephants that enter a new, open habitat, and become a stable part of that ecosystem?

    A. exponential growth   C. Malthusian growth

    B. irruptive growth   D. logistic growth

20. Which of the following types of population curves would best represent a group of elephants that enter a new, open habitat, and become a stable part of that ecosystem?

    A. norm-shaped curve   C. J-shaped curve

    B. S-shaped curve   D. cyclic oscillation-shaped curve

21. In the real world there are many factors that determine the numbers of organisms in any one population. Yet, a SUPERFLY with unlimited food and no mortality would show what type of growth?

    A. carrying capacity geometric increase   C. J-shaped curve

    B. irruptive growth   D. S-shaped curve

22. In the population oscillation graph below, the dieback phase is marked by the letter

    A. a   B. b   C. c   D. d

23. In the population oscillation graph below, the exponential phase is marked by the letter

    A. a   B. b   C. c   D. d

24. In the population oscillation graph below, the overshoot is marked by the letter

    A. a   B. b   C. c   D. d

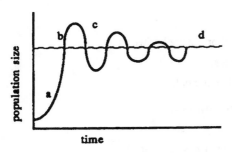

25. The horizontal line on the above population oscillation graph represents

    A. carrying capacity.   C. predator populations.

    B. biotic potential.   D. arithmetic growth.

26. Carrying capacity is the population

    A. of a species without predators.

    B. that a species' environment can support on a long-term basis.

    C. that remains after a catastrophic dieback has occurred.

    D. that an environment can support in an optimal year.

27. An island has formed off the coast of the Pacific Northwest. The Department of Natural Resources (DNR) has determined that there is enough land area for a herd of 100 elk, yet they say the carrying capacity is only 60 elk. This inequality can best be explained by the fact that the

    A. DNR is probably being careful not to overestimate.

    B. DNR must have added up the environmental resistance incorrectly.

    C. elk population will probably fluctuate between 60 and 100 animals.

    D. physical factor of space is only one of the determiners for population size in a community.

    E. law of limiting factors determines the maximum growth rate for a given population.

28. Which of the following is the correct equation?

    A. carrying capacity + environmental resistance = biotic potential

    B. biotic potential + environmental resistance = carrying capacity

    C. biotic potential - environmental resistance = carrying capacity

    D. carrying capacity - environmental resistance = biotic potential

29. Logistic growth rates are those in which a population

    A. grows very slowly when conditions are good as well as when they are not good.

    B. grows rapidly when conditions are good, then slows down as it approaches carrying capacity.

    C. overshoots and dies back repeatedly.

    D. remains significantly below carrying capacity.

    E. grows at a constant rate of increase per unit time.

30. Exponential growth rates are those in which a population

    A. grows very slowly when conditions are good as well as when they are not good.

    B. grows rapidly when conditions are good, then slows down as it approaches carrying capacity.

    C. overshoots and dies back repeatedly.

    D. remains significantly below carrying capacity.

    E. grows at a constant rate of increase per unit time.

31. Factors that limit growth and produce population equilibrium are known as

    A. predation resistance.   C. diebacks.

    B. environmental resistance.   D. biotic potential.

32. Which of the following is *not* a part of environmental resistance?

    A. predation   C. fecundity levels

    B. food limits   D. habitat or nesting space

33. The ability to produce rapid population overshoots can be a useful strategy for a species that tends to

    A. colonize new territory.   C. be part of a climax community.

    B. maintain a firm position in its current habitat.   D. develop intricate niche relationships.

34. You are studying an organism that is a pioneer species, is an opportunist, and does not care for its offspring. This organism probably has a _____ population growth strategy.

    A. logistic
    C. irruptive

    B. Malthusian
    D. catastrophic

35. You are studying an organism that is fairly large, matures slowly, lives fairly long, and cares for its offspring. This organism probably has a _____ population growth strategy.

    A. logistic
    C. irruptive

    B. Malthusian
    D. catastrophic

36. In considering the earth's carrying capacity for humans, which of the following factors *does not* have to be considered?

    A. Diets of the humans
    D. Doubling rate of humans

    B. Land use of earth
    E. All of these have to be considered.

    C. Cultural context of the humans

37. Natality is usually

    A. constant in a population.

    B. constant for a species.

    C. variable, depending on environmental conditions.

    D. variable, depending on the number of recent deaths.

38. An organism with _____ "strategies" would be considered to have _____ natality.

    A. logistic, high
    D. Malthusian, low

    B. Malthusian, high
    E. Both B and C

    C. logistic, low

39. The term "fecundity" refers to an organism's _____ while fertility is _____.

    A. physical ability to reproduce, actual number of offspring produced

    B. actual number of offspring produced, physical ability to reproduce

    C. average life span, physical ability to reproduce

    D. replacement level of reproduction, actual number of offspring produced

40. Which of the following is *not* closely associated to factors such as nutrient levels, climate, soil or water conditions?

    A. Natality
    C. Fertility

    B. Biotic potential
    D. All of these are closely associated to the listed factors.

41. If there is no migration, the size of a population is limited solely by interaction between

    A. natality and fertility.
    C. mortality and survivorship.

    B. mortality and fecundity.
    D. natality and mortality.

42. The graph below shows that fewer American women than men die
    A. between the ages of 40 and 80.   C. before age 40.
    B. after age 40.   D. at all ages.

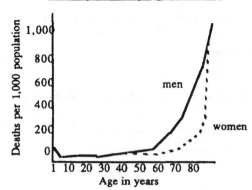

Mortality Curves by Age in the U.S.

43. Based on the graph above, the average _____ of people in the United States is around 80 years.
    A. survivorship   C. life expectancy
    B. mortality   D. life span

44. Life expectancy is the
    A. maximum life span that an individual of a given species could reach.
    B. number of individuals in a population that survive in a given year.
    C. number of years an individual of a certain age will probably live.
    D. probability that an individual will survive infancy.

45. Survivorship is determined by
    A. the percentage of a cohort that survives to a certain age.
    B. number of individuals in a population that survive in a given year.
    C. number of years an individual of a certain age will probably live.
    D. probability that an individual will survive infancy.

46. The longest period of life that a given type of organism can reach is known as
    A. survivorship.   C. life expectancy.
    B. life span.   D. mortality.

47. Which of the curves shown below should represent a normal survivorship in populations of large animals such as whales or elephants?
    A. a   B. b   C. c   D. d

48. Which of the curves below should represent a species such as sea gulls, which tend to die more-or-less randomly at any age?

A. a   B. b   C. c   D. d

Four Model Survivorship Curves

49. Which of the following statements best describes the species represented by curve "d"?

A. Reproductive adult species have the highest rate of survival for this species.

B. The rate of mortality is relatively constant throughout its life span.

C. It is highly susceptible to mortality early in life.

D. Once the individual reaches old age its survivorship decreases dramatically.

50. Because of population momentum, a country with many young people, such as Kenya, would _____ if birth rates suddenly dropped.

A. grow at an accelerating rate   C. quickly stop growing

B. continue to grow   D. begin to fall

51. In a population whose mortality and natality are balanced, there are

A. far more young people than old people.   C. about the same number of old and young.

B. far fewer young people than old people.   D. almost no young people.

52. A pyramid-shaped age-structure histogram is characteristic of a(n) _____ population.

A. stable   B. expanding   C. declining   D. unpredictable

53. Density-independent population control factors cause mortality

A. when the population becomes too large.   C. when the population becomes too small.

B. regardless of population size.   D. when the density becomes too low.

54. Widespread starvation is an example of _____ population control.

A. predator-caused   C. density-dependent

B. biotic   D. density-independent

55. External factors (such as predation or food availability) are especially important population regulators for

A. species low on the food chain.

B. species high on the food chain.

C. both a and b.

D. neither A nor B.

56. _____ factors of population growth are to intraspecific interactions as external factors are to _____ interactions.

    A. Intrinsic, interspecific   C. Intrinsic, intraspecific

    B. Extrinsic, interspecific   D. Extrinsic, intraspecific

57. Which of the following is an abiotic population control?

    A. predation   C. water shortages

    B. disease   D. prey shortages

58. In general, abiotic regulatory factors tend to be _____ while biotic factors tend to be _____.

    A. interspecific, intraspecific   C. density-dependent, density-independent

    B. intraspecific, interspecific   D. density-independent, density-dependent

59. Which of the following is an intraspecific interaction?

    A. mutualism   C. parasitism

    B. territoriality   D. predation

60. Emigration can benefit a species because it

    A. provides insurance against population loss in the home territory.

    B. can relieve stress.

    C. allows the species to take advantage of more resources.

    D. All of these can benefit a species.

CHAPTER 7
HUMAN POPULATIONS

1. Technological optimists argue that technological advances have

    A. led to the increase in human population but whether we can continue is of great concern.

    B. proven Marx wrong in his predictions of famine and disaster.

    C. proven Malthus wrong in his predictions of famine and disaster.

    D. been developed because there are more people. Therefore more people are the "ultimate resource."

2. Human ingenuity and intelligence as the "ultimate resource" is the central theme in the argument of

    A. Julian Simon.   C. Thomas Malthus.

    B. John Muir.   D. neo-Malthusians.

3. By 1997 the world's human population was about

    A. 5.8 million.   C. 5.8 billion.

    B. 90 billion.   D. 90 billion.

4. The world growth rate is about 1.7 percent. Therefore, the population is currently doubling about every ___ years.

    A. 10   B. 41   C. 70   D. 320

5. The world human population reached 1 billion in about

    A. 1400   B. 1600   C. 1700   D. 1800

6. Populations were held in check up to the middle ages by

    A. low fertility rates.   C. disease, famine, and war.

    B. culturally-imposed family planning practices.   D. religious restrictions on marriage.

7. In the population graph below, human population growth most closely resembles

    A. carrying capacity geometric increase.   C. S-shaped growth curve.

    B. irruptive growth.   D. J-shaped growth curve.

8. In the following population graph, the Industrial Revolution is most closely marked by the letter

    A. a   B. b   C. c   D. d

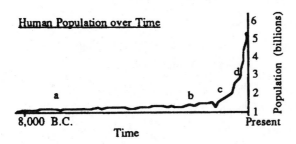

9. In the population graph shown in question 8, the plague is most closely marked by the letter(s)

    A. a.   B. between b and c.   C. c.   D. between c and d.

10. Malthus and Marx

    A. worked together to form their theories.

    B. agreed about the root causes of overpopulation, poverty, and social upheaval.

    C. disagreed about the root causes of overpopulation, poverty, and social upheaval.

    D. held the same beliefs but worked on different issues.

11. The population theory held by Thomas Malthus was that the human population would

    A. never reach its environment's carrying capacity.

    B. develop a modern utopia.

    C. outstrip its resources, then suffer starvation and misery.

    D. maintain equilibrium with its carrying capacity.

12. Neo-Malthusians argue that

    A. Malthus' eighteenth century theories apply to similar circumstances today.

    B. we should never return to the conditions observed by Malthus in his day.

    C. Malthus could be useful today if reinterpreted.

    D. Malthus was wrong from the start.

13. Disastrous famines in the past 200 years

    A. prove conclusively that Malthus was right.

    B. have resulted from war and politics more than from overpopulation.

    C. prove conclusively that Malthus was mistaken.

    D. have resulted from population overshoots based on overuse of resources.

14. The first major burst of human population growth (about 1 million years ago) probably resulted from

    A. the development of cities.   C. a human fecundity burst due to climate change.

    B. the discovery of tools and of fire.   D. the invention of agriculture.

15. The main reason that we have not suffered disastrous population crashes since the industrial revolution is that

    A. we use fewer resources per person than we did 200 years ago.

    B. we have replaced natural resources with synthetic resources through technological advances.

    C. despite the appearance of the numbers, there are actually fewer of us today.

    D. we have invented new ways to extract, process, and extend resources.

16. Graphs are widely used in communication because

    A. they can create powerful impressions by illustrating patterns of relationships.

    B. artifacts that distort the data can readily be seen by the untrained eye.

    C. they add interest and variety to textual material.

    D. they can be easily manipulated to distort the data presented.

17. Demography is the science that describes

    A. the earth's carrying capacity.   C. energy resources.

    B. population changes and characteristics.   D. food production.

18. Demographers are responsible for finding out how many people
    A. can live on Earth.
    C. there really are.
    B. there were long ago.
    D. can be supported with the earth's resources.

19. Ninety percent of the world's population growth in the next century is expected to occur in
    A. less-developed countries.
    C. developed countries.
    B. China.
    D. moderately-developed nations.

20. India's population, the second largest in the world, is
    A. almost as large as China's.
    C. less than half of China's.
    B. equal to China's.
    D. rapidly approaching China's.

21. Most of the world's human settlements are clustered
    A. in wide, arable plains.
    C. along coastlines and rivers.
    B. in mountainous regions.
    D. between 30 and 50 degrees north latitude.

22. What is one of the main reasons Mechai Viravaidya, the founder and director of the Community-Based Family Planning Service of Thailand, was successful in developing a birth control program in Thailand that worked?
    A. Viravaidya received strong support from religious leaders to develop a one-child policy.
    B. Viravaidya focused on the needs and wants of prosperous people in the urban areas.
    C. Viravaidya received strong government support to develop a one-child policy similar to China's.
    D. Viravaidya focused on the needs and wants of people in poverty.

23. Why is Russia's population declining?
    A. There is a one-child policy similar to the one in China and Thailand.
    B. The standard of living has decreased leading to higher death rates and lower birth rates.
    C. The standard of living has decreased leading to lower infant mortality and lower birth rates.
    D. Russia's population is not declining.

24. Crude birth rates are measured in terms of the number of children born
    A. in a single year.
    C. per 1000 people in the general population.
    B. per family.
    D. per 1000 people each year.

25. Crude birth rates are statistically "crude" because they do not account for
    A. pertinent population characteristics such as the number of reproductive women.
    B. the relative number of deaths occurring in a year.
    C. the total size of the population.
    D. the births of illegal immigrants.

26. The total fertility rate is the number of children born
    A. in a population during an entire generation.
    C. to the average woman per year.
    B. to the average woman during her lifetime.
    D. in a population during a single year.

27. The total fertility rate for upper class women in seventeenth and eighteenth century Europe was sometimes
    A. less than 1.
    C. between 1 and 2.
    B. greater than 20.
    D. about 8.

28. The zero population growth rate is slightly over two children per couple because
    A. we always need slightly more young people.
    B. the older generation is always dying off.
    C. some children die and some couples do not have children.
    D. that is as low as birth rates can reasonably be expected to get.

29. Demographers usually measure mortality in terms of
    A. deaths per 1000 persons per year.   C. the number of children who die per year.
    B. deaths per person per year.   D. the total number of deaths per generation.

30. Countries with poor sanitation and health care often have crude mortality rates of _____ per 1000 while most developed countries have crude mortality rates around ___ per 1000.
    A. 100, 10   B. 35, 20   C. 20, 10   D. 10, 20

31. The difference between "total growth rate" and "natural increase" is that total growth rates include
    A. only the number of births and deaths.   C. only immigration and emigration.
    B. immigration and emigration as well as births and deaths.   D. infant mortality as well as adult deaths.

32. With a natural increase rate of 0.8 percent, the population doubling time for Canada and the United States is about ____ years.
    A. 8   B. 18   C. 89   D. 700

33. The average age that a newborn can expect to attain in a given society is referred to as
    A. life expectancy.   C. life span.
    B. infant mortality.   D. survivorship.

34. The main cause of world population growth in the past 300 years has been
    A. increasing fecundity.   C. falling mortality.
    B. rising fertility.   D. increasing immigration.

35. The population represented by the age class histogram on the right (below) will
    A. have a large population of old people soon.
    B. not grow much in the coming years.
    C. begin to shrink in the next few years as old people die in greater numbers.
    D. continue to grow substantially in the future.

36. The following age class histogram on the right, could represent the population of
    A. the United States.   B. Sweden.   C. Mexico.   D. None of these.

37. The age class histogram on the left (shown in question 36), could represent the population of

    A. the United States.   B. Sweden.   C. Mexico.   D. None of these.

38. The left-hand histogram above represents a population whose birth rates

    A. have not changed for many years.   C. are gradually increasing.

    B. have recently decreased.   D. are sharply increasing.

39. A dependency ratio is a comparison between the numbers of

    A. working and nonworking people.   C. old people and young people.

    B. parents and children.   D. young children and older adults.

40. You were in a discussion with a classmate who complained that immigrants were taking away jobs and abusing social services. In response, another classmate who is a proponent of the open door policy explained that immigrants can actually be a bonus to a country. Which of the following statements would *not* be used by someone supporting an open door policy?

    A. Immigrants are usually of a different racial or ethnic background and add cultural diversity.

    B. Immigrants usually perform dangerous work that citizens are unwilling to do.

    C. Immigrants usually perform work at a payscale that citizens are unwilling to accept.

    D. Immigrants are usually welcomed by other immigrants or descendants of immigrants.

41. Pronatalist pressures are influences that lead people to

    A. increase fecundity.   C. have fewer children.

    B. have more children.   D. prevent early mortality.

42. Which of the following is considered a true pronatalist pressure?

    A. legitimate needs for support in old age

    B. the need for hands to help in farm work

    C. macho pride in men who have many children

    D. All of these

43. Birth rate would tend to be increased with a(n)

    A. increase in education.   C. decrease in infant mortality rate.

    B. increase in affluence.   D. decrease in average marrying age.

44. Women who _____ are least likely to have many children.

    A. cannot afford children   C. are subordinate to their husbands

    B. live where many children die young   D. are able to earn an income for themselves

45. Birth rates in the United States have _____ during the course of this century.

    A. remained fairly constant   C. fallen and risen repeatedly

    B. fallen steadily   D. risen steadily

46. There is some evidence that population growth today is _____ rather than _____.

    A. slowing slightly, continuing to accelerate   C. increasing, leveling off

    B. continuing to accelerate, slowing slightly   D. leveling off, decreasing

47. "Birth dearths" can be a problem because they cause

    A. labor shortages.   C. military weakness.

    B. declining strength of social support systems.   D. All of these.

48. Which of the following countries are facing serious problems because of low birth rates?

    A. England and Ireland
    C. Kenya and Tanzania
    B. Japan and Taiwan
    D. the United States and Canada

49. The demographic transition refers to a country's change from

    A. high birth and death rates to low birth and death rates.

    B. high to low birth rates and low to high death rates.

    C. a majority of elderly people to a majority of young people.

    D. a majority of young people to a majority of elderly people..

50. A demographic transition is expected to accompany

    A. colonization, as in Africa and Asia.
    C. the development of capitalism.
    B. economic development and stabilization.
    D. the introduction of modern medicine.

51. Many demographers believe that birth rates will fall as development proceeds because

    A. child raising becomes more expensive.

    B. people are better educated and have more economic options.

    C. women begin to have more influence in family planning.

    D. All of these.

52. The message from author Garret Hardin's "lifeboat ethics" is that

    A. helping poor people will, in time, reduce their rate of reproduction.

    B. helping poor people will simply increase their rate of reproduction.

    C. economic growth will reduce the birth rate of poor nations.

    D. the world has enough resources for everybody.

53. Proponents of social justice believe that environmental and social problems will decrease if

    A. we can educate poor people about family planning.

    B. resources are distributed fairly.

    C. better ethics are taught to poor, uneducated populations.

    D. we just reduce the number of people on Earth.

54. Supporters of "ecojustice" think we should

    A. send North American natural resources to the developing world.

    B. share our national parks with the developing world.

    C. share resources with other species as well as with other people.

    D. let the human population grow to the maximum possible size.

55. _____ are the most numerous vertebrate organisms on Earth.

    A. Humans   B. Insects   C. Rodents   D. Birds

56. The graph below indicates that more children die

    A. in the last stage of the demographic transition.

    B. when their mothers are poor.

    C. when their mothers are illiterate.

    D. when their mothers are literate.

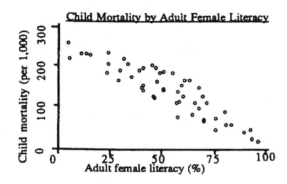

Child Mortality by Adult Female Literacy

57. The graph above indicates that there is

    A. a strong relationship between infant mortality and education for women.

    B. little relationship between infant mortality and education for women.

    C. a relationship between infant mortality and education in general.

    D. more importance for female rather than male education.

58. Family planning means enabling people to

    A. have fewer children so that the population growth rate can reach ZPG.

    B. have no children.

    C. have many children.

    D. decide in advance how many children they should have.

59. Breast-feeding children for long periods

    A. is a luxury that mainly wealthy women enjoy.   D. Both a and b

    B. limits fertility when calorie intake is low.   E. Both b and c

    C. can be a successful population control strategy.

60. Norplant is a trade name for

    A. an intrauterine device.

    B. the new female condom.

    C. an implanted source of contraceptive hormones.

    D. an injection of progesterone.

61. Which of the following is a mechanical barrier to conception?

    A. abortion   C. birth control pills

    B. condoms   D. vasectomies

62. RU 486 is a

    A. clinical name for injectable hormones.

    B. pill that prevents fertilization.

    C. pill that prevents fetal implantation.

    D. hormone injected in men to prevent sperm production.

63. Male contraceptives are less common than female contraceptives because

    A. women expect hormonal changes.

    B. men protest about possible hormonal changes and a repressed sexual drive.

    C. men are more likely than women to suffer from contraceptive use.

    D. All of these are reasons male contraceptives are less common than female contraceptives.

64. During the 1980s the Reagan administration _____ US international family planning assistance.

    A. decreased   C. maintained

    B. increased modestly   D. eliminated

1. Ecology and economy are both derived from the Greek word "Oikos" meaning

    A. the study of something.   C. household.

    B. how things work.   D. environment.

2. The effects of resource scarcity is/was the focus of

    A. political economic theory.   C. classical economic theory.

    B. neoclassical economic theory.   D. None of these dealt with resource scarcity.

3. Malthus' theory of diminishing returns stated that

    A. improved well-being leads to a labor surplus and subsequent starvation, disease, and crime.

    B. perpetual growth in material well-being is neither possible nor desirable.

    C. market competition leads to a balance where increased supply decreases the return on a product

    D. continued economic growth is necessary or products will decrease in value.

4. In economic terms, "demand" is how much of something

    A. people want.   C. people will buy at current prices.

    B. people need.   D. is available on the market.

5. In economic terms, "supply" is how much of something

    A. people want.   C. people will buy at current prices.

    B. people need.   D. is available on the market.

6. A(n) _____ relationship exists between supply and demand. Therefore, when supply is high, demand is _____.

    A. correlational, high   C. inverse, low

    B. inverse, high   D. correlational, low

7. On the classical supply-demand graph shown below, _____ is highest when prices are low.

    A. demand   B. supply   C. market equilibrium   D. cost

8. On the following supply-demand graph, market equilibrium is marked

    A. a.   B. b.   C. c.   D. d.

9. Using the supply-demand graph shown in question 8, what happens as the price of a good or service increases?

    A. the quantity of the good or service decreases.   C. demand increases and supply falls.

    B. market equilibrium is finally reached and the demand increases. D. demand falls and supply increases.

10. The price of natural gas doubles. What would happen to the quantity of the natural gas in a market system?

    A. The quantity decreases because it is too expensive to produce.

    B. The quantity increases because it is worthwhile to drill into lower quality fields.

    C. The quantity increases because new natural gas is being created.

    D. The quantity decreases because it is too expensive and people do not buy it.

11. Price elasticity is when _____ while price inelasticity is when _____.

    A. prices cannot be negotiated, consumers can negotiate a price

    B. consumers can negotiate a price, prices cannot be negotiated

    C. the supply/demand curve is followed, consumers buy a product regardless of cost

    D. consumers buy a product regardless of cost, the supply/demand curve is followed

12. Political economy theory incorporates _____ while neoclassical economic theory incorporates _____.

    A. the issues of social structures and value systems, objectivity and scientific analysis

    B. objectivity and scientific analysis, the issues of social structures and value systems

    C. the value of social systems, the value of natural resources

    D. birth and death rates, natural resources and social structures

13. Which of the following is *not* true with respect to natural resource economics?

    A. Natural resource economics views ecological processes as factors outside the economic system.

    B. The principles of thermodynamics and coevolution are incorporated into natural resource economics.

    C. Natural resources are seen as abundant in natural resource economics.

    D. Neoclassical economic theory is similar to natural resource economics.

    E. All of these describe natural resource economics.

14. Ecological economics is different from the other economic theories because it recognizes the

    A. scarcity of natural capital.

    B. recycling of ecological processes and the scarcity of manufactured capital.

    C. abundance of natural capital.

    D. fragility of the human economy and power of ecological systems.

15. A steady-state economy would be marked by

    A. high resource consumption, low volume, and low output.

    B. high resource consumption, high volume, and high-quality output.

    C. low resource consumption, high volume, and high-quality output.

    D. low resource consumption, low volume, and high-quality output.

16. Natural resources are those that are created by

    A. industrial processes.   C. natural Earth processes.

    B. human labor.   D. animal labor.

17. Which of the following is a human resource?

    A. timber   C. technology such as hydroelectric power

    B. solar energy   D. knowledge of history

18. _____ is an exhaustible resource.

    A. Scientific technology   C. Coal

    B. Hydroelectric power   D. Biomass

19. Renewable resources are those that

    A. will not be exhausted.

    B. will always renew themselves unless we destroy them.

    C. can be renewed through intensive investments of capital and labor.

    D. are intangible and inexhaustible.

20. Things like open space or beauty can be considered a resource because they are

    A. valued by people.   C. exhaustible.

    B. essential for efficient production. D. expensive.

21. An example of an intangible resource is

    A. solar energy.   C. human labor.

    B. space and beauty.   D. capital.

22. The supply of a natural resource depends on its

    A. availability in nature.   C. susceptibility to competition.

    B. extraction costs.   D. All of these.

23. Proven reserves of a mineral or fossil fuel resource are

    A. predicted according to current theory.

    B. mapped and recoverable at current prices and technology.

    C. already recovered and available for sale.

    D. identified but not yet mapped thoroughly.

24. The indicator species for selenium, Locoweed, is found on a site near your campus. Since you know that selenium is often found with uranium deposits, the uranium can best be described as a(n) _____ resource.

    A. nonrecoverable   B. unconceived   C. undiscovered   D. recoverable

25. The management of a wild area by a group of indigenous people such as the management of wild rice beds, is an example of

    A. tragedy of the commons.   C. communal open access system.

    B. "free-rider" system.   D. communal resource management system.

26. The tragedy of the commons is based on a view that

    A. communal systems can be sustained and promoted.

    B. community members will attempt, without success, to sustain a resource for future generations.

    C. only privatization or strict laws can overcome people's selfish and greedy nature.

    D. individuals will try to maximize gain for the group at a loss for the individual.

27. Which of the following is an example of an open access system?

    A. Cattle grazing on common woodlands and pastures in colonial New England.

    B. Maine lobster fisheries.

    C. Nearshore fisheries in many parts of the world.

    D. Native American management of wild rice beds and hunting grounds.

    E. None of these are examples of an open access system

28. Which of the following is an example of an communal property system?

    A. Cattle grazing on common woodlands and pastures in colonial New England.

    B. Maine lobster fishing.

    C. Privatization of Native American reservations in the US.

    D. Offshore fisheries in many parts of the world.

    E. None of these are examples of a communal property system.

29. In a frontier economy there is usually a relative abundance of _____ because of the inefficiency _____.

    A. natural resources, of the procedures for gaining access to resources

    B. labor, and lack of experience of workers

    C. capital (money), of the market economy at this first stage

    D. technology, of the processes to research and develop new technology

30. Pollution levels in frontier economies tend to be relatively low because

    A. few natural resources are wasted.

    B. recycling technology is used efficiently.

    C. people are scattered thinly over a large area.

    D. there is little resource use per person.

31. The graph below shows how _____ when economies develop.

    A. quantity increases as prices rise   C. prices and quantities fall simultaneously

    B. prices fall as quantities increase   D. quantities and prices naturally change through time

32. On the graph below, the price/quantity intersection marked "a" represents a/an _____ economy.

    A. developing   B. modern   C. elastic   D. frontier

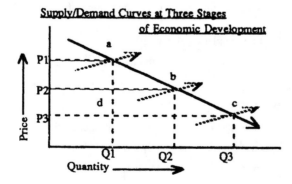

Supply/Demand Curves at Three Stages of Economic Development

33. On the graph above, the economy with the greatest volume of production is marked

    A. a.   B. b.   C. c.   D. d.

34. Which of the following is *not* an effective response to resource scarcity?

    A. Substituting different materials for scarce ones.

    B. Increasing efficiency.

    C. Diverting capital (money) to conventional industries.

    D. Increasing trade with other regions.

35. In *Limits to Growth*, the Club of Rome predicted that

    A. steady-state economic systems were not viable.

    B. sustained economic growth of most countries was likely for the foreseeable future.

    C. predicting the future was impossible.

    D. economic collapse is likely if we don't reduce population growth.

36. The computer models published in *Limits to Growth* predicted _____ in the next century.

    A. population stability

    B. population and resource crashes

    C. growth in both population and resources

    D. a decrease in pollution levels

37. In response to criticisms of *Limits to Growth*, a computer model was published in *Beyond the Limits* that

    A. predicted growth in both population and resources in the next century.

    B. predicted an increase in resources in the next century.

    C. includes technological progress and pollution abatement.

    D. includes a lower rate of world population growth.

38. To traditional economists, resources are most valuable

    A. for their own sake.   C. when preserved for the future.

    B. if saved and used sparingly.   D. when they are used now.

39. Which of the following indicators is *incorrectly* matched with the factors it takes into account?

    A. Gross National Product - goods and services purchased

    B. Index of Sustainable Economic Welfare - the value of unpaid labor and natural resource depletion

    C. Human Development Index - life expectancy and educational attainment

    D. Gender Development Index - gender and natural resource depletion

40. The use of Gross National Products as an indicator of economic well-being

    A. is criticized as an inaccurate measure of the quality of life.

    B. reflects social welfare.

    C. predicts ecological bankruptcy through recognition of decreased natural capital.

    D. takes into account life expectancy.

41. Which of the following would *not* be counted as part of the Gross National ?

    A. A new car purchase by a corporation.   D. Government purchases.

    B. Installation of cable television by a company.   E. Dental services for an individual.

    C. Home health care by a family member.

42. In 1997 ecological economists put a price on the goods and services provided by natural systems. This estimated annual value ranged from

A. $16,000,000,000,000 - $54,000,000,000,000   C. $16,000,000,000 - $54,000,000,000

B. $16,000,000 - $54,000,000   D. $16,000 - $54,000

43. An attempt to evaluate the long-term effects of a project or product is termed a

A. cost-benefit analysis.   C. tangible-intangible cost analysis.

B. supply-demand analysis.   D. benefit-need ratio analysis.

44. Cost-benefit analysis

A. is strictly an objective economic activity.

B. includes many subjective judgments.

C. is really a political process because it is based on many objective judgments.

D. includes many subjective judgments and is really a political process.

45. Which of the following factors would be most difficult to quantify in cost-benefit analysis?

A. depreciation of equipment   C. planning and consulting fees

B. the health of workers   D. future maintenance costs

46. The existence value of a grizzly bear in Alaska is highest for

A. a hunter who pays for the chance to shoot it.

B. a photographer who stalks and photographs it.

C. a tourist who might hope to see it one day.

D. It is impossible to be sure which of these is correct.

47. Which of the following is usually most difficult to include in economic planning?

A. exhaustible resources   C. intangible resources

B. renewable resources   D. human resources

48. The idea of discount rates is that a commodity is always

A. worth the same amount, unless you alter it.   C. worth more today than in the future.

B. going to be worth more in the future than today.   D. worthless unless you have sold it.

49. The idea of intergenerational justice is that we should consider the resource needs of people

A. who are young or unborn.   C. in other countries.

B. who are aging.   D. of the past.

50. When we purchase a product, the price we pay directly reflects the _____ cost of producing it. If the manufacture of the product degrades the quality of air or water, then the costs of this pollution are termed _____ costs.

A. internal, external   C. indirect, incidental

B. incidental, indirect   D. external, internal

51. When a factory pollutes a river, the costs and losses that affect people downstream would be called

A. indirect costs.   C. incidental costs.

B. external costs.   D. internal costs.

52. When the 1990 Clean Air Act put a price tag on volumes of pollution produced by manufacturers, Congress was attempting to _____ pollution costs.

A. eliminate   B. externalize   C. internalize   D. publicize

53. The function of the World Bank is to administer

    A. small, local development grants. C. major international development loans.

    B. small international grants. D. savings of major global corporations.

54. Why does the World Bank prefer to loan money for large projects rather than small ones?

    A. Small projects are not as impressive and there are more to manage.

    B. Although large projects are harder to manage, they are more successful.

    C. Small projects are not as successful for the country borrowing the money.

    D. In general, large projects are less environmentally destructive.

    E. The World Bank does not prefer to loan money for large projects rather than small ones

55. Market-based incentives for environmental protection are

    A. rigid laws outlawing pollution production.

    B. fees placed on certain types or volumes of a pollutant.

    C. fees charged to inventors of new control technologies.

    D. setting prices for pollution according to consumer demand.

56. Tradable permits are federally established allowable pollution limits that

    A. a company can sell if it produces less pollution than its limit.

    B. private citizens can buy for personal use.

    C. companies buy from the government, depending on how much pollution they plan to produce.

    D. All of these are characteristics of tradable permits.

57. The Grammeen Bank is a microlender whose business loans average $_____.

    A. 10,000   B. 5000   C. 475   D. 75

58. In recent decades, American business has _____ in establishing international markets in pollution control technologies.

    A. resisted or shown little interest C. participated vigorously

    B. exceeded even Japanese innovation D. led the world

59. "Sustainable growth" implies a balance between

    A. supply and demand. C. population growth and resource utilization.

    B. rich and poor. D. All of these are implied by sustainable growth.

60. Environmental protection has been proven to _____ the number of available jobs because _____.

    A. decrease, it limits the use of nonrenewable resources (as in the case of the logging industry)

    B. increase, labor is usually substituted for natural resources (as in the case of recycling)

    C. stabilize, the use of nonrenewable resources is stabilized and jobs are scarce anyway

    D. decrease, it negatively affects economic growth

61. Which of the following is *not* an essential component of sustainable development?

    A. stabilized birth and death rates

    B. increasing reliance on renewable resources.

    C. a marked decrease in military spending

    D. a broader sharing of the benefits of development

CHAPTER 9
ENVIRONMENTAL HEALTH AND TOXICOLOGY

1. The World Health Organization regards health as primarily a matter of _____ well-being.

   A. physical

   B. mental and physical

   C. social and mental

   D. physical, mental, and social

2. Diseases usually develop in response to _____ factors.

   A. nutritional and diet

   B. infectious or toxic

   C. physical

   D. psychological stress

   E. All of these.

3. Morbidity is another word for

   A. death.   B. health.   C. unhappiness.   D. illness.

4. Pathogenic organisms are those that
   A. cause diseases.

   B. are susceptible to diseases.

   C. carry and transmit diseases.

   D. are predatory.

5. Historically, the greatest threats to human health came from

   A. carcinogenic chemicals.

   B. psychological stress factors due to crowding.

   C. pathogenic organisms.

   D. teratogenic chemicals.

6. Which disease(s) cause(s) more deaths per year worldwide?

   A. HIV/AIDS

   B. Malaria

   C. Diarrhea

   D. Respiratory Diseases

7. Infectious diseases such as diarrhea are closely linked to

   A. emotional stress.   B. malnutrition.   C. toxicity effects.   D. overeating.

8. Oral rehydration therapy involves

   A. a special mixture of carbohydrates and proteins.

   B. a dose of calories and essential amino acids.

   C. a simple mixture of sugar and salts in water.

   D. All of these in sequence.

9. The best way to save children under five years old is to

   A. increase research in treating sick children.

   B. encourage bottle-feeding because of the increased sanitation benefits.

   C. use simple preventative medicine such as better nutrition.

   D. boil water used in bottle-feeding.

10. One of the _____ effective ways to stabilize populations is to _____.

   A. most, provide free contraceptives

   B. least, provide free contraceptives

   C. least, decrease child mortality

   D. most, decrease child mortality

11. Respiratory diseases are still the leading cause of death in

    A. many subtropical countries, including Latin America.   C. temperate regions of the world.

    B. developed countries, including the US and Canada.   D. both developed and developing countries.

12. Malaria is caused by

    A. nutritional deficiencies in moist tropical regions.

    B. an allergic reaction to mosquito bites.

    C. a parasitic protozoan.

    D. poor sanitary conditions.

13. Parasitic worms are very common in areas where

    A. the climate is dry.   C. the climate is hot.

    B. sanitation is poor.   D. urban development has been too rapid.

14. Large irrigation projects (e.g., Aswan Dam in Egypt) lead to increased crop yields, but also increased problems with

    A. waterborne leeches.   C. malaria.

    B. *Girardia.*   D. schistosomiasis.

15. Increased pesticide use has led to the _____ of many diseases as well as pesticide _____.

    A. decrease, resistance   C. increase, resistance

    B. decrease, toxicity for people   D. increase, toxicity for people

16. Historical evidence shows that plagues and diseases

    A. are highly effective at slowing population growth.

    B. cause only minor or temporary setbacks in population growth trends.

    C. affect relatively few people in a population.

    D. are devastating to human population growth.

17. Hazardous substances _____ while toxins are _____.

    A. react with specific cell components to kill cells, poisonous substances

    B. are dangerous substances, poisonous substances

    C. are usually of concern at all concentrations, are dangerous substances

    D. are poisonous substances, also poisonous substances

    E. All of these choices are true.

18. Toxic substances are dangerous because they

    A. react or interfere with specific cell functions.

    B. can physically remove or tear tissues.

    C. cause excessive water accumulation in tissues.

    D. cause debilitating, parasitic diseases.

19. Which of the following can be dangerous at the smallest concentrations (parts per trillion)?

    A. caustics   C. toxins

    B. acids   D. asphyxiants

20. Respiratory fibrotic agents are special irritants that

    A. are acidic, rather than basic.   C. cause scar tissue to grow in the lungs.

    B. fill the lungs with fluids.   D. introduce bacteria into the lungs.

21. Asphyxiants are substances that

    A. interfere with oxygen uptake.   C. cause physical damage.

    B. prevent proper nutrient digestion.   D. dehydrate cells.

22. Allergens are substances that

    A. repress the immune system.   C. prevent oxygen uptake.

    B. stimulate the nervous system.   D. activate the immune system.

23. Some particles or cells cause immune responses when your body's white blood cells recognize them as foreign objects. These are known as

    A. desensitizers.   C. active asphyxiants.

    B. antigens.   D. irritants.

24. Neurotoxins act by

    A. disrupting nerve cells.   C. repressing the immune system.

    B. altering genetic material.   D. repressing oxygen uptake.

25. Radiation can act as a mutagen because it

    A. deactivates the immune system.   C. causes muscles to grow at unusual rates.

    B. interferes with the activity of nerve cells. D. damages genetic material in cells.

26. Tumors can grow as a result of exposure to

    A. neurotoxins.   B. mutagens.   C. antigens.   D. parasitic organisms.

27. Teratogens cause abnormal growth specifically in

    A. nerve cells.   B. muscle cells.   C. embryos.   D. the liver.

28. Thalidomide was a sedative that caused

    A. children to have terrible birth defects.   C. malignant tumors in the children who took it.

    B. allergic reactions in mothers.   D. river blindness in many adults.

29. Fetal alcohol syndrome is caused by exposure to a(n)

    A. neurotoxin.   B. mutagen.   C. antigen.   D. teratogen.

30. Carcinogens are substances that cause

    A. a sensitized reaction.   C. birth defects.

    B. out of control cell growth and tumors.   D. immune responses.

31. A group of cells that grows extremely fast and begins to obstruct other cells' functions is known as

    A. a malignant tumor.   C. teratogenesis.

    B. a parasite.   D. a pathogen.

32. Two forms of cancer that now appear at increasing rates are

    A. bone and brain cancer.   C. liver and kidney cancer.

    B. prostate and lung cancer.   D. heart and skin cancer.

33. Electromagnetic fields (EMFs) occur

    A. primarily in large industrial areas.   C. mainly around nuclear power plants.

    B. very rarely.   D. around any electrical lines or appliances.

34. The links between EMFs and some forms of cancer were discovered

    A. after biologists demonstrated the cellular processes involved.

    B. when whole towns near power plants developed leukemia.

    C. when studies showed slightly higher cancer rates near power lines.

    D. when statistics proved conclusively the cause-and-effect relationship.

35. Natural chemicals have been in existence for a long time and our bodies should be accustomed to them. Therefore, when comparing the toxicity of natural and synthetic chemicals, natural chemicals are clearly _____ synthetic chemicals.

    A. less toxic than   C. as toxic as

    B. more toxic than   D. None of these -they cannot be compared.

36. Injuries caused by accidents or violence are known as

    A. morbidity.   C. distress.

    B. stress.   D. trauma.

37. The incidence of _____-related deaths is similar in less- and more-developed countries.

    A. trauma   C. parasite

    B. stress   D. disease

38. As a medical term, "stress" means _____ factors that cause strain on an organism.

    A. chemical   C. emotional

    B. physical   D. chemical, physical, or emotional

39. Which of the following are known to be physical responses to stress?

    A. strokes and ulcers   C. birth defects and leukemia

    B. cancer and toxic reactions   D. All of the above

40. Students who are more susceptible to the cold virus during final exams may be responding to

    A. overcrowded libraries.   C. less sleep.

    B. stress.   D. increased fat consumption (pizza, etc.).

41. Cardiovascular disease is strongly related to what dietary factors?

    A. vitamin deficiencies   C. excessive calorie consumption

    B. high salt and fat intake   D. protein imbalances

42. The best dietary measures to increase your health include eating

    A. more red meat and salt.

    B. less fat and cholesterol, but more processed foods.

    C. more whole grains, fruits, and vegetables.

    D. about 50 percent more than the minimum amount of needed calories.

43. Which of the following statements is true?

    A. If a substance is toxic, its toxicity is highly dependent on its form and where it is present in the environment.

    B. If a substance is toxic, it is equally toxic regardless of its form or where it is present in the environment.

    C. The most important factor in the toxicity of a substance is the route it enters our bodies.

    D. The most important factor in the toxicity of a substance is its persistence in the environment.

44. Among the most important characteristics of chemicals in determining their environmental risks is/are

    A. solubility.   C. reactivity.

    B. persistence.   D. All of these.

45. Solubility is an important characteristic in toxic material movement in the environment and body. Which of the following statements is true?

    A. Water-soluble compounds require carriers to enter cells.

    B. Oil-soluble compounds readily damage kidneys.

    C. Water-soluble compounds move slowly in the environment.

    D. Oil-soluble compounds accumulate in the body.

46. Bioaccumulation is a term that describes the way cells

    A. grow as they absorb all types of molecules.

    B. selectively absorb and store molecules.

    C. allow water-soluble compounds to pass through membranes.

    D. metabolize compounds that are absorbed.

47. Bioaccumulation is important because it allows cells to

    A. accumulate essential nutrients and minerals.   C. protect themselves against toxins.

    B. rid themselves of waste material.   D. reproduce more quickly.

48. Biomagnification is a concentration of toxins

    A. within certain cells of the body.

    B. as predators consume and store toxins stored in the bodies of their prey.

    C. within the liver as an organism gets older.

    D. within the bodies of organisms at low trophic levels.

49. Highly persistent toxic chemicals

    A. retain their toxicity as they cycle through the food chain and environment.

    B. lose their toxicity once released in the environment.

    C. accumulate within one organism but break down at higher trophic levels.

    D. are highly unusual among artificial chemicals.

50. A chemical interaction in which one substance exacerbates the other is termed

    A. an additive reaction.   C. an antagonistic reaction.

    B. a bioaccumulation.   D. synergism.

51. If 100 cups of strong coffee contain a lethal dose of caffeine, why don't all coffee drinkers die from caffeine overdoses?

   A. Few people drink 100 cups of coffee in a year.

   B. Because of its molecular form, this caffeine is not actually absorbed into the body.

   C. Our bodies metabolize the caffeine before lethal concentrations are reached.

   D. Coffee drinkers who drink 100 cups of coffee a month will eventually die from the bioaccumulation.

52. Our bodies minimize the effects of toxic compounds by all of the following *except*

   A. metabolic degradation.   C. antagonistic reactions.

   B. excretion.   D. repair mechanisms.

53. Which of the following tissues are more likely to develop cancers?

   A. skin because there is high cellular reproduction rates to replace injured cells.

   B. eyes because they are always exposed to light.

   C. fat because of bioaccumulation.

   D. bones because of the increased radiation in our environment.

54. The saying "the dose makes the poison" means that

   A. Almost nothing is toxic at low levels.

   B. Nearly anything can be toxic at some level.

   C. Some things are more poisonous than others.

   D. All things are equally poisonous at equal doses.

55. An advantage of testing for toxicity by exposing animals to chemicals is that using animals is

   A. cheaper than other methods.

   B. faster than other methods.

   C. a trusted and usually reliable way to get results.

   D. easier than using computer models.

56. In the dose/response curve below the greatest number of individuals respond to this toxin at a dosage of ____ ppm.

   A. 5   B. 10   C. 20   D. 40

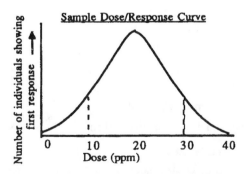

57. In the dose/response curve above, individuals represented by the left end of the curve (responding to doses between 0 and 10 ppm) are

   A. very sensitive.   C. about average sensitivity.

   B. very insensitive.   D. relatively insensitive.

58. LD50 is a dose of a toxin to which

    A. half of the population is sensitive.   C. all individuals react.

    B. only individuals over 50 years old react.   D. 0.5 percent of the population reacts.

59. Which of the following is *not* a problem with generalizing the results of LD50 to humans?

    A. Closely related species can have different reactions.

    B. Different individuals of the same species can have different reactions.

    C. Differences in physiology and metabolism can lead to different reactions.

    D. Smaller species generally have more sensitive reactions.

60. Acute effects of a toxin appear

    A. only after repeated exposure.   C. immediately after exposure.

    B. long after exposure.   D. when there is sustained contact.

61. Chronic effects of a toxic response

    A. are less harmful than acute effects.   C. rarely show up in time to be diagnosed.

    B. can last a long time or be permanent.   D. are unlikely to be lethal.

62. The dose/response curve below shows that

    A. some exposure is necessary before most individuals respond.

    B. any exposure causes immediate response.

    C. response levels off as dosage increases.

    D. the dose decreases as response increases.

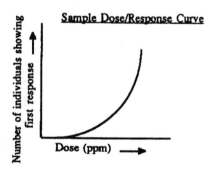

63. Detection of toxic chemicals depends upon

    A. how many chemicals are present.

    B. how sophisticated the sampling technology is.

    C. the sensitivity of measuring techniques and how many chemicals are present.

    D. whether or not individuals or groups of individuals are sensitive to them.

64. Most people do their own personal risk assessments based upon

    A. scientific data.   C. whimsical preference devoid of logic.

    B. logical reasoning about relative risks.   D. personal biases and preferences as well as logic.

65. As a society, we usually focus money and attention on health risks that are

A. most serious.

B. easiest to clean up.

C. most well-publicized and frightening.

D. All of these receive equal money and attention.

CHAPTER 10
FOOD, HUNGER, AND NUTRITION

1. After undergoing a terrible famine two decades ago, fewer than 3 percent of Chinese people are underfed. This proportion of underfed people is _____ than the United States.

    A. higher   C. the same

    B. lower   D. only slightly higher

2. China is able to feed its 1.2 billion people because the Chinese

    A. have more arable land than any other country.   C. farm efficiently and have simple diets.

    B. subsist mainly on fish.   D. All of these.

3. Agricultural policies in China's Great Leap Forward resulted in

    A. the worst famine in history.   C. a boom in rice exports in 1960.

    B. a sudden rise in nutrition for all Chinese.   D. the "Green Revolution."

4. In the past forty years world food supplies have shown

    A. modest gains.   C. no change.

    B. huge increases.   D. severe declines.

5. The United Nations Food and Agriculture Organization (FAO) estimates that the average minimum daily calorie intake worldwide is ____ calories per day.

    A. 500   B. 1000   C. 2500   D. 4800

6. "Undernourished" people are those who receive less than _____ percent of their minimum dietary requirements on a long-term basis.

    A. 100   B. 90   C. 50   D. 25

7. Undernourished parents often raise children who are undernourished because the parents

    A. transfer genetic deficiencies to their children.

    B. don't know any better.

    C. cannot afford to feed their children properly.

    D. All of these are reasons for the vicious cycle.

8. Children often suffer mental retardation and stunted growth when they are

    A. overnourished.   C. seriously undernourished.

    B. moderately undernourished.   D. seriously overnourished.

9. Over the past thirty years the *average* amount of food available per person has

    A. moderately decreased.   C. dramatically decreased.

    B. moderately increased.   D. dramatically increased.

10. Anemia is a common disease resulting from a shortage of dietary

    A. iron.   C. protein.

    B. iodine.   D. vitamin A.

11. In richer countries overnutrition is associated with

    A. heart attacks, weight problems, and marasmus.   C. anemia, strokes, and goiter.

    B. high blood pressure, heart attacks, and strokes.   D. All of these.

12. People can suffer malnourishment if they consume large amounts of _____ instead of _____.
    A. fat and sugar, vitamins and protein   C. vitamins, protein
    B. proteins, carbohydrates   D. proteins and minerals, vitamins

13. We get our ten essential amino acids by consuming
    A. vitamins.   C. complex carbohydrates.
    B. proteins.   D. minerals.

14. The basic structural material your body uses to create new cells and tissues is
    A. complex carbohydrates.   D. lipids.
    B. fiber.   E. Both A and B.
    C. proteins.

15. In order to flush out wastes and absorb toxins our digestive systems need
    A. complex carbohydrates.   D. lipids.
    B. fiber.   E. Both A and B.
    C. proteins.

16. What are two common diseases that result from protein deficiencies?
    A. dysentery and diarrhea   C. scurvy and pellagra
    B. marasmus and kwashiorkor   D. goiter and cretinism

17. People who subsist on starchy foods such as cassava, potatoes, and white rice
    A. often receive insufficient protein.   C. have the healthiest possible diet.
    B. are usually severely overweight.   D. are sure to meet all their nutritional needs.

18. Lipids are
    A. the building blocks of sugars.
    B. a source of essential amino acids.
    C. fats and oils.
    D. unnecessary components of our diet that we should avoid if possible.

19. The best way to ensure good nutrient intake is to consume
    A. vitamin supplements.   C. eggs and cheese.
    B. high-calorie and starchy foods.   D. a varied diet with grains, vegetables, fruit, and dairy products.

20. The main function(s) of fat in our body is to
    A. help metabolize energy.   D. All of these.
    B. build cellular components.   E. Both B and C.
    C. provide energy.

21. People who eat a diet of highly processed foods in more-developed countries are likely to have _____ deficiencies.
    A. iodine   B. mineral   C. protein   D. lipid

22. Our bodies *do not* use vitamins to

    A. help metabolize energy.   D. All of these.

    B. build cellular components.   E. Both B and C.

    C. provide energy.

23. People whose diet consists mainly of maize (corn) often suffer from a

    A. protein deficiency called pellagra.   C. vitamin deficiency called rickets.

    B. vitamin deficiency called pellagra.   D. protein deficiency called marasmus.

24. Vitamin A deficiencies are associated with

    A. dry eyes and retinal degeneration.   C. a lack of energy, or listlessness.

    B. weak bones.   D. anemia.

25. A completely vegetarian diet

    A. normally provides all necessary nutrients.   C. cannot ever provide complete nutrition.

    B. can provide all nutrients if well balanced.   D. can be harmful to health and digestion.

26. The US Department of Agriculture recently decided that the traditional four major food groups (meat, dairy, grains, and fruits/vegetables)

    A. are still the best guide to good eating.

    B. do not adequately support beef and milk consumption.

    C. give too little emphasis to whole grains, fruits, and vegetables.

    D. provide too few oils, salts, and sugars.

27. The three crops that humans rely on for the majority of nutrients and calories are

    A. potatoes, wheat, and oats.   C. barley, oats, and rye.

    B. wheat, rice, and maize.   D. maize, oats, and rice.

28. Most humans rely on just a few of the world's animal and plant species for food because only a few

    A. are edible.   D. few food types are what we are accustomed to eating.

    B. are available.   E. All of these are true.

    C. have been discovered.

29. Which of the following *does not* describe the current status of the world's wild fisheries?

    A. Fish farming has allowed wild fish to recover worldwide.

    B. Subsidies are necessary to make the fisheries profitable.

    C. Overharvesting threatens the fisheries.

    D. Habitat destruction threatens the fisheries.

30. What event occurred in the 1950s and 1960s that affects the world's current wild fisheries

    A. An increase in fishing technology led to more efficient fishing.

    B. The worldwide fishing harvests declined.

    C. Many fisheries (such as the Canadian Cod Fishery) collapsed.

    D. Many offshore fisheries became commercially inviable.

31. The 80 percent of the world's people who live in developing countries raise 60 percent of the world's ruminant livestock

    A. and therefore rely heavily on meat and milk.

    B. but consume only 20 percent of all animal products.

    C. but are nearly all vegetarians by persuasion.

    D. but eat well over 80 percent of world meat supplies.

32. Some people claim that the cod fishery collapsed because it developed along the industrial model. What do they mean by this claim?

    A. For 400 years the fishery was sustainable but the industrial revolution caused the collapse.

    B. Fisheries focus mostly on older fish because they are bigger and the higher price leads to more fishing.

    C. The allowable catch is based on the industrial need.

    D. Each fish becomes more valuable as stocks decline and the higher price leads to more efficient catching.

33. By the year 2025 cropland in Asia is expected to amount to about 0.09 hectares per person. This is about the area of

    A. an acre.   C. an average suburban garden plot in the US.

    B. an average suburban lawn in the US   D. a small farm.

34. Russia and Canada, the two largest countries in the world,

    A. have the world's greatest food production.

    B. each produce far more than China or the United States.

    C. lie too far north to be the biggest food producers.

    D. are too cold to produce any significant crops.

35. Most of the world's food is grown in

    A. China, India, and the United States mostly because these countries have the most land and workforce.

    B. Russia and the United States mostly because they are in the temperate growing zone.

    C. China, Russia, and the United States mostly because these countries have the most land and workforce.

    D. India and China mostly because these countries have the most workforce.

36. Indonesia's impressive improvement in their rice crop was due in part to

    A. decreased population growth.   C. increased use of labor in the fields.

    B. increased use of pesticides, fertilizers, and irrigation.   D. increased efficiency on less total cropland.

37. About 90 percent of US grain is used

    A. in making bread products.   C. to produce ethanol for fuel.

    B. to feed undernourished populations elsewhere. D. to feed cattle, hogs, and chickens.

38. What is the basis of the statement that we could feed more people if we eat grain rather than feeding it to livestock?

    A. the first law of thermodynamics   C. ecofeminism

    B. the second law of thermodynamics   D. biocentrism

39. India, which has about 300 million undernourished people,

    A. exports millions of tons of food annually.

    B. exports food only for humanitarian needs.

    C. chooses not to export any foods at all.

    D. has made it illegal to export food.

40. Thomas Malthus' gloomy predictions of worldwide famine and starvation

    A. are completely incorrect and laughable today.

    B. are incorrect so far.

    C. never really made any sense.

    D. have been proven solidly true today.

41. The most important step in ensuring food supplies in poor countries will be to

    A. stabilize population.

    B. protect the environment.

    C. solve political conflicts.

    D. All of these.

42. Croplands in Eastern Europe and the former Soviet region have declined in the past thirty years because of

    A. decreased food needs.

    B. increased forest cover.

    C. inappropriate farming methods.

    D. increased efficiency that made many croplands unnecessary.

43. "Miracle" crops of the green revolution produce tremendous yields

    A. even in severe drought conditions.

    B. with primitive farming techniques and no chemical use.

    C. in response to fertilizers, pesticides, and irrigation.

    D. in all conditions where standard crops fail.

44. Worldwide, traditional and native varieties of food crops have _____ since the introduction of green revolution varieties.

    A. become more widespread

    B. spread from region to region, leading to increasing diversity

    C. been slightly influenced by new varieties

    D. been widely replaced by new varieties

45. Gene banks are set up to

    A. preserve the genetic material of disappearing native crop varieties.

    B. stockpile surplus corn and wheat in the United States.

    C. keep safe the most valuable genetically engineered gene types.

    D. control the spread of green revolution crops.

46. Some of the important characteristics that gene banks and newer plant breeding programs have been working to preserve or develop include

    A. old-fashioned or traditional appearance.

    B. efficient response to fertilizers and irrigation.

    C. salt tolerance, drought resistance, and high nutrient value.

    D. the ability to grow taller and faster than other crops.

47. Fifty years ago there were several hundred varieties of wheat grown in the Middle East. Now a few of the more modern "miracle varieties" have replaced the indigenous species. What are the implications of this change?

    A. The productivity of wheat should continue to rise and increase the availability of food per person.

    B. Genetic resources are diminished and an epidemic of wheat disease is likely due to the reliance on few species.

    C. The miracle varieties will need specialized harvesting methods because they are so productive.

    D. The biodiversity of wheat species has increased because of the introduction of few hybrid species.

48. The "blue revolution" involves

    A. improved fish harvesting technology.   C. improved fish farming.

    B. producing single-cell protein from algae.   D. a combination of all of these.

49. One of the ecological problems associated with fish farming is the

    A. practice of some commercial trawlers of capturing hatchery fish.

    B. loss of native wetlands and species in favor of the fish tanks.

    C. overharvesting of young fish.

    D. No problems, there is actually a benefit from the organic material generated from the fish tanks.

50. In the United States, where farmers receive large subsidies and surplus food is stockpiled,

    A. malnutrition is unknown.

    B. diseases associated with undernourishment have been eliminated.

    C. at least 30 million people are undernourished .

    D. almost nobody receives adequate nutrition.

51. The best way to maintain or increase the world's productive agricultural land is to

    A. increase the use of pesticides.   C. stop producing food altogether.

    B. use modern mechanical agriculture more.   D. develop sustainable farming methods.

52. The conservation reserve program is designed to decrease

    A. the amount of active farmland in the United States.

    B. the price of farm goods to consumers.

    C. US dependence on food imports.

    D. the amount of food produced on US farms.

53. The United States gives most of its food aid to

    A. the world's most impoverished countries.

    B. countries with the highest population growth.

    C. countries that are politically aligned with us.

    D. countries with the least arable land.

54. Frequently, food aid _____ in receiving countries.

    A. drives down food prices and local farmers' income

    B. induces local food production

    C. causes increased malnutrition due to the increase of fats and oils

    D. does not support unpopular or repressive government

55. Cash crops growing is often criticized because it

    A. provides low income to farmers.   C. leads to malnutrition among farmers.

    B. often replaces the growth of local food crops.   D. raises foreign exchange.

56. One of your classmates is from Honduras and explains that her country's reliance on bananas for foreign exchange can lead to serious problems. You explain that you think increased foreign exchange is good for a country because there are funds available for development. She agrees, but explains further. Which of the following statements is probably *not* in her explanation?

    A. Since they are luxury foods people in a country like the US will not buy them if they are too expensive.

    B. Honduras farmers are not growing crops to feed people in their country because the land is used for bananas.

    C. If bananas are not bought abroad, there is no money for people in Honduras to buy needed food.

    D. Growing bananas leads to malnutrition in her country.

    E. All of these are explanations she would probably use.

57. In terms of the household environment, one of the most effective ways to improve family welfare and in turn, family nutrition is to provide support

    A. in the form of money to families so they can buy needed medicines.

    B. and infrastructure to women so they can grow a home garden.

    C. so that small scale farmers can have access to growing cash crops.

    D. for small scale farmers to convert their crops to annuals for an annual harvest time.

58. The comparison of Ethiopia and the Sudan with Zimbabwe and Cape Verde in the droughts of the early 1980s is a good illustration of the

    A. role of armed conflict and politics in famine.

    B. famine that killed so many people in the entire region.

    C. role of global climate change in the increase of famine in Africa.

    D. overharvesting that made croplands in the region vulnerable to drought.

59. Famines are most often serious when there is

    A. a very serious drought.   C. steady population growth.

    B. no room to expand agriculture.   D. drought and war together.

60. Food security has to do with

    A. a country's dependence on cash crop exports.

    B. preventing wars over diminishing food supplies.

    C. the ability of a population to obtain food on a day-to-day basis.

    D. the total volume of food imports and aid.

CHAPTER 11
SOIL RESOURCES AND SUSTAINABLE AGRICULTURE

1. What was the main cause of the dust storms of the 1930s?

    A. Diversified, subsistence farming was replaced.

    B. Shelterbeds were financed by the increased wheat prices.

    C. Stripcropping and other new tillage methods.

    D. All of these.

2. The Soil Conservation was founded in 1935 to combat the dust storms. What was one of the practices that the service did?

    A. Diversified, subsistence farming was replaced.

    B. Shelterbeds were replaced.

    C. Stripcropping and other new tillage methods were introduced.

    D. All of these.

3. Which is the best definition of soil?

    A. A complex of minerals that provide energy for plant growth

    B. A complex mixture of organic matter, minerals, and living organisms

    C. A mass of dead organic matter and detritus; dirt

    D. All of these adequately describes soil.

4. Red-colored tropical soils become red when rainwater leaches away _____.

    A. organic contents and soluble minerals   C. aluminum and clay

    B. iron and aluminum   D. insoluble minerals and inorganic content

5. Under favorable conditions, good topsoil accumulates at a rate of about _____ tons per hectare.

    A. .1   B. 1   C. 10   D. 100

6. It is possible that approximately ____ of the croplands in the world are losing topsoil faster than it is being replaced.

    A. 10-20%   B. 35-50%   C. 50-75%   D. 75-90%

7. Mineral particles in the soil are derived from

    A. underlying bedrock.   D. Both B and C

    B. materials transported and deposited by glaciers.   E. All of these.

    C. materials transported and deposited by rivers.

8. When compared to sand and gravel, small soil particles (clay and silt) have _____ pore space.

    A. more   B. about the same   C. less   D. significantly more

9. What component makes soil sticky, elastic, and impermeable?

    A. sands   B. organic matter   C. living organisms   D. clay

10. Spaces between sand particles give sandy soil

    A. the ability to hold water.   C. good drainage.

    B. low permeability to air or water.   D. the ability to store minerals.

11. A "heavy" soil would have a high _____ content.

    A. sand   B. organic matter   C. silt   D. clay

12. The soil types represented by the letters A, B, and C below are _____, _____, and _____.

    A. peat, sandy soil, loam   C. sandy soil, loam, peat

    B. loam, peat, sandy soil   D. peat, loam, sandy soil

Organic and Sand Content of Four Soils

13. In the graph above which soil type has the highest sand content?

    A. A   B. B   C. C   D. D

14. In the graph above which soil type has more humus?

    A. A   B. B   C. C   D. D

15. The critical organic component of soil that gives it its structure is termed

    A. clay   B. humus   C. parent material   D. heavy soil

16. Which of the following *cannot* be found in soil?

    A. fungus and algae   C. insects and bacteria

    B. algae and bacteria   D. All of these are found in soil.

17. Soil organisms usually stay _____ the soil.

    A. deep below the surface of   C. close to the surface of

    B. near the middle of   D. spread uniformly throughout

18. The stratified horizontal layers of soils are called

    A. soil profiles.   B. soil horizons.   C. soil textures.   D. soil types.

19. Soil leaching involves

    A. rainwater seeping through soil and dissolving nutrients.

    B. the accumulation of organic matter in the uppermost soil layers.

    C. the elimination of pore space in soil.

    D. All of these.

20. Topsoil contains predominantly

    A. organic material.   C. mixed organic and mineral particles.

    B. mineral material.   D. insoluble minerals and sand.

21. The letters A, B, C, and D on the graph below represent different horizons in a soil. The letters represent, in order,

A. topsoil; parent material; bedrock; subsoil.

B. subsoil; parent material; bedrock; topsoil.

C. parent material; topsoil; subsoil; bedrock.

D. topsoil; subsoil; parent material; bedrock.

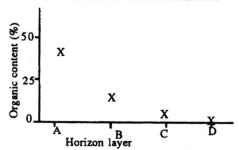

22. In which horizon layer of the figure above would you find the most plant roots?

A. A   B. B   C. C   D. D

23. Which horizon layer of the figure above would be impenetrable?

A. A   B. B   C. C   D. D

24. Which of the following would have nearly zero or zero topsoil?

A. virgin prairies

B. deserts

C. tropical rainforests

D. tundra

E. All of these have topsoil.

25. The parent material layer of a soil is composed of decayed or weathered

A. bedrock.

B. organic detritus and roots.

C. residual aluminum and iron.

D. soil.

26. The richest farming soils that form under the grasslands of central North America and under moist deciduous forests are the

A. latisols and aridisols.

B. ultisols and mollisols.

C. mollisols and alfisols.

D. entisols and ultisols.

27. Most recent increases in agricultural productivity have come from

A. irrigation in arid areas.

B. building up soil reserves on farms worldwide.

C. clearing rainforests.

D. new crop varieties and intensified farming.

28. Which of the following would indicate light soil erosion?

A. concentrations of salts and toxic minerals

B. soil doesn't retain water

C. part of topsoil removed

D. 30 - 70 percent of natural vegetation remains

29. Which of the following can cause serious degradation of soils?

    A. concentrations of salts and toxic minerals C. water erosion

    B. wind erosion   D. Any of these can cause serious degradation.

30. Which of the following are forms of chemical deterioration of soil?

    A. salinization and acidification   C. compaction and nutrient depletion

    B. waterlogging and laterization   D. pollution and waterlogging

31. Rill erosion leads to

    A. sheet erosion.   B. wind erosion.   C. gullying.   D. soil compaction.

32. Sheet erosion

    A. can remove much soil before it is noticed.

    B. generally has little importance on farmland.

    C. is usually stopped quickly because it is so easy to detect.

    D. can cause much damage but is unusual.

33. Wind erosion is most likely to cause problems in

    A. forested grazing lands on high mountains.   C. fertile river bottoms with annual floods.

    B. open, arid regions.   D. agricultural regions in the far north.

34. Canada's most severe water erosion rates are greatest in areas with

    A. strong winds and dry soils because the rain washes the dry soils away.

    B. hilly forested areas with high runoff due to melting snow.

    C. strip farming because the soil is exposed.

    D. soft soil with abundant rainfall and monoculture farming.

35. What are the implications of losing up to 2 bushels of soil for each bushel of corn produced from most Iowa farms?

    A. Corn prices are steadily increasing due to the loss of the soil.

    B. There is less availability of corn.

    C. We are mining the soil instead of using it.

    D. All of these are implications of losing the soil.

36. Which of the following areas has the greatest potential for future productive farmland?

    A. tropical moist forests in Asia   C. subtropical forests grassland in Texas

    B. tropical seasonal forests in Brazil   D. subtropical forests grassland in Argentina

37. Which is the best cropping method for reducing erosion?

    A. rotating corn, wheat, and clover

    B. raising only corn continuously

    C. raising wheat continuously

    D. raising a perennial such as bluegrass continuously

38. About what portion of world freshwater withdrawals is used for agriculture?

    A. 1/10   B. 1/20   C. 3/4   D. 9/10

39. Waterlogging results from
    A. toxic metal accumulation.
    C. excessive plowing.
    B. excessive irrigation.
    D. natural erosion processes.

40. Salinization is a common agricultural problem in what type of region?
    A. arid
    B. cold
    C. tropical
    D. humid

41. The most important mineral elements plants need to grow include
    A. iron, aluminum, manganese, and nitrogen.
    B. carbon, oxygen, hydrogen, and iron.
    C. nitrogen, potassium, phosphorus, and calcium.
    D. calcium, magnesium, and sulfur oxides.

42. Legumes are plants whose roots contain bacteria that can fix nitrogen and naturally fertilize the plant. Which of the following are legumes?
    A. peas, beans, and alfalfa
    C. peas, spinach, and rhubarb
    B. carrots, potatoes, and beets
    D. celery, carrots, and onions

43. "Green manure" is
    A. fresh animal wastes.
    C. plants raised for animal fodder.
    B. green plants, especially legumes.
    D. commercial fertilizer that is certified organic.

44. Which of the following uses the least amount of energy in industrialized farming practices?
    A. fuel for tractors and other machines
    C. pumping groundwater
    B. production of chemical fertilizers
    D. drying the crops

45. Sustainable farming
    A. is cheaper and safer than conventional farming.
    B. is safe, even though it causes weed problems.
    C. uses fewer chemicals but more water than conventional methods.
    D. is an invention of modern agricultural research.

46. Annual row crops such as _____ cause the highest topsoil erosion rates because _____.
    A. corn and coffee, they use so many nutrients
    B. wheat and coffee, they need so much water
    C. tea and beans, plowing in the fall is required for planting of these annual spring crops
    D. corn and beans, soil is left bare for the majority of the year

47. Compared to the Dust Bowl Era, farming practices are _____ and there is currently _____ topsoil loss.
    A. more intensive, about the same
    C. more intensive, more
    B. less intensive, about the same
    D. less intensive, more

48. An effective way to eliminate soil loss in a region is to measure the
    A. amount of dust in the air.
    C. amount lost on crop fields.
    B. sediment load of rivers.
    D. All of these are effective ways to measure the loss.

49. The efficiency of irrigation water use is _____ in most countries. One of the reasons for this is

    A. low, the lack of availability of technology to distribute the water where it is needed.

    B. high, the careful use of water because it is so expensive.

    C. high, the technology to distribute the water where it is needed is available.

    D. low, evaporative losses from unprotected water channeling.

50. What is the main reason a conversion from conventional agriculture to organic farming occurred in Cuba?

    A. The demands of consumers.

    B. The collapse of the socialist bloc.

    C. The high rate of deaths from heavy pesticide use.

    D. The change to a main crop of sugarcane.

51. What is one method that Cubans use on the large scale to fertilize their soil?

    A. They use humus from earthworm farms.

    B. They use imported synthetic organic fertilizers.

    C. They use synthetic organic fertilizers produced in Cuba.

    D. They import organic fertilizers.

52. Contour plowing and strip farming are methods designed to

    A. prevent weed spreading.   C. prevent water and soil loss.

    B. improve plowing and harvesting efficiency.   D. make farms more attractive.

53. Which of the following is the best way to ensure soil health?

    A. maintaining clean, open ground between rows

    B. strip farming and leaving residues on fields after harvest

    C. clearing fields immediately after harvesting.

    D. establishing ridges running up and down hills.

54. Another word for cover crops is

    A. mulch.   B. strip farming.   C. green manure.   D. All of these.

55. Which of these is *not* a benefit found with reduced tillage farming?

    A. water conservation   D. soil aeration and loosening

    B. soil preservation   E. decreased insects and weeds

    C. increased crop yields

56. The graph below shows that

    A. runoff and soil loss increase simultaneously.

    B. runoff decreases as soil loss rises.

    C. runoff and soil loss change in opposite ways as land uses change.

    D. soil loss causes increased runoff.

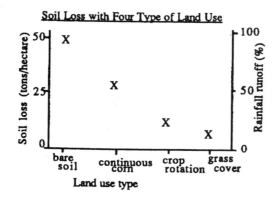

57. According to the above graph, which is the most sustainable type of land use?

    A. bare soil   C. crop rotation

    B. continuous corn cropping   D. maintaining grass cover

58. One of the drawbacks of leaving crop residues on a field after harvest is increased

    A. cost due to the high cost of fertilizers.   C. salinization.

    B. pest, disease, and insect problems.   D. energy use of machinery.

59. The benefits of leaving crop residues on a field after harvest include

    A. protecting soil organisms.

    B. reducing evaporation and soil temperatures.

    C. breaking the erosive effects of wind and water.

    D. All of these.

60. Organic foods

    A. are healthy for you but have little impact on farmers.

    B. are good for farmers but bad for society and the economy.

    C. are good for you, for farmers, and for the environment.

    D. are good for farmers but bad for the environment.

1. DDT accumulation in North American eagles, pelicans, and other birds disrupted birds' calcium metabolism, causing

    A. infertility.
    B. thin eggshells.
    C. severe nerve damage.
    D. adult deformities.
    E. All of these.

2. DDT is

    A. equally toxic to mammals and insects.
    B. soluble only in water.
    C. cheap to produce and easy to apply.
    D. All of these.

3. Pest organisms tend to be _____ species.

    A. specialist   B. generalist   C. migratory   D. endemic

4. Which of the following is *not* true of pesticides?

    A. They are expensive and difficult to use.
    B. They have been used to save human lives.
    C. They can be found in most American homes.
    D. They are used to kill animals *and* plants.

5. Of the millions of living species, only about ____ cause 90 percent of the worldwide crop damage.

    A. 100   B. 1000   C. 10   D. 500

6. Herbicides are used to kill

    A. leafy herb plants.   B. plants.   C. algae.   D. fungus.

7. A broad-spectrum biocide is designed to kill

    A. a wide range of plants.
    B. microbes that are neither plant nor animal.
    C. all sorts of living organisms.
    D. specifically multicellular organisms.

8. Alcohol and pickling solutions were probably widely developed because they

    A. neutralize toxins in foods.
    B. preserve food due to their pesticidal properties.
    C. have more interesting flavors than other solutions for seasoning.
    D. are effective insecticides in the home.

9. A goose is used in pest control to

    A. control weeds.   B. catch insects.   C. eat grass.   D. All of these.

10. What is considered the "modern era of chemical pest control"?

    A. The use of predatory ants in China.
    B. The discovery of the insecticidal properties of some plants.
    C. The recent decrease in the use of pesticides in agriculture.
    D. The discovery of the insecticidal properties of DDT.

11. The population growth curve of a pest organism would probably be _____ because they are _____ species in ecological succession.

    A. exponential, pioneer   C. stable, pioneer

    B. exponential, climax   D. stable, climax

12. The rates of pesticide use are _____ in the wealthiest, more developed countries. When compared to these wealthier, more developed countries the rates of pesticide use in developing countries are _____.

    A. about the same; rising   C. highest; rising

    B. about the same; decreasing   D. highest; decreasing

13. Worldwide, what are most pesticides used for?

    A. Household applications   C. Personal protection against disease carrying insects

    B. Agriculture   D. All of these.

14. The world's three highest pesticide consumers are

    A. the United States, Germany, and Italy.   C. India, China, and Brazil.

    B. Russia, the United States, and Canada.   D. the United States, India, and Egypt.

15. Most of the pesticides applied in the United States are used in

    A. landscaping for private homes.   C. private homes.

    B. agriculture.   D. landscaping for both private homes and businesses.

16. Which of the following categories of agricultural pesticide use is highest in the US?

    A. biocides   B. fungicides   C. insecticides   D. herbicides

17. Why is it useful to classify pesticides by their chemical structure?

    A. It is easier to keep them organized by type.

    B. Scientists have done this for years and it would be inefficient to change it now.

    C. Similar chemical structures often relate to similar toxicological characteristics.

    D. This is how they are named and looking them up for reference is easier.

18. Which of the following are inorganic pesticides?

    A. rotenone and nicotine   C. carbon tetrachloride and ethylene dibromide

    B. arsenic, copper, and mercury   D. DDT and mothballs

19. Inorganic pesticides are generally

    A. highly toxic and remain in the soil for a long time.

    B. highly toxic and break down soon in the environment.

    C. moderately toxic and remain in the soil for a long time.

    D. moderately toxic and break down soon in the environment.

20. DDT is a

    A. chlorinated hydrocarbon (organochloride).   C.   chlorinated inorganic pesticide.

    B. natural organic pesticide.   D. organophosphate.

21. Organophosphates operate by attacking an organism's _____ system.

    A. muscular   B. blood   C. immune   D. nervous

22. Natural organic pesticides are *not*

    A. extracted from plants.   C. safe for all animals.

    B. toxic to humans.   D. stable in their natural form.

23. Chlorinated hydrocarbons have ____ toxicity for humans and remain in the soil for a _____ time.

    A. high; long   B. high; short   C. low; short   D. low; long

24. In general, microbial agents are

    A. wide spectrum agents.

    B. used in place of chemical pesticides.

    C. small molecules that gasify easily.

    D. small molecules that penetrate rapidly into a variety of materials.

25. Organophosphates and _____ are similar in that they lack environmental persistence and have low bioaccumulation.

    A. chlorinated hydrocarbons   C. inorganic pesticides

    B. carbamates   D. fumigants

26. The introduction of DDT and other pesticides has greatly reduced deaths from _____ over the past fifty years.

    A. malaria   B. polio   C. diphtheria   D. tuberculosis

27. Which of the following diseases cannot be decreased with insecticides?

    A. malaria   B. sleeping sickness   C. bronchitis   D. plague

28. In terms of agriculture, pesticides have lead to _____ for consumers.

    A. lower monetary costs   C. more attractive produce

    B. better produce quality   D. All of these.

29. When a new pesticide is developed the best thing to do is to use it

    A. sparingly so pests won't develop a resistance.

    B. widely and liberally, to knock out pests.

    C. sparingly then liberally to prevent resistance and knock out pests.

    D. liberally then sparingly to prevent resistance and knock out pests.

30. Approximately what percentage of the pesticides we use never reach the intended target?

    A. 15   B. 20   C. 90   D. 50

31. Significant monetary losses are due to the destruction of _____ through pesticide spray drift and residues on flowers.

    A. lady bird beetles   C. praying mantises

    B. honeybees   D. Monarch butterflies

32. Pesticide resurgence is part of the problem of pesticide resistance and happens when a pest organism

    A. that was dormant during pesticide application becomes active and produces offspring.

    B. adapts to the pesticide and produces tolerant offspring.

    C. adapts to the pesticide and produces even more pesticide-tolerant offspring.

    D. that is tolerant to the pesticide survives and produces tolerant offspring.

33. Pesticide resistance occurs when a population of pests

    A. becomes too numerous for chemicals to control.

    B. develops genetic resistance to chemicals.

    C. grows extremely large because of chemical misapplications.

    D. is not affected because the pesticide chemicals do not break down in the environment.

34. How could an organism be resistant to a chemical that it has never been exposed to?

    A. Genes for pesticide resistance can be transferred through vectors such as viruses.

    B. Pesticide resistance does not require chemical exposure and eventually all organisms become resistant.

    C. The pesticide treadmill causes pesticide resistance.

    D. There is probably some exposure that we are not aware of.

35. The pesticide treadmill occurs when

    A. a virus transfers pesticide resistance to a new species.

    B. constantly increasing doses of pesticides are needed to control pests.

    C. nontarget agricultural species are destroyed by insecticides.

    D. predators of the pest species are killed by broadcast spraying.

36. Pesticide resistance only occurs in _____ species.

    A. weed   B. insect   C. plant pathogen   D. All of these.

37. Why are pest predator populations so adversely affected by broad-spectrum pesticides?

    A. In general, predators are more susceptible to the pesticides.

    B. There is less food for the predators when the pest species is destroyed.

    C. Predators in higher trophic levels are more likely to be wiped out than lower trophic levels.

    D. Broad-spectrum pesticides leave more residues than other pesticides and these kill the predators.

38. Pesticides

    A. have no positive effects.   C. have benefits that outweigh all costs.

    B. can be beneficial if used cautiously.   D. are rarely as dangerous as people think

39. When pesticide residues are found in such remote areas as the St. Lawrence estuary, which of the following is probably *not* responsible?

    A. bioaccumulation   C. the circle of poison

    B. pesticide rain   D. pesticide persistence and mobility

40. There are many pesticides that are illegal to use in North America but that are still produced here. The irony for the United States occurs when these chemicals

    A. bioaccumulate in developing nations.

    B. accumulate in foreign waterways and return in ocean currents.

    C. return on or in foreign-grown produce.

    D. start being produced overseas.

41. Which of the following is a long-term effect of pesticides on humans?

    A. cancer   C. fetal deformities

    B. an allergic response   D. Parkinson's disease

42. What happened in Bhopal, India in 1984?

   A. A cure for DDT poisoning was discovered.

   B. Peasants demonstrated against pesticide use.

   C. There was a pesticide-related cancer outbreak.

   D. A pesticide plant exploded, killing many.

43. In the US the farm workers who are exposed to the highest doses of the most toxic agricultural chemicals are usually

   A. the workers who apply the pesticide.

   B. migrant workers who use machines to harvest grains.

   C. the workers who transport the chemicals.

   D. migrant workers who hand-pick fruits and vegetables.

44. Which of the following usually has the most intensive use of pesticides?

   A. a soybean field   C. an average US kitchen

   B. a golf course   D. All of these are comparable.

45. What types of symptoms are possibly caused by exposure to DDE?

   A. skin lesions   B. decreased sperm counts   C. kidney failure   D. nerve damage

46. Which of the following is *not* a result of the DDT spill in the Florida Lake Apopka population of alligators?

   A. Alligator eggs were infertile.

   B. Male hatchlings had smaller penises.

   C. Female alligators had elevated estrogen levels.

   D. All alligator hatchlings were males.

47. In the Florida Lake Apopka population of alligators DDE seemed to interfere with _____ because of a _____.

   A. sex hormones; similarity in chemical structure

   B. egg development; similarity in chemical structure

   C. kidney function; toxic reaction in the body

   D. nerve development; toxic reaction in the body

48. The scientific and legal proof of pesticide effects on humans is generally

   A. obvious and quickly established.   C. impossible to establish.

   B. clear and therefore easy to put into policy.   D. difficult to establish.

49. What does the process Dick and Sharon Thompson developed in Iowa called regenerative agriculture do?

   A. The process regenerates populations of pest predators.

   B. The process relies on natural processes to rebuild and protect the soil.

   C. The process generates a profit without subsidies.

   D. The process regenerates crops with significantly lower production costs.

50. The yields of the Thompson's regenerative agriculture land in Iowa are _____ yields and the costs are _____ when compared to their neighbors' conventional cropping systems.

   A. similar; lower   C. lower; about the same

   B. higher; about the same   D. similar; about the same

51. Behavioral changes as an alternative to current pesticide use would *not* include

   A. switching from monoculture fields to mixed polyculture fields.

   B. rotating crops.

   C. flooding fields before planting.

   D. making sure the soil in row crops is weed free.

   E. All of these are behavioral changes as alternatives to current pesticide use.

52. Knowledge of the life cycle of an insect population enables biological controls to be used in place of current pesticide use. Examples include the use of *Bacillus thuringiensis* (Bt) which affects _____ stage(s) of moths and the use of predators to attack _____ of the pests.

   A. all; all stages

   B. all; the larval stage

   C. the larva; all stages

   D. the pupa; the adult stage

   E. the adult; the pupa stage

53. In order to institute an integrated pest management program, it is necessary to

   A. have large amounts of money.

   B. use large amounts of space.

   C. understand local plants and animals.

   D. burn all fields to eliminate biological elements.

54. With respect to chemical pest controls, integrated pest management (IPM) uses

   A. none.

   B. the maximum amount as determined by economic thresholds.

   C. broad-spectrum products.

   D. the minimum amount necessary as a last resort.

55. Why did Indonesia's President Suharto ban 56 of 57 pesticides previously used in the country?

   A. Increasing cancer rates among people in Indonesia

   B. Insect resistance to the pesticides

   C. Expense of pesticides for the local farmers

   D. High mortality of rice harvesters

56. The Delaney Clause, added to US Federal Food and Drug laws in 1958, aimed to

   A. keep known carcinogens out of food.

   B. decrease pesticide use in agriculture.

   C. support IPM research in the United States.

   D. support organic food production.

57. One part per quintillion is a detectable level of some chemicals. This concentration equals one liquid tablespoon mixed into

   A. a lake.

   B. an oil tanker.

   C. the human body.

   D. the Great Lakes.

58. The Delaney Clause was amended in 1996 to replace the zero risk requirement with a

   A. 1% risk requirement.

   B. uniform regulation for all states regardless of local conditions.

   C. cost/benefit approach to risks.

   D. All of these.

59. Which of the following things that can you do to reduce pesticide residues in your diet is related to bioaccumulation?

    A. Peel fruits and vegetables when possible.

    B. Trim the fat from meat, chicken, and fish.

    C. Cook foods that you think have been exposed to chemicals.

    D. Ask for organically grown produce at a farmer's market.

60. Which of the following alternative methods is *not* helpful in reducing your exposure to pesticides?

    A. Accept slightly blemished fruits and vegetables.

    B. Purchase praying mantises and lady bugs to protect garden plants.

    C. Use only natural chemicals as pesticides.

    D. Wash aphid-infested vegetation with pure water.

CHAPTER 13
BIODIVERSITY

1. Which of the following factors probably led to the rapid and extensive Cichlid speciation in Lakes Victoria, Malawi, and Tanganyika?

   A. predation

   B. interspecific competition

   C. symbiosis

   D. resource partitioning

2. How is the introduction of the Nile Perch affecting the native people near Lake Victoria?

   A. They are able to feed their families because the perch is larger than the small bony cichlids.

   B. The perch is oilier than the cichlid so they don't need to dry the fish and can eat them throughout the year.

   C. Protein malnutrition is common because the perch is too large for traditional harvesting methods.

   D. The thriving international fishery of native people has been taken over by international fishing companies.

3. How is the introduction of the Nile Perch affecting the ecosystem of Lake Victoria?

   A. Since there is another species in the lake, biodiversity has increased.

   B. Algae growth has increased due to the lack of cichlids with a corresponding decrease in oxygen levels.

   C. Algae growth has increased due to the increased perch fecal matter providing increased food availability.

   D. There is no real difference, eutrophication is due to increased amounts of untreated sewage.

4. We are usually referring to species diversity when we talk about biodiversity. However, genetic diversity is also important to ecological systems because diverse genes

   A. increase the efficiency and productivity of a system because all niches are filled.

   B. allow an individual organism to adapt to its changing environment.

   C. are necessary for a population to evolve in a changing environment.

   D. lead to diverse ecological processes in a biological community.

5. Ecological diversity is a measure of the number of

   A. different kinds of organisms within a community or ecosystem.

   B. different versions of the same gene in an ecological community.

   C. sizes, colors, and shapes of organisms within an ecological community.

   D. niches, trophic levels, and ecological processes of a biological community.

6. In terms of the definition of a species, a "lumper" would probably declare the red wolf as a _____ and a "splitter" would probably declare it as a _____.

   A. separate species, hybrid between a gray wolf and coyote

   B. hybrid between a gray wolf and coyote, separate species

   C. separate species, separate species

   D. hybrid between a gray wolf and coyote, hybrid between a gray wolf and coyote

7. The total number of living species is probably

   A. between 3 million and 50 million.

   B. between 500,000 and 1 million.

   C. about 450,000.

   D. at least 300 million.

8. Approximately how many species have been identified on Earth?

   A. 500,000   B. 1 million   C. 2.1 million   D. 30 million

9. Most of the species that are yet undiscovered are probably

    A. mammals and reptiles.   C. birds and fish.

    B. invertebrates and vertebrates.   D. invertebrates, bacteria, and fungi.

10. Species diversity is most concentrated in

    A. North America and Europe.   C. South Africa, Australia, and Europe.

    B. South America, Africa, and Southeast Asia.   D. Oceania, East Asia, and Antarctica.

11. One of the reasons humans rely heavily on only a few food crops is because

    A. we haven't explored the cultivation of thousands of edible wild species.

    B. there are few edible wild species.

    C. we have already focused on the best tasting species for domestication and cultivation.

    D. it would be difficult for small farmers to cultivate the fragile wild species.

12. Which of the following is *not* a benefit of biodiversity for humans?

    A. aesthetics   C. ecological services

    B. food   D. All of these are benefits of biodiversity.

13. How is Costa Rica dealing with the problem of biopiracy?

    A. They are writing stricter laws to prevent the export of local knowledge and products for medicinal use.

    B. They are selling data and specimens to finance scientific work and biodiversity protection.

    C. They are developing local pharmaceutical companies to screen local plants and animals for medicinal uses.

    D. They are making more areas inaccessible to foreign visitors.

14. Which of the following drugs is *not* derived from a naturally occurring organism?

    A. penicillin   D. morphine

    B. aspirin   E. All of these are natural products.

    C. cortisone

15. An important drug for treating Hodgkin's disease was discovered in a periwinkle native to _____ and is valued at approximately _____ per year.

    A. Madagascar, $15 million   C. Costa Rica, $15 million

    B. New Guinea, $1 million   D. Greenland, $1 million

16. The pharmaceutical industry has an interest in preventing species extinction because

    A. people are healthier in a healthy environment.

    B. undiscovered species may provide important new drugs.

    C. most taxonomists are drug makers.

    D. it wants to increase diversity in North America.

17. Soil formation and water purification are examples of _____ based on the biodiversity that benefit humans.

    A. aesthetic benefits   C. ecological services

    B. geological cycles   D. health benefits

18. Which of the following is true of the idea of "existence value"?

    A. It is a good idea but not a practical one.

    B. Only religious people have reason to believe in it.

    C. It may be an ethic with very practical implications.

    D. It sounds nice, but no one knows its practical implications.

19. Which of the following is or would be an example of a natural cause of extinction?

    A. Freshwater Great Lakes mussels that compete with the Zebra Mussel.

    B. Genetic assimilation as in the case of the hybridization of gray wolves or black ducks and mallards.

    C. The passenger pigeon that went extinct at the beginning of this century.

    D. An insect species in the tropical forest that cannot escape predation by native bird species in the forest.

    E. All of these are examples of a natural cause of extinction.

20. Habitat fragmentation usually leads to a(n)

    A. decrease in biodiversity.

    B. reduction in the number of introduced species.

    C. increase in biodiversity due to the isolated populations.

    D. increase in the number of introduced species.

    E. more stable environment.

21. Extinction is the term used when all members of a species

    A. disappear in a locality.   C. live in zoos.

    B. die.   D. are threatened with imminent habitat loss.

22. Which of the following is *true*?

    A. Humans may have been causing extinctions thousands of years ago, but our impact has recently increased.

    B. Humans are responsible for most of the mass extinctions in the geologic record.

    C. Humans began causing extinctions only in the past 150 years.

    D. Humans have never had significant impact on species extinctions until the past four decades.

23. Generally speaking, an animal whose population is widely scattered geographically is _____ as/than one whose population is geographically restricted.

    A. more likely to become extinct   C. equally likely to become extinct

    B. less likely to become extinct   D. equally unlikely to become extinct

24. The main reason for the high rate of animal extinctions at the present time is

    A. uncontrolled sport hunting in the developed world.

    B. commercial harvesting of wildlife in Africa.

    C. drought conditions caused by the greenhouse effect.

    D. habitat destruction worldwide.

25. The graph below tells us that

    A. species extinctions will continue to rise in the next fifty years.

    B. species extinctions first occurred in 1600.

    C. species extinctions have accelerated since about 1800.

    D. there has been little change in species extinctions in recent history.

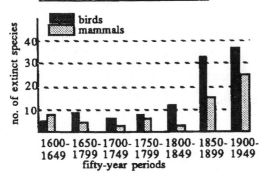

26. The above graph of species extinctions shows us that

    A. birds have disappeared at a faster rate than mammals.

    B. birds have lost more habitat than have mammals.

    C. mammals are hardier than birds.

    D. birds have been hunted more than mammals.

27. The US Army participated in extermination of the American bison because

    A. the Army desperately needed meat.

    B. the United States wanted the Great Plains free for agriculture.

    C. the Army needed leather for shoes.

    D. native peoples depended on the bison for food and shelter.

28. Iceland and Japan continue to justify whaling by arguing it is necessary for

    A. cultural survival.   C. scientific research.

    B. food production.   D. fish habitat protection.

29. According to trends of the last twenty five years (as shown below), the African black rhinoceros should be extinct by the year

    A. 1995.   B. 2000.   C. 2010.   D. 2015.

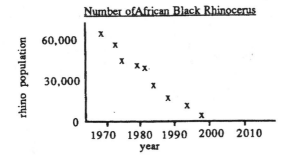

30. The drastic reduction in rhinoceros as shown by the graph in question 29 was due mostly to

    A. the supposed medicinal value of, and corresponding demand for, their horns.

    B. overharvesting for their meat and hide.

    C. introduction of exotic species that compete for their food.

    D. habitat destruction.

31. From the graph below you can tell how many elephants died

    A. in 1980 and 1990.

    B. during the Civil War in Zimbabwe.

    C. compared to the surviving population.

    D. when ivory was worth $50 per ton.

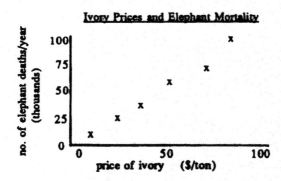

32. The graph above suggests that

    A. the price of ivory depends on the number of surviving elephants.

    B. more elephants die when ivory is valuable.

    C. the total elephant population is shrinking.

    D. ivory has become more valuable now that it is hard to find and trade.

33. What did CITES (the Convention on International Trade in Endangered Species) do in 1989 to help save the African elephant population?

    A. established parks

    B. banned all trade in ivory

    C. established breeding programs

    D. wrote laws making it illegal to kill or transport elephants

34. The main reason for continued trade in endangered species is

    A. a surplus of these species in their home countries.

    B. ruthless traders and collectors in tropical countries.

    C. the need for international capital exchange in developing countries.

    D. pet lovers and collectors who like exotic species.

35. If you have an aquarium with salt-water fish, 75 percent of your fish probably came from

    A. captive breeding programs in the United States.

    B. captive breeding in Indonesia or the Philippines.

    C. wild fish populations caught with cyanide or nets.

    D. hybrid crosses of native United States fish.

36. Which of the following statements about trade in endangered species is *false*?

    A. The principal importers of endangered species are developed countries.

    B. Overharvesting affects animals more than plants.

    C. People who say they are animal lovers are the main contributors to the trade.

    D. The principal exporters of endangered species are developing countries.

37. What is the argument of the critics of the animal control program in the United States?

    A. It is expensive to taxpayers.

    B. It kills nontarget species.

    C. Other controls are more effective and more humane.

    D. All of these are arguments of critics of the animal control program.

38. The argument against harvesting baby seals is largely based on

    A. emotions because the seals are cute, appealing, and babies.

    B. ecological principles because the annual harvest is wiping out the seals.

    C. human needs because the products from the seals are used for feeding and clothing humans.

    D. All of these arguments are used against harvesting baby seals.

39. The argument for harvesting baby seals includes

    A. the renewable resource of wild fur contrasted with synthetics based on nonrenewable petrochemicals.

    B. maintaining viable populations of seals requires preservation of large areas of land.

    C. harvesting seals can employ more people than jobs in producing cotton, wool, or synthetic fabrics.

    D. All of these arguments are used in defense of harvesting baby seals.

40. "Exotic" is another word for

    A. tropical.   B. foreign.   C. rare.   D. beautiful.

41. Introduced (exotic) species tend to _____ the balance of ecosystems and _____ biodiversity.

    A. increase, decrease   C. maintain, enhance

    B. increase, enhance   D. upset, decrease

42. The zebra mussel was introduced to the Great Lakes

    A. as a food source.   C. intentionally by recreational fishermen.

    B. accidentally in ocean-going ship ballast. D. from the Mississippi.

43. Which of the following would be a characteristic of an exotic (introduced) plant species?

    A. Produces a few seeds after many years to reach maturity.

    B. Is a specialist, for example, has a low range of tolerance for different soil conditions.

    C. Opportunist that is desired by humans for food or ornamental value.

    D. Has many predators and diseases.

44. Introduced disease organisms are especially dangerous to new environments because they completely destroy the non-native host. This happens because the disease organisms

    A. have not evolved with this host to achieve the normal balance for long-term success.

    B. are opportunists and in order to survive must out compete all other species.

    C. are specialists and destroy the individual organisms that have not developed resistance.

    D. do not have natural predators.

45. It is clear that a heavy dose of pesticides or other toxic pollutants can kill species. However, chronic exposure to pollutants seems to cause recent high mortality in marine mammals by

    A. decreasing the plants that are normally in their environment, such as kelp, that they use for shelter.

    B. killing off the prey species that they depend on for food.

    C. direct bioaccumulation of the chemicals, such as lead, in their tissues.

    D. causing weakened immune systems and increased vulnerability to infection.

46. Genetic assimilation occurs when a rare species

    A. disappears through cross-breeding with a related species.

    B. is strengthened through cross-breeding.

    C. mutates to adapt to environmental conditions.

    D. is so similar that genetic diversity is lost.

47. A species in imminent danger of extinction is classified by the US Endangered Species Act as

    A. vulnerable.   B. threatened.   C. valuable.   D. endangered.

48. The US Endangered Species Act was enacted by Congress in _____.

    A. 1973   B. 1950   C. 1988   D. 1905

49. Canada's legal equivalent of the US Endangered Species Act is called the

    A. Endangered Species Act of Canada (ESAC).

    B. Committee for the Prevention of Extinction.

    C. Committee on the Status of Endangered Wildlife in Canada (COSEWIC).

    D. Canadian Green Party.

50. A species that is naturally rare or that has been depleted to dangerous levels is known, according to the Endangered Species Act, as a(n) _____ species.

    A. endangered   B. threatened   C. unusual   D. vulnerable

51. A threatened species may be extinct or near extinction

    A. already.   C. in certain localities.

    B. in the near future.   D. only in the distant future.

52. The main reason that there are relatively few invertebrates categorized as endangered species is because

    A. we consider other groups, such as mammals, to be more interesting and desirable.

    B. worldwide there are relatively few invertebrates when compared to plants.

    C. it is extremely difficult to identify and count invertebrates.

    D. Since there are 532 invertebrates considered endangered, none of the above is true.

53. The bar graph of listed endangered species below shows that we know of four times as many endangered mammals as endangered fish. Which of these conclusions is most reasonable?

   A. There are four times as many mammals as fish in the United States.

   B. Mammals are more likely than other species to be endangered.

   C. Few fish and invertebrate species have lost habitat.

   D. We may be more interested in studying mammals than fish or invertebrates.

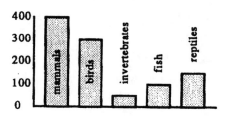

54. Canada has fewer listed endangered species than the United States because

   A. much of Canada lies in the far north, where diversity is low.

   B. Canadians are more careful with wildlife.

   C. there are fewer people in Canada when compared to the United States.

   D. the United States has more wild areas.

55. In general, funding for recovery programs is given to species that are

   A. in the most danger.   C. most well known.

   B. the most important.   D. most numerous.

56. The objective of a species recovery plan is to

   A. scientifically interbreed threatened species with common species.

   B. increase an endangered species population until it is no longer endangered.

   C. invest corporate capital in species maintenance.

   D. study the species for a better understanding of its role in the biological community.

57. Island biogeography explains the phenomenon of _____ terrestrial species on islands small and far from the mainland when compared to larger, closer islands that have _____ terrestrial species.

   A. fewer, more   B. more, fewer   C. larger, smaller   D. smaller, larger

58. How does island biogeography apply to ecosystems other than islands?

   A. Relatively rare ecosystems such as coastal areas are more stable if they have high species diversity.

   B. Habitats that are large and close to development are more adversely affected than smaller fragmented habitats.

   C. Habitat fragmentation has formed islands of habitat in "oceans" of development and the principles apply.

   D. Island biogeography is only concerned with islands in oceans and lakes.

59. Small populations are more vulnerable to harmful effects that limit adaptability, reproduction, and species survival. Genetic diversity is lost in a small population when

A. the ecological diversity is high.

B. genetic mutations cause some individuals in a population to be different in coloration or size.

C. individuals from other populations are introduced into the population and the genes are diluted.

D. only a few individuals survive a catastrophe.

60. The DNA studies that suggest that all existing cheetahs originated from a single female cheetah in recent times is an example of _____ or _____. Since all male cheetahs are basically genetically identical the cheetah population is vulnerable and in fact, suffering from _____.

A. the founder effect, a demographic bottleneck, inbreeding

B. a demographic bottleneck, the founder effect, genetic drift.

C. genetic drift, inbreeding, the founder effect

D. inbreeding, genetic drift, a demographic bottleneck

61. Conservationists and wildlife managers use gap analysis to

A. predict the next evolutionary change an organism will undergo.

B. find unprotected landscapes that are rich in species.

C. bring different managing agencies into closer accord.

D. isolate and contain populations.

62. When Aldo Leopold said "the first rule to intelligent tinkering is to save all the pieces," he meant that we should

A. save records of all species that have disappeared.

C. not cause species to disappear.

B. not interfere with the disappearance of species

D. not interfere with nature.

1. Buffalo Commons proponents say open buffalo range would be a good use of the Great Plains because

    A. agricultural settlements are not proving sustainable in this arid region.

    B. buffalo have become extremely rare.

    C. some people are nostalgic about old times.

    D. the Great Plains have never been useful for anything else.

2. Looking at the world land use pie graph shown below lets you know

    A. how many hectares are devoted to each land use.

    B. approximately what proportion of earth's land surface is used in each of four ways.

    C. the relative amounts of land uses for different parts of the world.

    D. precisely what percentage of land uses exist.

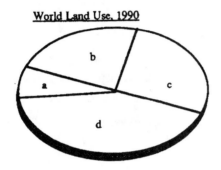

World Land Use, 1990

3. "Closed canopy" forests are those in which tree crowns

    A. include all sizes of trees.   C. cover about 20 percent of the ground surface.

    B. are filled in by smaller vegetation.   D. cover at least 90 percent of the ground surface.

4. You have been asked by a conservation group in the United States to help them research the use of open woodlands and savannas in a sustainable manner to prevent desertification. One of the members of the group mentions that her family lives in the largest remaining area of open woodlands where there is mainly dry savanna and thorn bush. She believes that you should visit her family so they can share their knowledge. Where does her family live?

    A. Africa   C. the former USSR

    B. United States   D. Costa Rica

5. _____, _____, and _____ have vast areas of temperate deciduous or boreal coniferous forest.

    A. Costa Rica, Ecuador, Mexico   C. Brazil, Africa, Southeast Asia

    B. Canada, Europe, the United Kingdom   D. Russia, Canada, the United States

6. A "woodland" is an open

    A. forest with at least 20 harvestable trees per hectare.

    B. forest with trees at least 20 meters tall.

    C. canopy forest where tree crowns cover less than 20 percent of the ground.

    D. canopy forest where tree crowns cover at least 50 percent of the ground.

7. Africa's largest remaining closed canopy forests are in which region?

  A. North Africa
  C. East Africa
  B. South Africa
  D. Central Africa

8. A large portion of industrial timber comes from managed, replanted forests in

  A. North America and Europe.
  C. Africa and Latin America.
  B. Southeast Asia and South Asia.
  D. None of these.

9. Developed countries produce _____ of all industrial wood and account for _____ of its consumption.

  A. more than half, less than half
  C. more than half, about 80 percent
  B. less than half, about 80 percent
  D. less than half, about half

10. Ironically, as the world's largest net importer of wood, _____ has strict environmental laws against harvesting local forests. Therefore, this country's forests are preserved while it clears other country's forests.

  A. England
  B. Costa Rica
  C. Japan
  D. Russia

11. Fuelwood harvests

  A. make up about half of all wood harvests.

  B. make up only 1 percent of industrial timber harvests.

  C. are far greater than industrial timber harvests.

  D. make up about 10 percent of all wood harvests.

12. One of the ways to increase the efficiency of fuel used for cooking is to use

  A. sustainably harvested fuelwood.
  C. food that doesn't require as much cooking time.
  B. biomass for fuel instead of wood.
  D. stoves to replace cooking over open fires.

13. When fuelwood demand exceeds supplies,

  A. forest regeneration becomes more difficult.

  B. fewer people rely on fuelwood.

  C. increased sunlight improves forest regeneration.

  D. agricultural land usually improves and expands.

14. "Forest management" means planning for

  A. gaining maximum, quick profit from trees.

  B. sustainable harvest and forest regeneration.

  C. a continual increase in forest complexity.

  D. building the maximum biodiversity in a forest.

15. After losing nearly all its trees in the civil war, South Korea is now

  A. beginning to plan replanting.
  C. 70 percent reforested.
  B. nearly 10 percent reforested.
  D. an eroded wasteland.

16. A disadvantage of monoculture agroforestry is that it is

  A. difficult to harvest with clear-cut methods.
  C. difficult to replant.
  B. susceptible to pests and requires pesticides.
  D. economically inefficient.

17. Leucaena trees are notable because they

  A. enrich soil.
  C. provide animal fodder.
  B. provide a fast-growing wood source.
  D. All of the above are true.

18. Refer to the graph below. Which region loses the greatest total amount of forests each year?

   A. East Asia   C. West Africa

   B. South America   D. One can only read the percentage of loss with accuracy.

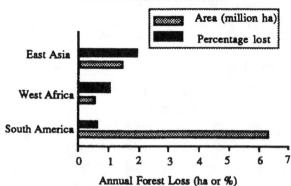

Rates of Tropical Forest Loss

Area (million ha)
Percentage lost

East Asia
West Africa
South America

Annual Forest Loss (ha or %)

19. Milpa and swidden agriculture are alternative terms for

   A. slash and burn.   C. monoculture agroforestry.

   B. single-crop agriculture.   D. conservation tillage.

20. Mixed perennial polyculture involves

   A. crops of different species of edible plants.   C. both corn and beans.

   B. a few carefully selected, hybridized plant species.   D. foraging for wild foods.

21. Milpa agriculture usually produces harvestable foods

   A. in profusion in late fall.   C. after several years of work.

   B. in early spring.   D. in a steady sequence year-round.

22. Since tropical forests typically have only a few commercially valuable trees per acre, logging operations

   A. usually do little damage to the trees that are left.

   B. do extensive damage because of road building and injury to surrounding trees.

   C. generally do not encourage conversion of the forest to farmland.

   D. are usually not successful.

23. The most sustainable land use in tropical forests is probably

   A. logging.   C. periodic mixed (swidden) agriculture.

   B. cattle grazing.   D. intensive, efficient modern row-cropping.

24. Monoculture agroforestry involves

   A. harvesting a single crop of trees, then using the land for agriculture.

   B. multiple-species plantations whose trees are highly resistant to disease.

   C. single-species tree plantations that are efficient but subject to diseases.

   D. harvesting only a single species of trees that is especially useful.

25. Although most of the world's forests are shrinking, biologists are especially concerned about tropical forest loss because

    A. they contain such high biodiversity.

    B. tropical trees are the biggest in the world.

    C. they contain irreplaceable wood resources.

    D. there are fewer remaining tropical forests than any other forest type.

26. Extracting just a few large trees often destroys tropical forest canopy cover because

    A. there are so few trees that make up the canopy.

    B. the shade of the largest trees is essential for other trees' survival.

    C. vines and interlocking branches pull down many trees at once.

    D. undergrowth below the tall trees is so thin.

27. Satyagraha movements in India work to achieve social and environmental goals

    A. by controlling national politics.

    B. by force.

    C. using large amounts of money.

    D. through passive, peaceful methods.

28. India's Chipko Andolan movement was charismatic,

    A. and saved a large portion of forests in watersheds.

    B. using children to plant tees in a reforestation project.

    C. but it failed to actually save any forests.

    D. but is now no longer active.

29. International lending institutions are willing to cooperate in debt-for-nature swaps because

    A. they want to encourage indigenous lifestyles.

    B. they don't really expect to recover much of their loans.

    C. they are concerned about the greenhouse effect.

    D. the size of the loans is really negligible.

30. Debt-for-nature swaps are beneficial mainly to

    A. lending institutions.

    B. governments of developing countries.

    C. environmental groups.

    D. All of these.

    E. None of these.

31. One-quarter of the world's largest temperate forest reserves are in

    A. Siberia.   B. the United States.   C. Western Europe.   D. China.

32. Old growth forests are notable for containing species that

    A. are exotic to North America.

    B. have an unusually high market value.

    C. are highly adapted to their special environment.

    D. are common in other North American forests, in very different environmental conditions.

33. Of all the old growth forests that stood in the United States before European settlement, how much remains today?

    A. about 35 percent

    B. slightly over 25 percent

    C. about 15 percent

    D. less than 10 percent

34. Spotted owls became the subject of national controversy in 1989 because the Forest Service was forced to

    A. plant thousands of acres of new habitat.

    B. limit logging to save habitat.

    C. halt all mineral exploration.

    D. cease issuing hunting permits.

35. Environmentalists say that the loss of logging jobs in Washington and Oregon result from

    A. industry mechanization and raw log exports.   C. the disappearance of owls.

    B. low quality work in timber communities.   D. legal limits on timber harvests.

36. President Clinton's 1993 proposed compromise on logging in the Pacific Northwest seeks to protect _____ forests.

    A. steep hillside   C. all publicly owned

    B. privately held   D. streamside and old growth

37. Most commercial loggers prefer "clear-cut" harvesting because it is the most

    A. environmentally sustainable type of harvest.

    B. efficient way to get valuable small timber without disturbing the larger early successional trees.

    C. efficient, cheapest harvest method using large, fast machinery instead of costly labor.

    D. effective way to refresh soil with sun and rain.

38. Economically, monoculture forestry is advantageous for the loggers because

    A. it produces large quantities of a single type of tree for a particular use, such as building timber or paper pulp.

    B. it is labor-intensive and thus increases job opportunities for local people.

    C. high levels of pesticides and herbicides may be needed, therefore there is more money spent and in the system.

    D. the increase in wildlife diversity is beneficial to the tourism industry.

39. In the process of selective cutting, loggers

    A. cut all trees in only 30 percent of a forest.   C. take all small vegetation as well as trees.

    B. cut some of the mature trees every 5 - 10 years.   D. take only small trees.

40. One of the main drawbacks of clear-cutting is the

    A. wastage of many small trees.

    B. elimination of habitat for many forest species.

    C. increased soil erosion that pollutes streams with siltation.

    D. All of these are drawbacks of clear-cutting.

41. The profits from a year's harvest of salmon in a British Columbia river

    A. can exceed the value of nonrenewable old growth trees.

    B. are negligible compared to timber values.

    C. benefit fewer people than do logging proceeds.

    D. can be gained only through sport fishing.

42. In below-cost timber sales the Forest Service's price for trees is less than

    A. the cost of growing trees.   C. management, clean-up, and road-building costs.

    B. the price charged by foreign governments.   D. the cost companies incur harvesting trees.

43. The primary aim of the US Forest Service has historically been to provide _____ based on Pinchot's philosophy of _____.

    A. public recreation and education, pragmatic conservation

    B. timber to logging companies, pragmatic conservation

    C. wildlife habitat, biocentric preservation

    D. fire patrols to protect ancient forests, biocentric preservation

44. What type of harvest method would you use if you wanted to manage a forest for early successional species such as jackpine, lodgepole pine, or loblolly pine?

    A. selective cutting

    B. coppicing

    C. seed tree harvesting

    D. clear-cutting

    E. shelterwood harvesting

45. What type of harvest method would you use if you wanted to manage a forest for spruce and fir, later successional species that are sensitive to abiotic factors such as increased wind or sunlight?

    A. selective cutting

    B. coppicing

    C. seed tree harvesting

    D. clear-cutting

    E. shelterwood harvesting

46. What would be the best way to remove logs from an area that has a forest floor sensitive to compaction?

    A. helicopters or balloons

    B. tractors or articulated

    C. horse or mule skidding

    D. both A and C

47. Why would someone deliberately set fire to a forest?

    A. To create jobs or help businesses rent expensive equipment to government agencies.

    B. To remove an area from wilderness status so the timber is available for harvesting.

    C. To protect fire-adapted ecosystems from large uncontrollable fires.

    D. All of these are reasons someone would deliberately set fire to a forest.

48. Why is there a need to reeducate people about the role of fire in natural systems?

    A. People are still throwing away cigarette butts that can start forest fires.

    B. People who camp are not putting their campfires out causing fires in inaccessible areas.

    C. People do not understand that fire is a natural part of many biological ecosystems.

    D. both A and B

49. Most rangelands are found on open grasslands where forests and crops don't grow because

    A. temperatures are too high for forests or crops.

    B. rainfall is too scarce or seasonal for forests or crops.

    C. soil is too thin for forests or crops.

    D. rainfall is too heavy for forests or crops.

50. Enclosed domestic meadows and managed grazing lands are known as

    A. open range.

    B. closed range.

    C. clear-cuts.

    D. pastures.

51. Seasonal migration allows grazing livestock to

    A. use the most fertile pastures continuously.

    B. use marginal lands year after year with modest environmental damage.

    C. produce more young animals with less range.

    D. depend more on domestic pastures.

52. Nomadic pastoralists live by

    A. foraging and hunting.

    B. raising seasonal crops.

    C. herding grazing animals.

    D. raising chickens, ducks, and pigs.

53. Today nomadic herders often find their traditional migration routes blocked by

    A. political borders.   C. expanding farm lands.

    B. wars.   D. All of these.

54. The first symptom of range overgrazing is usually

    A. gullying.   C. the disappearance of palatable herbs.

    B. the absence of trees.   D. desertification.

55. World deserts are

    A. decreasing as world climate becomes wetter.

    B. increasing because of the increase in global carbon dioxide.

    C. increasing because of logging and grazing.

    D. decreasing because of massive reforestation.

56. According to the graph below, agriculture causes about what percentage of worldwide soil degradation?

    A. 28 percent   B. 82 percent   C. 33 percent   D. 8 percent

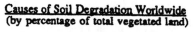

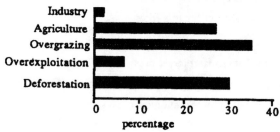

57. Desertification results from overgrazing because

    A. the dry surface reflects the sun's heat and wind drives off rain producing clouds.

    B. bare soil erodes and rainwater runs off.

    C. temperatures rise as plants disappear

    D. All of these.

58. Places most susceptible to desertification are

    A. jungle clearings.   C. temperate deciduous forests.

    B. desert margins.   D. boreal landscapes.

59. Grazing animals such as cattle and goats are particularly adapted to a diet of coarse plant material because they

    A. utilize symbiotic bacteria in their stomachs to digest cellulose.

    B. do not need as much water as other animals do.

    C. have developed more efficient digestive enzymes.

    D. have teeth that are better adapted to grinding vegetation.

60. Meat from wild animals may become a more important source of human food because

    A. increased leisure time in the developed countries will encourage sport hunting.

    B. wild animals are generally more efficient at converting food into meat.

    C. genetic engineering is decreasing flavor in domestic meat animals.

    D. wild animals are easier to breed and control.

61. Most public rangelands are in poor condition due to

    A. excessive populations of wild ungulates.

    B. overcrowding of private livestock.

    C. too many publicly owned animals on public lands.

    D. excessive urban settlement in the West.

62. The BLM and US Forest Service charge _____ as much for grazing fees as the average private land owner.

    A. about equally   C. significantly less

    B. more than five times   D. about twice

63. Grazing fees on public lands have changed little because

    A. political pressures ensure they remain low.

    B. they remain at market value, so there is no reason to change them.

    C. the public feels that the price is right.

    D. livestock owners cannot afford higher fees.

64. Land reform focuses on

    A. modernizing farming systems.   C. collecting land into a few large landholdings.

    B. replanting forests.   D. distributing land to poor populations.

65. Environmentalists are often concerned about land reform because

    A. small farmers usually damage land more than large landowners.

    B. tenant farmers are usually better stewards than are independent peasants.

    C. landless squatters and absentee landowners are both responsible for major environmental problems.

    D. they are afraid it will facilitate similarities to colonial rule.

66. Land reform is an important political issue in many countries because

    A. land is traditionally the main source of wealth and power.

    B. land is a highly marketable commodity worldwide.

    C. crowded urban populations are jealous of large landholders.

    D. massive peasant populations are usually the most powerful landowners and politicians.

67. Why would governments in the Philippines, Cameroon, and Tanzania consider indigenous people living in the forests as squatters?

    A. These governments had the right to take the land because it was uncultivated land.

    B. These governments fail to recognize the rights of indigenous people.

    C. The indigenous people sold their land to the governments and are still living on it.

    D. The indigenous people recently moved to the forests and have recently claimed it.

CHAPTER 15
PRESERVING NATURE

1. How is the Annapurna Conservation Area Project different from other ecotourism regions in Nepal?

    A. It is visited by tourists less often and therefore suffers from less environmental damage.

    B. It was recently opened to tourists but is currently suffering from environmental degradation.

    C. It is the only pristine wilderness area that tourists can visit in Nepal.

    D. It is managed so that the fees paid by tourists go directly to local people.

2. Natural landscaping involves

    A. a natural geometry of straight lines and symmetry.

    B. mimicking nature.

    C. no human input; letting nature go.

    D. topiary and bonsai pruning styles.

3. Frederick Law Olmsted, known as the father of American landscape architecture, is known for designing _____ and then becoming the original commissioner of _____ National Park.

    A. New York's Central Park, Yosemite

    B. Niagara Falls, Yellowstone

    C. Greek-style public gardens, Yellowstone

    D. Yellowstone National Park, Yosemite

4. The United States' first two national parks are

    A. Glacier and Great Smoky Mountains.

    B. Olympic and Yosemite.

    C. Yellowstone and Everglades.

    D. Yosemite and Yellowstone.

5. _____ is believed to be the first national park in the world.

    A. Glacier National Park

    B. Yellowstone National Park

    C. Banff-Jasper National Park

    D. Yosemite National Park

6. The Alaska Lands Act, passed in 1980, _____ the area of US National Parks.

    A. tripled   B. decreased   C. determined   D. doubled

7. National parks are an important part of our heritage,

    A. and they remain pristine and undisturbed because of their park status.

    B. but they lack any protection from mining, logging, and grazing.

    C. but they are endangered by overcrowding, pollution, and in some places, mining.

    D. that, unfortunately, exist only in remote, inaccessible areas.

8. Over the past decade the number of park visitors has _____ and park budgets have _____.

    A. increased by more than one half; increased by about 25%

    B. increased by one third; decreased by about 25%

    C. decreased by more than one half; decreased by about 25%

    D. decreased by one third; increased by about 25%

9. Which of the following factors is probably the *most* important in the success of the reintroduction of wolves in Yellowstone National Park?

    A. The cooperation of local residents.

    B. The genetic diversity in the population.

    C. The availability of prey species.

    D. The hybridization of the species with coyotes.

10. The National Park Service controls game animal populations by

    A. hiring professional hunters.   C. letting nature take its course.

    B. allowing sportsmen to hunt.   D. releasing predators.

11. One way to control herd sizes in national parks could be the reintroduction of predators, but this course is opposed by

    A. animal rights activists.   C. wilderness advocates.

    B. neighbors and local ranchers.   D. scientists.

12. Changes in park policies in recent years have supported the removal of shabby hotels, laundries, and gas stations because

    A. they conflict with visitors' experience of nature.   C. they stop visitors from coming.

    B. park officials wish to operate more expensive facilities.   D. the rents were too low.

13. According to current national park policies, it is most important that visitors have access to

    A. visible wildlife.   C. an experience of nature or wilderness.

    B. amusement rides and concessions.   D. good hotels and other facilities.

14. The most important goal of national parks is to

    A. provide protection for the environment.   D. All of these.

    B. provide education for visitors.   E. None of these.

    C. preserve our natural heritage.

15. The International Union for the Conservation of Nature (IUCN) has described 5 categories of protected areas based on _____.

    A. size   B. importance   C. human impact   D. world cultural value

16. The boundaries of a park or nature preserve are usually based on

    A. how much land can be effectively managed.   C. animal territories.

    B. political considerations.   D. an entire ecosystem.

17. Why do park managers argue that a biogeographical region must be managed if a park is to remain biologically viable in the long term?

    A. A biogeographical region contains an airshed.

    B. A biogeographical region contains a watershed.

    C. A biogeographical region contains wildlife territories for minimum viable population sizes.

    D. The components of "A," "B," and "C" work together to form a system whose parts are interconnected.

18. A biogeographical area is

    A. the entire range of a given species.   C. usually the size of a continent.

    B. a watershed.   D. an entire ecosystem.

19. The complete Yellowstone ecosystem is

    A. several times larger than the park itself.   C. slightly larger than the park.

    B. approximately the size of the park.   D. slightly smaller than the park.

20. Even Yellowstone National Park may be too small to support viable populations of _____.

    A. black bears   B. moose   C. grizzly bears   D. elk

21. What is the most recent addition to the US Park and Preserve System?

   A. The Columbia Gorge in Washington and Oregon.

   B. The Grand Staircase-Escalante National Monument in Utah.

   C. Lake Tahoe in Nevada and California.

   D. Thousand Islands in New York.

22. The 1990 _____ is a plan to double the size of Canada's protected areas.

   A. Biogeographical Plan   C. Crétien Initiative

   B. Watershed Plan   D. Green Plan

23. The largest number of nature preserves are in _____ and _____.

   A. tropical dry forests, temperate deciduous forests

   B. boreal tundra, tropical dry forests

   C. temperate grasslands, boreal tundra

   D. temperate conifer forests, temperate grasslands

24. Which of the following are severely underrepresented in protected areas?

   A. deserts, arctic tundra, and grasslands

   B. grasslands, aquatic ecosystems, and islands

   C. islands, tropical rain forests, and deserts

   D. aquatic ecosystems, tropical dry forests, and temperate deciduous forests

25. Biosphere reserves are areas recognized _____ for their ecological value.

   A. by the National Park Service   C. internationally

   B. in the United States and Canada D. by local residents

26. The graph below shows that land acquisitions for parks and preserves peaked in about

   A. 1910   B. 1940   C. 1980   D. 1985

Growth in Number of World Protected Areas

27. There are about _____ designated Biosphere Reserves worldwide.

   A. 30   B. 300   C. 3000   D. 30,000

28. The IUCN world conservation strategy is directed at protecting

   A. resources from human use.   C. ecosystems and biodiversity.

   B. endangered species.   D. world climate stability.

29. Corridors effectively enlarge which of the following?

    A. preserve areas   C. feeding ranges

    B. genetic pools   D. All of these

30. Which of the following preserve shapes has the greatest interior area relative to perimeter area?

    A. a   C. c

    B. b   D. All have the same interior/perimeter measurements.

31. Which of the above preserve shapes is the worst shape for a species which requires a core area?

    A. a   C. c

    B. b   D. All have the same measurements.

a   b   c

32. Which of the above preserve shapes would support the most species which require a core area?

    A. a   C. c

    B. b   D. All have the same measurements.

33. In the Upper Peninsula of Michigan an area was clear-cut. Trees at the edge of the clear-cut died within a few months after the logging began. Due to the edge effects, the core forested area _____ and species in the core area were more vulnerable to catastrophic events such as a fire or severe storm. However, as a consultant to the state of Michigan you suggest that _____ might help the core species survive in the long term.

    A. decreased, corridors

    B. decreased, fences to protect the species from human impact

    C. increased, corridors

    D. increased, fences to protect the species from human impact

34. The amount of interior area in a preserve is important because

    A. humans and other hardy species encroach on preserve margins.

    B. it is more economical to buy large land areas.

    C. many threatened species cannot survive environmental conditions on preserve margins.

    D. All of these.

    E. A and C.

35. If you were going to hypothesize about the results of the experiment in the Brazilian rainforest to determine the effects of shape and size on biological reserves you would probably use the model of _____ and expect the quick disappearance of some species -especially those species that are _____ and located in _____ areas.

    A. island biogeography; specialists; small

    B. biogeographical areas; generalists; small

    C. island biogeography; specialists; large

    D. biogeographical areas; generalists; large

36. Poor people in developing countries often threaten wildlife preserves because

    A. they dislike unsettled territory.

    B. they need the resources to survive.

    C. they enjoy sport hunting.

    D. vandalism is a popular use of spare time.

37. In which part of a biosphere reserve does the most intensive human impact occur?

    A. in the core zone　　　　　　　　　C. in the multiple use zone

    B. in the buffer zone　　　　　　　　D. there is no human impact in a biosphere reserve.

38. Ecotourism benefits natural areas by giving economic value to land and water resources

    A. that have no other value.　　　　　C. that never existed before.

    B. that no one is interested in.　　　　D. without destroying them.

39. Which of the following has *not* happened since the inception of the CAMPFIRE Program in Zimbabwe?

    A. Illegal poaching has increased.

    B. Governmental costs of reserve management have decreased.

    C. Local communities receive funds and food from the wildlife in their region.

    D. Foreign hunters are allowed to hunt local wildlife.

40. Many developing countries in Africa find their wildlife is worth the most money

    A. as products for export.　　　　　　C. as photographic subjects.

    B. as meat for local people.　　　　　D. when replaced by domestic livestock.

41. As officially defined by Congress in the 1964 Wilderness Act, "wilderness" is

    A. any area with important scenic, historic, and recreational value.

    B. undeveloped land where humans have little impact and temporary presence, and visitors can find solitude.

    C. a place where people live in harmony with nature, building only low-impact structures and roads.

    D. an area of at least 100,000 acres with no human intrusion.

42. A "de facto" wilderness is an area that

    A. is legally classified as wilderness.　　　C. is gradually returning to wilderness conditions.

    B. contains only small human settlements.　D. is wild but not legally recognized or protected.

43. Many rural communities object to nearby wilderness designations because they

    A. depend on natural resources in the area.　C. object to subsidies for wildlife.

    B. dislike and misunderstand wildlife.　　　D. dislike having wilderness nearby.

44. Ninety-six percent of the United States is open to development; the remaining four percent consists mainly of areas developers historically

   A. could not enter because of legal restrictions.   C. agreed was culturally important.

   B. felt was too beautiful to ruin.   D. could not reach or did not want.

45. The first wildlife refuges were established in the United States shortly after _____.

   A. 1780   B. 1900   C. 1960   D. 1985

46. Which of the following statements regarding wildlife refuges is true?

   A. While they may face other obstacles, wildlife refuges rarely have notable pollution problems.

   B. Hunting is not allowed in wildlife refuges.

   C. The Bureau of Land Management has made it a priority to expand designated wilderness areas on their lands.

   D. Wildlife refuges are managed by the United States Fish and Wildlife Service.

   E. All of these are true.

47. The Serengeti is home to the world's

   A. rarest tropical rainforests.   C. driest deserts.

   B. most endangered zebra and wildebeest populations.   D. highest density of ungulates.

48. The greatest threat to animals of the Serengeti comes from

   A. natural dry spells.   C. poachers.

   B. predation.   D. pollution.

49. Wetlands are critical for wildlife survival because they

   A. are productive sources of food.   C. contain few, but rare, species.

   B. allow animals too cool off.   D. provide vast amounts of habitat.

50. Coastal wetlands are important because they

   A. provide food for off-shore species.   C. stabilize shorelines.

   B. prevent saltwater intrusions into groundwater.   D. All of these.

51. Which of the following has caused the most wetland loss in the United States?

   A. conversion to farmland   C. dredging transportation canals

   B. urban development   D. the greenhouse effect

52. In the following graph of existing wetlands in the United States, "swampbuster" provisions were probably passed in the year marked

   A. a.   B. b.   C. c.   D. d.

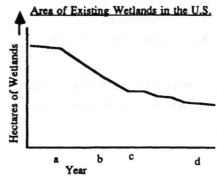

193

53. According to the graph shown in question 52, the effect of the "swampbuster" laws was to

    A. halt all wetland destruction.   C. return wetlands to their pre-settlement levels.

    B. decrease the rate of wetland destruction.   D. further increase the rate of wetland drainage.

54. Wetlands and floodplains control flooding by

    A. temporarily storing water.   C. evaporating most of the water.

    B. diverting water to other drainage basins. D. helping rain flow faster into rivers.

55. In the graph of rainfall storage capacity per hectare shown below, the letters a, b, and c represent, in this order,

    A. parking lot, wetland, cornfield.   C. cornfield, wetland, parking lot.

    B. cornfield, parking lot, wetland.   D. parking lot, cornfield, wetland.

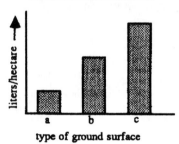

Rainfall Storage Capacity

liters/hectare →

a   b   c

type of ground surface

56. Floods are worse after levees are built and wetlands are drained because

    A. water moves into rivers more quickly.   C. the total volume of water increases.

    B. rainfall becomes more intense per unit area. D. people complain more about damage.

57. Which of the following statements regarding wetlands and floodplains is *true*?

    A. Since the early nineteenth century the U. S. and Canadian governments have encouraged wetland preservation.

    B. Because floodplains are subject to flooding, they are rarely developed or built on.

    C. Although floodwalls contribute to flood severity, the United States government is legally responsible for rebuilding them when they are damaged.

    D. All of these are false.

58. An estuary is a place where a

    A. river begins.   C. barrier island is broken.

    B. river enters a sea or ocean.   D. floodplain meets a river.

59. An essential food source for many marine shellfish and fish is

    A. along shorelines.   C. in the open ocean.

    B. in deep ocean trenches.   D. in trenches near coastal shelves.

60. Barrier islands are formed by

    A. volcanic activity.   C. wind and waves piling up sediments.

    B. tectonic plate slippage.   D. river floods depositing sediment.

CHAPTER 16
THE EARTH AND ITS CRUSTAL RESOURCES

1. In the diagram below representing a cross-section of the Earth, the mantle is labeled

    A. a.   B. b.   C. c.   D. d.

2. In the diagram below the semisolid part of the Earth is labeled

    A. a.   B. b.   C. c.   D. d.

Hypothetical cross-section of Earth

3. In the above diagram, the most dense part of the Earth is labeled

    A. a.   B. b.   C. c.   D. d.

4. In the above diagram, the part of the Earth that is composed mainly of oxygen, silicon, and aluminum is labeled

    A. a.   B. b.   C. c.   D. d.

5. The continental crust of the earth is _____ while the oceanic crust is _____.

    A. rich in silicon; thicker and lighter than the oceanic crust

    B. thicker and lighter than the oceanic crust; rich in silicon

    C. similar in composition to the mantle; rich in silicon

    D. rich in silicon; similar in composition to the mantle

6. _____ in the mantle and core make tectonic plates move.

    A. Conduction movements   C. Radioactive decay

    B. Earthquakes   D. Convection currents

7. "Subduction" is the process of a tectonic plate

    A. falling freely into the mantle.   C. melting without moving.

    B. being forced below another plate.   D. sliding alongside another plate.

8. Which of the following statements regarding tectonics is *true*?

    A. As a result of tectonic movements, Europe and Africa are drifting slowly toward the Americas.

    B. When continental plates collide with continental plates, both plates usually subside.

    C. When oceanic plates collide with continental plates, the continent usually rides up over the seafloor.

    D. As a result of tectonic movements, the Pacific Ocean is slowly increasing in size.

9. The "ring of fire" is the source of more earthquakes and volcanic activity than any other place on earth. What causes the ring of fire?

   A. the subduction of Pacific plates under continental plates

   B. the drift of Europe and Africa away from the Americas

   C. the collision of two continental plates

   D. mid-oceanic ridges

10. Which of the following bodies of water is growing due to tectonic movement?

    A. Pacific Ocean   D. Indian Ocean

    B. Atlantic Ocean   E. None of these

    C. Black Sea

11. Rocks are _____ in the process called the rock cycle.

    A. moved from place to place   C. broken down and re-formed

    B. incorporated into living organisms   D. cycled through the core and mantle

12. Rocks are classified according to their

    A. chemical composition.   D. mode of formation.

    B. physical properties.   E. All of these are used to classify rocks.

    C. internal structure.

13. A mineral is composed of

    A. other minerals.   C. inorganic elements.

    B. any noncrystalline elements.   D. organic material.

14. What is the basic material of rocks?

    A. minerals.   C. inorganic elements.

    B. any noncrystalline elements.   D. organic material.

15. Rock formed from magma extruded to the surface through volcanic vents is classified as

    A. sedimentary.   B. igneous.   C. metamorphic.   D. evaporitic.

16. _____ is an example of an igneous rock.

    A. Basalt   B. Shale   C. Marble   D. Sandstone

17. The word "igneous" comes from a Latin word meaning

    A. water.   B. fossil.   C. sediment.   D. fire.

18. Water, wind, and glaciers are examples of forces that cause

    A. chemical weathering.   C. abrasion.

    B. mechanical weathering.   D. sedimentation.

19. Sinkholes are produced by

    A. chemical weathering.   C. abrasion.

    B. mechanical weathering.   D. plant growth and soil acidity.

20. The selective removal or alteration of specific components of a rock that leads to its weakening is called

    A. the rock cycle.   C. chemical weathering.

    B. sedimentation.   D. mechanical weathering.

21. Sedimentary rocks are formed from material deposited by

    A. rivers.   B. glaciers.   C. wind.   D. All of these.

22. Which of the following is an important product of biogenic sedimentation?

    A. halite   B. gypsum   C. limestone   D. gabbro

23. Salts such as gypsum and halite are often produced as _____ deposits.

    A. sedimentary   B. igneous   C. metamorphic   D. mechanical weathering

24. Evaporative sedimentation involves

    A. soluble chemicals reacting with water to make insoluble products.

    B. water and ice moving materials to a different location.

    C. living organisms.

    D. the accumulation of minerals left by water that has vaporized.

25. Metamorphic rocks are produced when rocks are

    A. chemically weathered.   C. physically broken down.

    B. recrystallized by heat and pressure.   D. melted in the mantle and recrystallized.

26. _____ is an example of metamorphic rock.

    A. Basalt   B. Shale   C. Marble   D. Sandstone

27. _____ rocks are often the source of metal ores such as gold, silver, and copper.

    A. Igneous   C. Sedimentary

    B. Metamorphic   D. All of these are sources of metal ores.

28. Economic mineralogy is the study of rocks that

    A. contain useful materials.   C. are extremely rare, such as diamonds.

    B. contain metals.   D. are valuable, but not useful.

29. Evaporites, formed from _____, are important economically because they are often found at or above 97% purity and are _____.

    A. sedimentary rocks; therefore concentrated in economically recoverable levels

    B. metamorphic rocks; important due to their strength, lightness and malleability

    C. sedimentary rocks; important due to their strength, lightness and malleability

    D. igneous rocks; therefore concentrated in economically recoverable levels

30. Strategic minerals are minerals that a country

    A. depends on selling.   C. uses in military and industrial processes.

    B. has in abundance.   D. needs but cannot produce itself.

31. The United States keeps large stockpiles of bauxite in order to ensure a supply of aluminum. This is an example of

    A. economic mineralogy.   C. a strategic mineral.

    B. an evaporite.   D. a metal consumed in South America.

32. Which of the following statements is *false*?

    A. Many of the world's major metal resources are found in South Africa and Russia.

    B. Worldwide, trade in minerals is mostly local.

    C. Resource substitution can be an effective way of conserving strategic minerals.

    D. Many European colonies of the eighteenth and nineteenth centuries were established specifically to provide Europe with strategic minerals.

33. Why would the environmental degradation associated with mining be a low priority for a less-developed country?

    A. The country relies on the export of a mineral for most of their foreign exchange.

    B. Both consumers and producers depend on the minerals so much that environmental consequences are of less importance.

    C. Less-developed countries are more likely to import minerals so environmental degradation is not as important to them.

    D. The environmental impact of mining is low.

34. Placer mining causes environmental damage chiefly by

    A. destroying streambed habitats.   C. introducing toxic compounds to streams.

    B. clogging streams with silt.   D. All of these.

35. Subsidence is most likely to occur with _____ mining.

    A. placer mining   C. underground mining

    B. strip mining   D. spoil bank mining

36. If metals are deposited in streambeds _____ would probably be used.

    A. placer mining   C. underground mining

    B. strip mining   D. spoil bank mining

37. Since the passage of the Strip-Mining Reclamation and Control Act in 1977, mine cleanup has been

    A. almost completed in the United States.   C. usually required in the United States.

    B. largely disregarded.   D. usually accomplished in the United States.

38. Reclamation of strip-mined land is difficult chiefly because

    A. nobody can afford it.   C. there is no legal enforcement.

    B. top soil is mixed up and buried.   D. no plants exist that will grow.

39. Under the US General Mining Law, mining companies are required to pay what percentage of their profits in taxes?

    A. 3 percent   C. 12.5 percent

    B. 7 percent   D. No taxes are paid on mining profits.

40. Heap-leach extraction removes gold from ore by

    A. pouring gravel into holding tanks.   C. roasting ore to release the gold.

    B. spraying cyanide on a pile of ore gravel.   D. high-pressure spraying of ore.

41. Smelting ore, as in Ducktown, Tennessee, releases toxic chemicals in the form of

    A. gases, from baked ore.   C. dust, from grinding ore gravel.

    B. liquids, from leaching processes.   D. All of these simultaneously.

42. _____ is a toxic gas released in the process of smelting.

    A. Carbon monoxide B. Chlorine   C. Sulfur dioxide   D. Ammonia

43. Recycling waste aluminum (e.g., beverage cans) consumes _____ of the energy of extracting new aluminum from bauxite.

    A. half   B. twice   C. one-twentieth   D. two-thirds

44. On average, producing steel from scrap metal takes about _____ as much energy as producing steel from raw ore.

    A. half   B. twice   C. one-twentieth   D. equally

45. In terms of mineral resources, recycling is slowly _____ as raw materials become more _____ and _____ are more plentiful.

    A. increasing, scarce, wastes   C. increasing, expensive, environmental laws

    B. decreasing, scarce, environmental laws   D. decreasing, scarce, wastes

46. Aftershocks of earthquakes are sometimes more severe than the principal tremor because

    A. their motion is converted into waves.

    B. they occur so frequently.

    C. they are caused by reverberations within the Earth.

    D. they can be amplified as they travel through the ground.

47. A giant sea swell known as a tsunami is caused by

    A. typhoons.   C. lunar gravity.

    B. earthquakes.   D. unusual tides combined with seasonal storms.

48. Nueés ardentes are

    A. massive clouds of volcanic ash.   C. mixtures of hot gases and ash.

    B. large lava flows.   D. mud slides caused by volcanic eruptions.

49. How would the eruption of a volcano cause global climate changes?

    A. Dust from the volcano blocks sunlight.

    B. Sulfuric acid is produced which interferes with solar radiation.

    C. It can cause stratospheric ozone reduction allowing increased ultraviolet light to reach the Earth's surface.

    D. Both a and b.

50. An example of mass wasting is

    A. a landslide.   C. land slumping.

    B. erosion.   D. All of these are examples of mass wasting.

CHAPTER 17
AIR, CLIMATE, AND WEATHER

1. Weather is a term for atmospheric moisture and temperature on a _____ basis.

    A. daily   B. annual   C. short-term   D. permanent

2. Climate is a description of _____ weather conditions.

    A. long-term, regional   C. temporary

    B. stable and unchanging   D. temporary, local

3. Understanding climate and weather is important for ecologists because

    A. biome activities commonly alter climate conditions.

    B. ecosystem conditions are largely dictated by climate.

    C. biologists need to know what biome to expect when climate changes.

    D. they both affect human activities.

4. The earth's earliest atmosphere was probably composed mainly of _____, which has/have since largely dissipated into space.

    A. hydrogen and helium   C. oxygen

    B. carbon dioxide and methane   D. water

5. Elements such as carbon, nitrogen, oxygen, and sulfur were added to the Earth's early atmosphere through

    A. the mechanical and chemical weathering of rocks.   C. contact with space.

    B. photosynthesis.   D. volcanic emissions.

6. Aerosols are

    A. gases produced by industry.

    B. tiny particles and droplets suspended in the air.

    C. the principal gas involved in the greenhouse effect.

    D. tiny droplets of a very specific chemical composition.

7. The two main gases making up the lower atmosphere are

    A. helium and hydrogen.   C. oxygen and methane.

    B. carbon dioxide and nitrous oxide.   D. nitrogen and oxygen.

8. The atmospheric zone where most weather events occur is the

    A. stratosphere.   C. troposphere.

    B. thermosphere.   D. mesosphere.

9. The correct sequence of atmospheric zones upward from the earth's surface is

    A. stratosphere, troposphere, mesosphere, thermosphere.

    B. troposphere, stratosphere, mesosphere, thermosphere.

    C. mesosphere, stratosphere, troposphere, thermosphere.

    D. thermosphere, stratosphere, troposphere, mesosphere.

10. The different layers of the atmosphere are kept from mixing by

    A. sharp temperature boundaries.

    B. contrasting gas compositions.

    C. the extreme stillness within each layer.

    D. physical barriers composed of thick layers of atmospheric dust.

11. The "ozone hole" that causes concern among scientists and the public is an ozone depletion in the

    A. troposphere.   C. thermosphere.

    B. stratosphere.   D. mesosphere.

12. Heat in the atmosphere comes from

    A. radioactive decay of gas particles.   C. gravitational pressure on air molecules.

    B. radioactive decay of elements in the Earth.   D. solar radiation.

13. Insolation is a term that means

    A. heat reflectivity of clouds.   C. incoming solar radiation.

    B. the energy retentive ability of gases.   D. the total amount of energy released by the sun.

14. Albedo is a term describing the Earth's

    A. reflection of solar radiation.   C. production of radiant heat.

    B. refraction of energy.   D. use of energy in biomass production.

15. Which of the following would have the highest albedo?

    A. a field of black soil   C. a dark forest

    B. a snowfield   D. an asphalt parking lot

16. Eventually all the energy that reaches the Earth's surfaces is

    A. absorbed into the Earth.   C. used in heating.

    B. turned into biomass.   D. reflected or radiated back to space.

17. Energy absorbed at the Earth's surface is radiated back to space in the form of

    A. visible light.   C. infrared radiation.

    B. ultraviolet radiation.   D. microwaves.

18. Much of the ultraviolet light from the sun is absorbed by _____ as it passes through the atmosphere.

    A. carbon dioxide   B. water vapor   C. nitrogen gas   D. ozone

19. The phenomenon causing the greenhouse effect is that _____ in the lower atmosphere selectively absorbs reradiated _____ radiation.

    A. ozone; visible light   C. hydrocarbons; very short wavelength

    B. carbon dioxide, methane, and other gases; infrared (heat)   D. carbon dioxide; ultraviolet

20. One reason the energy flux is considerably lower at the poles than at the equator is because

    A. there is more cloud cover at the poles.   C. there is more ozone in polar regions.

    B. sunlight comes in at an oblique angle.   D. sunlight comes in vertically.

21. Convection currents in the atmosphere are driven by

    A. the different temperatures and densities of warm and cold air masses.

    B. the jet stream dipping down into the troposphere.

    C. forces that scientists cannot yet explain.

    D. bursts of energy emitted by the ionosphere.

22. When an area of the earth's surface becomes very hot, the air above it

    A. condenses and cools.   C. warms, condenses, and releases rain.

    B. warms, expands, and rises.   D. expands and sinks.

23. _____ is/are the driving force(s) of the hydrologic cycle.

    A. Wind   B. Jet streams   C. Evaporation   D. Convection currents

24. When cool, dry air sinks from the upper atmosphere toward the Earth's surface, it is

    A. compressed and cooled further.   C. compressed and becomes warmer.

    B. allowed to expand and become warmer.   D. forced to release any remaining moisture.

25. The circular convection currents near the equator in the zone marked "A" below are known as

    A. Milankovitch cycles.   B. the jet stream.   C. wind.   D. Hadley cells.

26. The convection cells shown above create a band of _____ in the zone marked "A."

    A. deserts   C. tundra

    B. humid tropical forests   D. temperate rainy zones

27. The Coriolis effect is caused by the

    A. jet stream.   C. heating and cooling of air masses.

    B. rotation of the Earth.   D. seasonal changes in air temperature and humidity.

28. Water draining from a bathtub will swirl in a _____ spiral according to the _____.

    A. clockwise, location of the bathtub in the Southern Hemisphere

    B. clockwise, location of the bathtub in the Northern Hemisphere

    C. counterclockwise, location of the bathtub in the Southern Hemisphere

    D. counterclockwise, location of the bathtub in the Northern Hemisphere

    E. clockwise or counterclockwise, shape of the bathtub

29. Rising, expanding air masses create a region of

    A. low pressure.   B. warming air.   C. high pressure.   D. dry air.

30. A westward flowing wind is called a(n) _____ due to the direction _____.

    A. east wind, it is blowing   C. west wind, it is blowing

    B. east wind, from which it originates   D. west wind, from which it originates

31. The Southern Hemisphere has _____ wind patterns because of the presence of _____ than the Northern Hemisphere.

    A. more stable, more ocean and less landmass

    B. less stable, less ocean and more landmass

    C. less stable, more ocean and less landmass

    D. more stable, less ocean and more landmass

32. Two jet streams run over North America. These tend to run approximately

    A. along the Atlantic and Pacific coasts.

    B. between the southern and northern borders of Mexico.

    C. at 30° north latitude and over northern Canada.

    D. from southern California toward Maine.

33. Due to the influence of the _____, in the month of January your flight from Chicago to the United Kingdom will take _____ than the return trip from the United Kingdom to Chicago.

    A. Coriolis effect, longer   C. jet stream, longer

    B. Coriolis effect, shorter   D. jet stream, shorter

34. The boundary between two air masses of different temperature and density is known as a

    A. front.   B. cold front.   C. warm front.   D. Hadley cell.

35. A cold front is a situation in which cold air

    A. remains stationary for weeks at a time.   C. recedes in the face of warmer air.

    B. displaces a mass of warmer air.   D. is heated by seasonal changes in solar energy.

36. As a cold front forces its way under a mass of warm air, the warm air is forced to

    A. rise, become warmer, and absorb more moisture.   C. retreat laterally and become more dense.

    B. rise, cool, and release its moisture.   D. fall, condense, and lose its moisture.

37. Narrow, violent bands of rain and storms are characteristic of

    A. advancing cold fronts.   C. both warm and cold fronts.

    B. advancing warm fronts.   D. stationary bends in the jet stream.

38. If you see high wispy cirrus clouds with layers of other clouds in a wedge shape you can expect _____ due to an _____.

    A. heavy rain and thunderstorms, advancing cold front

    B. heavy rain and thunderstorms, advancing warm front

    C. drizzle and cloudy skies, advancing warm front

    D. drizzle and cloudy skies, advancing cold front

39. Hurricanes are powered by

    A. the hydrologic cycle.   C. sinking air masses.

    B. rising air masses.   D. heat released from condensing water vapor.

40. Why don't storms over land have as much energy as those over oceans?

    A. Convection currents are intensified by the latent energy of condensation.

    B. Convection currents are intensified by the latent energy of warm dry air.

    C. High pressure cells are more common over oceans.

    D. There aren't as many low pressure systems over land.

41. Monsoons occur over India when air heated over the Indian subcontinent and the Indian Ocean

    A. is forced to rise because of convection.

    B. is forced to rise when it meets the Himalayas.

    C. begins to sink as fall approaches.

    D. is forced out over the Indian Ocean.

42. Efforts to "seed" clouds and force rainfall artificially have been

    A. completely hypothetical, never tried in practice.

    B. somewhat successful and highly controversial.

    C. totally unsuccessful.

    D. outstandingly successful.

43. Milankovitch cycles involve the periodic _____ and could be responsible for _____ weather changes.

    A. convection currents in the lower atmosphere, drastic

    B. summer/winter seasonality on the Earth, gradual

    C. wobbling of the earth's axis and orbital shifts, cyclic

    D. tidal cycles from month to month, seasonal

44. When El Niño occurs every three to five years, a mass of warm Pacific water that is usually pushed westward by trade winds

    A. surges back eastward toward South America.

    B. becomes much hotter than usual, strengthening trade winds.

    C. cools dramatically.

    D. surges northward toward Japan.

45. As far as we are currently aware, who were the first people to notice the El Niño Southern Oscillation cycle?

    A. scientists studying atmospheric changes

    B. indigenous people in South America

    C. meteorologists

    D. Peruvian fishermen

46. Computer models predict that doubled carbon dioxide levels could raise average temperatures by 1.5°C to 4.5°C. The difference between today's temperatures and the last ice age is about

    A. 1°C.   B. 5°C.   C. 9°C.   D. 14°C.

47. Most of the excessive carbon dioxide that is expected to cause global warming is generated by

    A. green plants.

    B. burning of fossil fuels.

    C. production of cement and clearing of forests.

    D. All of these.

    E. B and C only.

48. What are the ecological implications of global warming?

    A. Plants and animals that are residing in fragmented habitats may not be able to move to a suitable habitat.

    B. In general, plants and animals will probably benefit from warmer temperatures.

    C. Since farmland may be lost, the habitats for plants and animals will increase in area.

    D. Since biodiversity is usually higher in warmer, milder climates, it will probably be increased.

49. Given what we know about the probability of the greenhouse effect the best thing to do is

    A. immediately cease all industrial activity.

    B. wait and see how much temperatures change before we change our habits.

    C. severely cut back on production of greenhouse gases.

    D. not worry about greenhouse gas production.

50. Higher temperatures and carbon dioxide levels of the greenhouse effect could possibly be counteracted by

    A. greater growth of green plants.

    B. higher humidity, more cloud cover and greater reflection of incoming solar energy.

    C. increased growth of oceanic plankton.

    D. All of these.

51. Scenarios and computer models describing the greenhouse effect

    A. all agree on what will happen.   D. should be heeded in case they are correct.

    B. disagree on their predictions.   E. Both b and d are correct.

    C. are useless because they contradict each other.

52. The greenhouse effect in the atmosphere occurs because

    A. clouds reflect sunlight back into space.

    B. oceans absorb heat and then release it slowly at night.

    C. stratospheric ozone absorbs UV radiation.

    D. CO_2, water vapor, methanol, and other gases absorb infrared radiation.

    E. All of the above.

1. Human-produced pollutants are different from natural particulates and gases because they are

    A. almost always chemically distinct.

    B. almost always chemically more dangerous.

    C. often produced in very high quantities and concentrations.

    D. generally more abundant than natural pollutants.

2. Primary pollutants are those that are

    A. released directly in dangerous forms.   C. the most dangerous.

    B. produced in the greatest quantities.   D. the most threatening to people.

3. Secondary pollutants

    A. harm only vulnerable members of a population.   C. are produced in lesser quantities.

    B. become dangerous after reacting in the atmosphere.   D. are less dangerous than others.

4. _____ are examples of secondary pollutants.

    A. Aerosols   C. Photochemical oxidants

    B. Volatile organic compounds   D. Combustion gases

5. Fugitive emissions are produced by

    A. smokestacks.

    B. power plants and other heating equipment.

    C. reactions between pollutants and atmospheric gases.

    D. strip mining, rock crushing, and other dust-producing activities.

6. Criteria pollutants are those that

    A. contribute the most to air quality degradation.   C. are easiest to get rid of.

    B. are most highly toxic even in small quantities.   D. cause the most damage to buildings.

7. Of the following criteria pollutants, _____ is produced in the largest amount.

    A. carbon monoxide   B. sulfur dioxide   C. nitrogen oxide   D. methane

8. Sulfur trioxide

    A. is a secondary pollutant.   C. reacts with water to form sulfuric acid.

    B. is formed by the oxidation of sulfur dioxide.   D. All of these.

9. The term NOx is often used because

    A. there are many different oxides of nitrogen.

    B. it is usually unclear how oxidized nitrogen is.

    C. NO_2 and NO easily convert into each other.

    D. many different molecules often attach to NO.

10. The brown haze in smog is caused by

    A. sulfuric acid.   B. NO_2.   C. carbon monoxide.   D. chlorofluorocarbons.

11. A common example of a photochemical oxidant is

A. NO_2.　　　　B. H_2S.　　　　C. CO_2.　　　　D. methane.

12. Carbon monoxide is produced by

A. normal respiration.　　　　C. incomplete burning of fuels.

B. the burning of sulfur-laden coal.　　　　D. photochemical oxidation of carbon.

13. Carbon dioxide levels in the atmosphere are increasing at the rate of about _____ percent per year.

A. 0.4　　　　B. 0.9　　　　C. 1　　　　D. 5

14. The most common metallic air pollutant is

A. iron.　　　　B. cadmium.　　　　C. lead.　　　　D. mercury.

15. Lead is dangerous because it acts as a(n)

A. neurotoxin.　　　　B. asphyxiant.　　　　C. irritant.　　　　D. respiratory fibrotic agent.

16. An aerosol is

A. a chemical propellant.　　　　C. any liquid droplet or solid particle suspended in air.

B. a rigidly defined chemical composition.　　　　D. liquids condensing from air on leaves.

17. The most dangerous air-borne particulates are those

A. large enough to damage skin and eyes.　　　　C. produced by artificial means.

B. small enough to breathe.　　　　D. that are liquid.

18. Which of the following is *not* a volatile organic compound?

A. benzene　　　　B. methane　　　　C. formaldehyde　　　　D. chlorofluorocarbons

19. A major source of VOCs is

A. incomplete burning of hydrocarbons.　　　　C. photochemical oxidation.

B. combustion of sulfur-containing fuel.　　　　D. decaying organic matter.

20. Photochemical oxidation reactions are driven by

A. the great instability of the reactants.　　　　C. solar energy.

B. the heat of industrial activity.　　　　D. entropy.

21. Ozone is produced by

A. incomplete burning of fuels.　　　　C. decaying organic matter.

B. combustion of sulfur-containing fuel.　　　　D. photochemical oxidation.

22. Unconventional (noncriteria) pollutants include _____ and are mostly _____ in origin.

A. especially hazardous or toxic chemicals, anthropogenic

B. most forms of dust and soot, biogenic

C. many naturally-produced compounds, biogenic

D. most photochemical oxidants, anthropogenic

23. Aesthetic degradation is a term that describes

A. health risks associated with pollution.　　　　C. noises, odors, and light pollution.

B. primarily the brown color of smoggy air.　　　　D. the discomfort of knowing the air is dirty.

24. Which of the following statements is *true*?

   A. Most carbon monoxide produced in the United States comes from internal combustion engines (cars).

   B. Nearly all emissions of sulfur compounds are anthropogenic.

   C. Overall, in the past twenty years air pollution conditions have steadily decreased in most North American and West European cities.

   D. Volatile organic compounds are produced exclusively by human activity.

25. The pollution control measure that would be most effective in saving human lives would be

   A. upgrading smokestack scrubbers.
   C. banning all forms of mining.

   B. banning smoking.
   D. eliminating petroleum refineries.

26. Formaldehyde is an especially problematic indoor pollutant because it is

   A. far more toxic than most other substances.
   C. so difficult to detect.

   B. produced naturally by the Earth below buildings.
   D. used in so many household materials.

27. Which of the following statements is *false*?

   A. The likelihood of having radon gas in your home depends largely upon the geology and soil types in your region.

   B. According to the EPA, toxic air pollutants are generally much more concentrated indoors than outdoors.

   C. One of the reasons indoor air pollutants are so dangerous is the high amount of time people spend indoors.

   D. In the less-developed countries of Africa, Asia, and Latin America there is less indoor air pollution than in developed countries.

   E. All of these are true.

28. Radon in houses comes from

   A. building materials in walls.
   C. radioactive decay in the Earth below a house.

   B. emissions from furnaces.
   D. solar radiation coming through the roof.

29. Radon in homes is suspected of causing

   A. cancer.   B. heart disease.   C. kidney infections.   D. emphysema.

30. A temperature inversion occurs when

   A. two warm air layers surround a cold air layer.
   C. stable, cold air overlays warm air.

   B. air turbulence causes mixing between air layers.
   D. stable warm air overlays cold air.

31. Los Angeles has especially bad inversion problems because it

   A. lies on a flat space by the ocean.
   C. occupies such a large geographical area.

   B. is in a warm climate and is partly ringed by mountains.
   D. All of these.

32. Stable air masses over cities and warm updrafts between tall buildings often create _____ in and near cities.

   A. dust domes of suspended pollutants
   C. convective rain storms

   B. cyclonic dust storms
   D. low pressure zones that dissipate pollution

33. Which of the following statements about long range pollutants is *true*?

   A. Wind can transport dust for tens of thousands of kilometers, or from Africa to the Americas.

   B. The North and South Polar regions are almost alone in still having pristine, unpolluted air today.

   C. Although they persist for a long time in the Arctic region, pollutants take a long time to reach the region.

   D. Controlling long range pollutants is more of an ecological rather than a political process.

34. Native peoples living in the Canadian Arctic have some of the highest recorded PCB concentrations in their bodies because of

    A. unusually high susceptibility to contamination.

    B. concentrated natural occurrence of PCBs in that region.

    C. local production of PCBs.

    D. long-range transport of airborne pollutants.

35. _____ ozone is harmful, damaging plants and human health while ozone at the _____ level screens out mutagenic ultraviolet radiation.

    A. Stratospheric, troposphere

    B. Thermospheric, mesosphere

    C. Tropospheric, stratosphere

    D. Mesospheric, thermosphere

36. The "ozone hole" is a depletion currently most serious

    A. at the most populated latitudes.

    B. over North America.

    C. in tropical latitudes.

    D. near the poles.

37. Pollutants such as chlorofluorocarbons deplete atmospheric ozone

    A. when nitrogen combines with O_3 to form NOx.

    B. when chlorine-containing molecules are oxidized at the expense of O_3.

    C. because chlorine is most stable as ClO_3.

    D. All of these are correct.

38. There are serious signs that ozone depletion may lead to

    A. UV-caused skin cancers.

    B. UV-caused blindness.

    C. IR-caused sunburn.

    D. All of these.

    E. A and B only.

39. The most common human health response to air pollution is

    A. inflammatory responses in sensitive tissues.

    B. lung cancer.

    C. blindness caused by deteriorating eye tissues.

    D. skin cancer.

40. Persistent inflammation of bronchi in the lungs is known as

    A. asthma.   B. fibrosis.   C. pulmonary toxicosis.   D. bronchitis.

41. Asthma is a shortness of breath caused by

    A. tumors in the bronchial walls.

    B. sudden muscle spasms in the bronchial walls.

    C. spasms in the heart.

    D. physical obstructions in the lungs.

42. An irreversible obstructive lung disease is

    A. asthma.   B. bronchitis.   C. emphysema.   D. fibrosis.

43. Sudbury, Ontario's copper-nickel smelter is notorious for having

    A. destroyed the local ecosystem with sulfur-laden smoke.

    B. caused brown lung disease in miners.

    C. spread cyanide in nearby rivers.

    D. All of these.

44. Which of the following is the best example of synergistic effects?

    A. the disappearance of plant life around Sudbury, Ontario

    B. the prevalence of cancer among smokers exposed to asbestos fibers

    C. the appearance of PCBs in residents of remote Arctic villages

    D. cancer caused by fibrosis in the lungs

45. Pollutants such as sulfur dioxide and ozone cause

    A. relatively little damage to plants.

    B. mortality in most plants.

    C. reduced yields in crop plants as well as visible damage.

    D. damage mainly to highly sensitive species.

46. Acid precipitation often occurs downwind from _____ industries.

    A. dust-producing

    B. coal-burning or smelting

    C. wood product

    D. hydropowered manufacturing

47. On a pH scale, pH 4 is _____ as pH 8.

    A. half as acidic

    B. ten times as acidic

    C. 100 times as acidic

    D. 10,000 times as acidic

48. One of the principal ways lakes suffer from acid deposition is that

    A. rocks on the bottom begin to dissolve.

    B. fish eggs die and fish populations fall.

    C. aquatic vegetation turns yellow.

    D. plants grow excessively and choke other life.

49. Streams and lakes are especially sensitive to acid deposition when

    A. fish populations are already small.

    B. soils and rocks provide little buffering capacity.

    C. they are alkaline, with calcium-rich bedrock.

    D. they lie in hot, dry regions.

50. High altitude forests are especially susceptible to acid deposition because

    A. acidic clouds surround them much of the time.

    B. high winds blow acids into leaf tissues.

    C. low moisture levels fail to dilute acids.

    D. high altitude species are especially delicate.

51. What type of buildings and monuments are most susceptible to acid damage?

    A. granite and basalt

    B. wood

    C. limestone and marble

    D. concrete and brick

52. Tall smokestacks are effective ways of

    A. decreasing pollution.

    B. displacing and dispersing pollution.

    C. cleaning up air pollution.

    D. eliminating the effects of pollution.

53. Large bags can be used by industries to _____ airborne pollutants.

    A. electrostatically precipitate

    B. displace

    C. disperse

    D. filter

54. Electrostatic precipitators prevent fly ash escape by

   A. filtering them.

   B. using electrodes to give particles an electrostatic charge.

   C. preventing their production in the first place.

   D. gravity.

55. Many industries prefer electrostatic precipitators to filter bags because

   A. precipitators are cheaper.   C. precipitators are easy to use.

   B. bags are difficult to use.   D. precipitators save energy.

56. Mixing limestone with coal can reduce sulfur emissions because the limestone's

   A. pH decreases the acidity of the sulfur dioxide.

   B. calcium bonds with the sulfur to make gypsum.

   C. particle size filters out the sulfur.

   D. burning temperature completely combusts sulfur.

57. Cars use _____ to reduce nitrogen oxide emissions.

   A. afterburners.   C. fluidized bed combustion.

   B. electrostatic precipitators.   D. catalytic converters.

58. Hydrocarbon emissions are produced mainly by _____ industries.

   A. chemical and solvent   C. cement manufacturing

   B. coal-burning   D. nuclear power

59. The graph below shows that _____ are now produced at 50 percent or less of 1940 levels.

   A. nitrogen oxides

   B. sulfur oxides, volatile organic compounds, and carbon monoxide

   C. volatile organic compounds, carbon monoxide, solid particulate matter, and lead

   D. solid particulate matter and lead

Air Pollution Trends in the U.S., 1940-1984

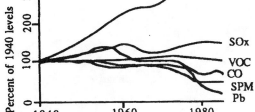

60. The Clean Air Act of 1970 established _____ standards for criteria pollutants at levels to protect crops, the climate, and visibility.

   A. criteria   B. primary   C. secondary   D. tertiary

61. National Ambient Air Quality Standards (NAAQS) set _____ for acceptable public exposure to specific pollutants.

    A. time limits

    B. concentration limits

    C. population size limits

    D. time and concentration limits

62. Worldwide, air pollution control efforts are least advanced or least successful in

    A. major cities of leading industrialized countries.

    B. major cities of developing countries.

    C. small towns in developing countries.

    D. rural areas in industrialized countries.

63. Eastern European cities and farming regions have been notable in recent years for their

    A. widespread and terrible pollution conditions.

    B. miraculous cleanup successes.

    C. complete lack of industrial pollution.

    D. steady and successful cleanup accomplishments.

CHAPTER 19
WATER USE AND MANAGEMENT

1. The hydrologic cycle describes the process of water

    A. running from small streams to rivers to the sea.

    B. being used and reused in different communities.

    C. running from large streams to smaller, then evaporating to fall as rain or snow.

    D. falling as rain, running toward the sea, and evaporating to rain or snow again.

2. About ___ of the earth's surface is covered by water.

    A. 70 percent   B. 50 percent   C. 85 percent   D. 33 percent

3. One acre-foot is the amount of water that would cover an acre

    A. of ground.   C. one inch deep.

    B. of ground one acre deep.   D. one foot deep.

4. Evapotranspiration is the way plants

    A. return large amounts of rain to the atmosphere.

    B. absorb water from the atmosphere.

    C. absorb water from the ground.

    D. return large amounts of water from the atmosphere to the ground.

5. Evaporation is

    A. the way plants absorb water.

    B. liquid water turning to vapor well below boiling temperature.

    C. liquid water boiling to produce water vapor.

    D. the way water seeps into the ground.

6. Natural evaporation processes are mainly driven by

    A. living plants.   C. solar energy.

    B. radiative heat from the ground.   D. the natural instability of liquid water.

7. Water can transform from a solid form to a gaseous form in a process called

    A. evapotranspiration.   C. disintegration.

    B. evaporation.   D. sublimation.

8. The amount of water vapor that air can hold varies greatly. Warm air is able to hold _____ humidity when compared to _____ air.

    A. more, cold   B. more, hot   C. less, cold   D. the same, cold

9. Saturation point is the maximum amount of water vapor that

    A. can be added to a certain volume of air.   C. air can give up if it cools 5 degrees.

    B. air at a certain temperature can hold.   D. a certain amount of solar heat can evaporate.

10. Relative humidity is a measure of water vapor in air compared to the

    A. maximum vapor air can hold.

    B. average vapor that air holds.

    C. maximum vapor air can hold at that temperature.

    D. maximum vapor that volume of air can hold.

11. Condensation is the process of water molecules

    A. aggregating when saturation point is exceeded.

    B. aggregating when temperatures rise.

    C. disaggregating in solar heat.

    D. disaggregating from solid to gaseous form.

12. The dew point is

    A. another word for relative humidity.

    B. the temperature at which a certain concentration of water vapor will begin to condense.

    C. the temperature at which rain will turn to snow.

    D. the humidity level that a certain temperature of air can hold without producing rain.

13. Condensation nuclei such as smoke or dust can make water vapor

    A. less dense.   C. reach dew point more slowly.

    B. evaporate more easily.   D. condense more easily.

14. When temperatures are below 0°C, condensation

    A. does not usually occur.   C. produces snow instead of rain or mist.

    B. occurs only in the presence of condensation nuclei.   D. produces dew, but not precipitation.

15. A cloud is formed of

    A. condensation nuclei with some water vapor.   C. water in gaseous form.

    B. condensed water in liquid drops or solid crystals.   D. condensed water droplets.

16. Rain drops that form in high, cool, humid clouds sometimes fail to reach the ground because

    A. lower air layers are warmer and less saturated and reevaporation occurs.

    B. gravity pulls them apart as they near the Earth resulting in precipitation.

    C. convection currents keep them in a layer above the ground.

    D. lower layers of air are colder and freeze them.

17. The rainiest or snowiest zone on the mountain drawn below would be in the area marked

    A. from A to B.   B. from B to C.   C. from C to D.   D. at A and at D.

18. The rainshadow on the mountain drawn in question 17 would be in the area marked

    A. from A to B.   B. from B to C.   C. from C to D.   D. at A and at D.

19. Air moving in the direction indicated on the drawing in question 17 will become warmer as it moves from

    A. B to D.   B. A to B.   C. C to A.   D. None of these is correct.

20. Intense sunlight causes a band of hot, rising air laden with evaporated water near the equator. This moisture then falls because

    A. its potential energy increases with height.

    B. warm air cannot hold much moisture.

    C. the rising air cools and loses its ability to hold water vapor.

    D. moisture is condensed as convection currents carry air over hotter, drier regions.

21. A band of deserts rings the Earth at about 23° north and south latitude because these are regions of

    A. descending, warming air.   C. the earth's most intense solar energy.

    B. rising hot air.   D. air that cools as it descends.

22. Residence time of water in oceans is a measure of the

    A. age of the oceans.

    B. average amount of time a water molecule spends in the ocean.

    C. average amount of time needed for the entire ocean to be replaced by rainfall.

    D. time an average water molecule spends in one region before it circulates to another.

23. Which of the following statements regarding the water budget is *false*?

    A. Eventually even groundwater makes its way to the oceans.

    B. Circulation patterns in the oceans are an important factor in distributing heat on the Earth.

    C. Circulation systems on land, in the ocean, and in the atmosphere balance the water budget.

    D. Most of the evaporation in the water budget equation occurs over tropical rainforests.

24. Most water in the atmosphere has evaporated from the ocean, and _____ rain falls back into the sea. About _____ percent of the earth's total rain falls on land.

    A. most, 10   B. most, 20   C. less, 55   D. less, 70

25. The hydrologic compartment that contains the greatest amount of fresh water is

    A. groundwater.   C. living organisms and biomass.

    B. the Great Lakes.   D. ice and snow.

26. Water enters groundwater by

    A. infiltration.   C. evapotranspiration.

    B. entering the runoff stream.   D. interception.

27. A water table is the _____ in the ground.

    A. top of a saturated zone   C. number of saturated zones

    B. thickness of the saturated zone   D. lowest level of saturated zones

28. The zone of saturation is the portion of groundwater where

    A. water vapor turns to liquid.   C. all soil or rock pore spaces are filled with water.

    B. an aquifer is deepest.   D. all soil or rock pore spaces are filled with air.

29. The place where aquifers are most likely to be contaminated is at
    A. artesian springs.   C. recharge zones.
    B. seeps and other outlets.   D. all discharge and recharge areas.

30. The amount of water in aquifers in the United States is
    A. nearly as great as the amount of surface water.
    B. greater than all the Great Lakes together.
    C. a small portion of surface water in the United States.
    D. over thirty times greater than all surface water in the United States.

31. Aquifer discharge is measured in terms of
    A. meters per second of flow.   C. square meters in a cross-section of the stream.
    B. liters or gallons per second or minute. D. cubic meters in the entire streambed.

32. The atmosphere has the greatest _____ of the earth's hydrologic compartments.
    A. water volume   C. discharge rate and water content
    B. turnover rate and smallest water volume   D. All of these.

33. The United States has a drought cycle that brings dry periods about every _____ years.
    A. 100   B. 60   C. 30   D. 10

34. Withdrawal is the total amount of water
    A. lost in transmission, due to evaporation or leakage.   C. used in manufacturing or agriculture.
    B. taken from rivers, lakes or aquifers.   D. altered or polluted in human activities.

35. Technically speaking, when water is consumed it
    A. has been used.   C. is no longer available for other purposes.
    B. is no longer suitable for any other purpose.   D. is lost to evaporation or leakage.

36. In the United States we withdraw about _____ gallons of water per person per day.
    A. 100   B. 600   C. 1400   D. 15,000

37. Human water withdrawals have been increasing at about _____ rate as worldwide population growth.
    A. the same   B. half the   C. three times the   D. twice the

38. Which of the following statements regarding the water budget is *true*?
    A. US taxpayers pay for about 70 percent of the water piped to farmers in the Central Valley of California.

    B. About 40 gallons of water is consumed in commercial processing of a single egg.

    C. Most people in the world now have water piped to their homes, and it is rare for people to have to carry water for household uses.

    D. Agricultural conservation of water supplies is a good idea, but it would have little impact on overall water supplies.

39. As a rule, water use in poor countries is dominated by
    A. agricultural use.   C. industrial activities.
    B. domestic needs.   D. use as drinking water.

40. On the following graph of water use per person, each letter represents a country. Which of the following is most likely?

    A. A is the United States; B is China.
    C. A is the United States; B is Canada.

    B. B is the United States; A is China.
    D. B is India; A is China.

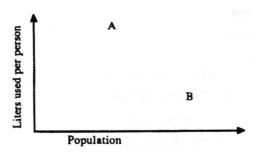

41. The World Health Organization considers the minimum amount of good water that each person needs per year to be _____ cubic meters.

    A. 500   B. 2000   C. 25   D. 27,000

42. Groundwater is the source of drinking water for _____ Americans.

    A. nearly all   B. nearly all urban   C. relatively few   D. 95 percent of rural

43. The Ogallala Aquifer supplies water to _____ and once held more water than the surface water _____.

    A. California's Central Valley, in the world

    B. the Rocky Mountain states, in the United States

    C. the central Plains states, in the world

    D. most of New England, in the United States

44. Withdrawal of groundwater often causes subsidence, which is a situation in which

    A. aquifer volume decreases sharply.   C. water quality and water tables fall.

    B. withdrawals exceed recharge rates.   D. porous rocks settle and ground level falls.

45. In some regions groundwater withdrawals can contribute to sinkholes, in which

    A. ground level over a large area sinks.

    B. buildings slowly settle at odd, perilous angles.

    C. empty underground caverns suddenly collapse.

    D. a whole city suddenly falls into the ground.

46. Subsidence and sinkholes

    A. can, with difficulty, be reversed and the ground surface raised again.

    B. are probably a permanent loss of an aquifer.

    C. can never be reinflated with the ground surface raised again.

    D. are a consequence of saltwater intrusion.

47. A method of increasing water supplies that has been successful, if expensive, is

    A. desalinization by reverse osmosis.   C. towing icebergs by ship from polar regions.

    B. cloud seeding.   D. altering the climate's convective currents.

48. Principal problems that have resulted from the construction of large dams include

A. evaporation and siltation.

B. leakage and weakening of bedrock.

C. earthquakes.

D. All of these.

49. One of the consequences of the Aswan High Dam in Egypt is the

A. increase in the need for buying fertilizer.

B. increase in the occurrence of schistosomiasis.

C. decline in the Mediterranean fisheries.

D. Both b and c are consequences of the Aswan High Dam in Egypt.

E. All of these are consequences of the Aswan High Dam in Egypt.

50. The activity that uses the greatest share of US household water is

A. bathing.

B. drinking and cooking.

C. flushing the toilet.

D. washing clothes and dishes.

51. Because industry and agriculture use more water than households in the United States, industry and agriculture

A. pay far more per gallon of water.

B. pay far less per gallon of water.

C. are taxed heavily to encourage conservation.

D. have strict legal limits on their withdrawals.

1. Density differences resulting from the nutrient-rich, well oxygenated, warm, top layer and a cold, hydrogen sulfide-rich anaerobic lower layer has existed for centuries in the Black Sea. How has this layering affected recent pollution and eutrophication of the Black Sea?

   A. The toxic bottom layer is now mixing with the top layer causing the catastrophic collapse of ecosystems.

   B. The deeper dense layer keeps the pollutants from dispersing so they are trapped in the relatively shallow top layer.

   C. The density differences do not have any relationship to the many pollutants that are introduced into the Black Sea.

   D. The pollutants are sinking to the more dense lifeless layer and are having a minimal effect on the top layer.

2. How has the introduction of the comb jellyfish affected the Black Sea?

   A. The jellyfish are preying on the algae blooms that result from eutrophication of the Black Sea.

   B. The jellyfish are serving as food for the native fish.

   C. The jellyfish are experiencing S-shaped population growth and are becoming a stable part of the ecosystem.

   D. The jellyfish are filtering out some of the toxins in the Black Sea.

   E. None of these are true.

3. Factories, sewage treatment plants, and oil wells are _____ sources of water pollution.

   A. point   B. primary   C. nonpoint   D. tertiary pollutant

4. _____ sources of water pollution are relatively easy to monitor and regulate.

   A. point   B. primary   C. nonpoint   D. tertiary pollutant

5. The discharge from a nonpoint source of pollution is

   A. usually constant throughout the year.   C. usually less polluting than point sources.

   B. generally easier to regulate than a point source.   D. highly seasonal in quantity.

6. Atmospheric deposition of contaminants is an excellent example of

   A. the properties of water that allow it to disperse contaminants.

   B. nonpoint pollution.

   C. a point source of pollution.

   D. the relative ease in determining sources of contaminants.

7. The water pollutant that most commonly threatens human health is

   A. pathogenic organisms.   C. toxic and hazardous chemicals.

   B. dissolved plant matter.   D. thermal pollution.

8. Coliform bacteria populations are routinely monitored in drinking water supplies, swimming pools, and at beaches because these bacteria

   A. cause several deadly diseases.

   B. may mutate into severely pathogenic strains.

   C. indicate the presence of feces in water.

   D. usually live in pesticide-contaminated water.

9. High oxygen content in water is an indication that

    A. water is clean enough to support game fish.

    B. there are no contaminants present at all.

    C. there is a large population of coliform bacteria.

    D. water is only able to support algae and bacteria.

10. An oxygen sag occurs most often

    A. 7 - 9 miles downstream from a pollution source.   C. just upstream of a pollution source.

    B. just downstream of a pollution source.   D. at any of the above places.

11. On the graph below the horizontal (X) axis should be labeled

    A. Temperature.   B. Time.   C. Distance from outfall pipe.   D. Depth.

12. Referring to the graph below, which of the following units would probably be used to label the numbers on the horizontal (X) axis?

    A. Degrees Centigrade   B. Hours   C. Meters   D. Miles   E. Days

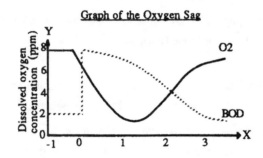

Graph of the Oxygen Sag

13. On the above graph, the most active decomposition occurs in the area marked _____ on the horizontal axis.

    A. -1 to 0   B. 0 to 1   C. 1 to 3   D. 2 to 3

14. Which of the following organisms would probably be found in the area marked 3 and above?

    A. mayfly and stonefly larvae   C. Bullhead catfish and gar

    B. mosquito larvae   D. blackfly and midge larvae

15. When natural waters are overloaded with plant nutrients, such as nitrate and phosphate ions, they become

    A. oligotrophic.   B. dystrophic.   C. eutrophic.   D. metatrophic.

16. Cultural eutrophication results from

    A. natural sediment and nutrient levels.   C. the disappearance of tributary streams.

    B. a change in animal life as well as plants.   D. human activity.

17. Red tides are a common problem in the Mediterranean Sea because of

    A. the particular species of algae there.   C. nutrients from extremely active agriculture.

    B. heavy tourism and untreated sewage.   D. the heavy storms and waves that occur there.

18. Toxic metals such as lead, cadmium, and mercury

    A. rarely threaten water supplies.

    B. can be toxic if high concentrations are reached.

    C. can be toxic in extremely minute quantities.

    D. are the most common health threat in water.

19. The following are inorganic toxic substances sometimes found in water supplies.

    A. salts and lead   C. fecal coliform bacteria

    B. algal blooms and red tides   D. All of these

20. Minamata disease, named after a town in Japan, was caused by

    A. fecal coliform bacteria.   C. mercury poisoning.

    B. salt poisoning.   D. acidic precipitation.

21. Rivers in California's dry agricultural valleys are often toxic because they

    A. run through toxic soils.   C. are so highly acidic, due to acid rain.

    B. originate in coastal industrial areas.   D. have high concentrations of metals and salts.

22. Acid precipitation is especially disruptive when it occurs in areas with

    A. limestone.   B. alkaline soils.   C. granite bedrock.   D. All of these.

23. Dioxins, pesticides, and polychlorinated biphenyls are all types of

    A. inorganic toxic substances.   C. suspended solids and BODs.

    B. heavy metals.   D. toxic organic compounds.

24. The largest category of water pollutants by volume is

    A. heavy metals.   C. suspended soil and other sediments.

    B. human and animal wastes.   D. toxic organic compounds.

25. The range of tolerance for temperature in an aquatic organism is likely to be _____ the tolerance range of a terrestrial organism.

    A. the same as   B. less than   C. more than   D. significantly more than

26. In order to avoid producing thermal plumes, power plants often

    A. increase the efficiency of their energy use.   C. chemically alter their effluent.

    B. warm entire rivers to ease temperature gradients.   D. build cooling towers or ponds.

27. The main reason that surface water pollution has largely decreased in the United States since 1950 is

    A. the Clean Water Act.

    B. a series of epidemics that inspired action.

    C. the discovery of newer technology that makes it cheaper not to pollute than to pollute.

    D. decreases in water withdrawal for industrial uses.

28. Feedlots are a major cause of _____ in water.

    A. viruses   B. coliform bacteria   C. nitrates and phosphates   D. All of these

29. _____ is an example of a natural process that is accelerated by human activities.

  A. Eutrophication

  B. The weathering and release of toxic inorganic minerals from rocks

  C. The mobilization and concentration of soluble salts from groundwater

  D. Sediment loading of rivers

  E. All of these are examples of natural processes that are accelerated by human activities.

30. A river that was severely polluted with industrial chemicals and human sewage and has since been restored to excellent health is the

  A. Vistula in Poland.   C. Ganges in India.

  B. Cuyahoga in Indiana.   D. Thames in England.

31. Water contamination in Eastern European countries results

  A. mainly from inadequate sewage treatment.

  B. from both industrial and human waste.

  C. from agricultural pesticide runoff.

  D. mainly from radioactivity from power plants.

32. Aquifers are especially susceptible to contamination

  A. around wells.   C. when they are shallow.

  B. near their recharge zones.   D. All of these.

33. The following statements explain why contamination of aquifers are dangerous. Which of the statements is *false*?

  A. The contaminants are concentrated by the different densities of water in the aquifers.

  B. Pollutants are extremely stable once they contaminate an aquifer.

  C. Minuscule amounts of a pollutant can contaminate an entire aquifer.

  D. Aquifers can take an extremely long time to turn over their water content.

34. Oceans are

  A. usually pristine because no one lives in them.   C. legally protected from most dumping.

  B. normally better cared for than rivers and lakes.   D. universal dumping grounds for all sorts of pollutants.

35. Dumping sewage effluent into bays and estuaries causes _____ in fish and crabs caught by fishermen.

  A. prolific reproductive rates   C. little change

  B. disease and deformities   D. unusually large sizes

36. The Exxon Valdez disaster in Prince William Sound, Alaska, in 1989 was

  A. the biggest oil spill on record.

  B. an example of a rare but serious occurrence.

  C. one of many huge spills every year.

  D. responsible for nearly all the oil pollution Alaska has seen.

37. Municipal sewage can be an excellent source of _____ that are otherwise expensive to mine.

  A. useful metals   C. organic compounds

  B. inorganic salts   D. toxic chemicals

38. In reality, the cheapest and most effective way to reduce water pollution is to

A. recycle materials.

B. improve land use practices.

C. divert runoff from surface waters.

D. prevent production or release of the pollutant.

39. The problem with natural decay for human waste is that

A. it never really works.

B. it only works where population density is low.

C. it is an expensive process to maintain.

D. unlike sewage treatment, it produces toxic by-products.

40. _____ should never be allowed down a drain when a septic tank and drain field system is being used for sewage disposal.

A. Kitchen wastes from cooking

B. Dog or cat urinary or fecal matter

C. Chlorine and antimicrobial cleansers

D. Oils and greases

41. Primary sewage treatment involves

A. removing solids from water.

B. removing all organic matter from water.

C. making water transparent again.

D. removing all bacteria.

42. Tertiary treatment of sewage produces water that is usable for

A. agriculture.

B. drinking.

C. industrial activities.

D. watering livestock.

43. Tertiary sewage treatment is designed to remove

A. large solids.

B. suspended solids.

C. sludge.

D. nitrates and phosphates.

44. The advantage of effluent sewerage is that

A. since solids are removed, pipes and pumps can be small and cheap.

B. since solids remain in the liquid, disposal is easy and cheap.

C. families can do all their processing at home.

D. large, expensive municipal systems are no longer needed.

45. The city of Arcata, California, is notable because it designed a _____ to treat its sewage.

A. system of modern outhouses

B. fully modern, technologically advanced system

C. natural marsh

D. corporate sponsorship system

46. Best practical technology (BPT) is legally required for all

A. point source polluters.

B. priority toxic pollutants.

C. pollution and polluters.

D. common toxic pollutants.

47. Best available economically achievable technology (BAT) standards are standards set for

A. nonpoint pollution. C. radioactive waste, specifically.

B. toxic substances.

D. all point sources.

48. The 1990 London Dumping Convention is directed at controlling

A. European municipal sewage sludge.

B. all British nonpoint pollution.

C. Ontario's toxic and hazardous pollution.

D. dumping at sea by all nations.

49. Using duckweed in a lagoon as low-tech sewage treatment plants is an example of

    A. a containment method of remediation.   C. bioremediation.

    B. tertiary sewage treatment.   D. extraction techniques of remediation.

50. Using Bentonite slurries to stabilize liquids in porous substances is an example of

    A. a containment method of remediation.   C. bioremediation.

    B. tertiary sewage treatment.   D. extraction techniques of remediation.

CHAPTER 21
CONVENTIONAL ENERGY

1. The application of force over distance is known as

    A. power.   B. work.   C. fuels.   D. All of these.

2. Power is the

    A. rate of energy delivery (work done per second).   C. capacity to do work (force over distance).

    B. amount of energy available.   D. a combination of A, B, and C.

3. One megawatt is equal to _____ watts.

    A. 100   B. 1000   C. 1 million   D. 1 billion

4. Coal replaced wood as industrialized countries' major energy source in the nineteenth century because

    A. coal was easier to transport, store, and burn.   C. wood is not as energy efficient as coal.

    B. coal was a cleaner fuel.   D. wood supplies were diminishing.

5. A major force leading Americans to begin thinking carefully about energy conservation was the

    A. industrial revolution.   C. near depletion of domestic coal supplies.

    B. 1973 Arab oil embargo.   D. invention of nuclear energy.

6. Which of the following is not considered a fossil fuel?

    A. coal   B. natural gas   C. oil   D. uranium

7. Fossil fuels currently supply about _____ percent of all world commercial energy supplies.

    A. 95   B. 75   C. 50   D. 33

8. Which of the following energy sources does not contribute to the greenhouse effect?

    A. coal   B. gas   C. nuclear fission   D. wood

9. _____ dependence on wood and other biomass for more than 90 percent of total heating and cooking energy contributes to its loss of _____.

    A. China's, agricultural land   C. Mexico's, biodiversity

    B. Haiti's, soil and forests   D. East Germany's, forests

10. The United States and Canada, making up 5 percent of the world's population, use more than ___ of the world's commercial energy production.

    A. 9/10   B. 2/3   C. 1/2   D. 1/4

11. Sweden, Denmark, and Switzerland have higher standards of living than Americans or Canadians

    A. because their energy consumption is much greater.

    B. because they are closer to energy supplies.

    C. even though their energy use is about equal to ours.

    D. even though their energy use is much less than ours.

12. The graph in question 13 confirms that

    A. standard of living depends on energy consumption.   C. energy consumption depends on wealth.

    B. energy consumption depends on standard of living.   D. None of these.

13. The graph below reflects a relationship between energy consumption and

    A. geographical location.   C. wealth.

    B. population of a country.   D. well-being of all citizens in the country.

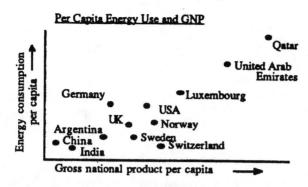

14. According to the graph above, Norway uses at least _____ energy as the United States with _____ standard of living as measured by GNP.

    A. the same amount of, a lower   C. three times as much, a higher

    B. one-third as much, about the same   D. half as much, a lower

15. Slightly over half of US electricity production is produced by

    A. coal burning.   C. solar and wind conversion.

    B. nuclear power.   D. hydroelectric dams.

16. Natural gas is the most _____ fuel with _____ of its energy content lost in shipping and handling.

    A. expensive, over 70 percent   C. environmentally damaging, over 50 percent

    B. efficient, only 10 percent   D. polluting, only 1 percent

17. One _____ of natural gas is that it is _____ than either coal or oil.

    A. advantage, easier to ship and store   C. disadvantage, harder to sell

    B. advantage, easier to build infrastructure for transporting it   D. disadvantage, harder to find

18. Which of the following statements is *true*?

    A. World coal reserves are substantially smaller than petroleum reserves.

    B. The fossil fuel most readily available and abundant in the United States and Canada is petroleum.

    C. The United States has only enough proven oil supplies to last ten years at current rates of consumption.

    D. World coal reserves are only large enough to provide power for about 100 years.

19. Worldwide, coal deposits are

    A. widespread but rarely in economic quantities.   C. highly unusual formations.

    B. relatively difficult to find.   D. widespread and extensive.

20. Black lung disease results from

    A. the radioactivity in coal and around coal-fired power plants.

    B. coal dust causing inflammation and fibrosis in lungs.

    C. careless strip-mining methods.

    D. coal dust literally filling lungs like dust in a vacuum cleaner bag.

21. _____ power plants release radioactivity as well as toxic metals under normal operating conditions.

    A. Coal-fired   B. Hydroelectric   C. Nuclear   D. All of these.

22. The main pollutant released by coal burning is

    A. mercury vapor.   B. methane.   C. sulfur oxides.   D. volatile organic compounds.

23. Most useful oil deposits are usually found

    A. in a liquid pool under a layer of impermeable shale.

    B. saturating porous rocks, like water in a sponge.

    C. locked in the mineral structure of a rock formation.

    D. in pools on the earth's surface, where geologic pressures have forced them to collect.

24. Oil wells are usually able to extract _____ of the petroleum present in an oil reservoir.

    A. all   C. 30 to 40 percent

    B. about 75 percent   D. less than 10 percent

25. Secondary recovery techniques are ways to

    A. force more oil out of a drying well.

    B. extract new types of fuels from an empty well.

    C. recover nonfuel materials from an oil well.

    D. distill usable fuels from raw petroleum.

26. The graph below shows that the Middle East has about _____ of the world's proven recoverable oil.

    A. 1/2   B. 2/3   C. 3/4   D. 1/3

World Proven Recoverable Oil Reserves

27. For much of the past decade battles have been going on over oil and gas drilling in

    A. the Arctic National Wildlife Refuge.   C. Buffalo Commons Wildlife Refuge.

    B. the Everglades National Wildlife Refuge.   D. All of these.

28. Oil shale and tar sands are examples of _____ oil.

    A. unrecoverable   B. unproven   C. unknown   D. unconventional

29. Natural gas is the _____ source of commercial energy worldwide.

    A. largest single   B. second largest   C. third largest   D. fourth largest

30. The graph below shows that most of the world's natural gas reserves are located
    A. exactly where oil reserves are.
    C. in Western Europe and Africa.
    B. very near to the world's main industrial areas
    D. far from major world industrial areas.

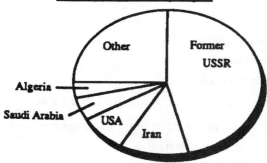

Natural Gas Reserves by Region

31. Unconventional gas sources are sources of natural gas
    A. locked in geological formations.
    D. All of these.
    B. produced from the digestion of organic matter.
    E. Both A and B are true.
    C. produced as a by-product of oil processing.

32. With respect to natural gas, many developing countries
    A. cannot afford this expensive fuel.
    B. cannot afford to build the pipes needed to transport this fuel.
    C. have excellent success in using this fuel.
    D. are the major importers of this fuel.

33. Methane from animal waste is an example of a(n)
    A. conventional gas source.
    C. by-product of human activities.
    B. unconventional gas resource.
    D. nonrenewable energy source.

34. Interest in nuclear power as a major world energy source
    A. was immense in the 1950s but has since faded.
    B. gradually built to a peak in the 1980s and 1990s.
    C. reached another peak of interest due to the Gulf War.
    D. has been consistently low since it was invented.

35. The fuel used in a conventional PWR or BWR nuclear power plants is
    A. plutonium.   B. uranium.   C. thorium.   D. any one of these.

36. A notable factor in the Chernobyl disaster was that Soviet authorities
    A. failed to respond immediately, unnecessarily endangering many lives.
    B. failed to respond at all.
    C. responded immediately, saving many lives.
    D. immediately notified all citizens and neighboring countries of events at the plant.

37. Which of the following statements regarding nuclear energy is *true*?

   A. In a nuclear power plant, electricity is collected directly from electrons splitting off from fuel atoms.

   B. Nearly all nuclear power plants worldwide are built far from water sources to prevent contamination.

   C. Decommissioning a nuclear power plant costs up to ten times as much as building it.

   D. The Pressurized Water Reactor and the Boiling Water Reactor are essentially the two main designs for a nuclear power plant.

38. Uranium fuel is _____ before it can be put into a reactor.

   A. extensively processed to clean and purify it

   B. found in concentrated form in the Earth and simply washed

   C. produced by bombarding it with electrons from radioactive plutonium

   D. All of these are correct.

39. A fuel assembly in a nuclear power plant consists of many

   A. fuel pellets packed into a hollow rod.

   B. pellet-filled rods bundled together.

   C. fuel pellets arranged in a cube and encased in plastic.

   D. thousands of fuel rods.

40. Nuclear fission occurs when a high-energy subatomic particle, a neutron, strikes a uranium atom and releases energy and

   A. breaks in half, causing another atom to break.   C. releases protons.

   B. releases an electron in a gamma wave.   D. releases neutrons.

41. Control rods in a nuclear reactor are used to

   A. absorb neutrons.   C. provide neutrons to initiate reactions.

   B. move fuel rods around in the chamber.   D. provide cooling.

42. The most likely disaster in a nuclear power plant is that

   A. the plant would explode like a bomb.

   B. cooling systems could fail, causing rapid overheating.

   C. fuel rods could fail to maintain chain reactions.

   D. All of these are equally likely.

43. Most nuclear plants in the United States use _____ to cool fuel rods and run turbines.

   A. pressurized water   C. freon, as in a refrigerator

   B. forced air   D. pressurized water and steam

44. A breeder reactor is designed to

   A. burn on multiple types of fuels.   C. operate on a very small scale.

   B. create rather than consume fuel.   D. be safer than any other type of reactor.

45. The liquid sodium that must be used to cool a breeder reactor

   A. is explosive in contact with water.   D. All of these.

   B. burns intensely when exposed to oxygen. E. None of these.

   C. is highly corrosive.

46. Radioactive waste dumping in oceans has been

   A. considered by many governments but not yet carried out.

   B. common worldwide until last year.

   C. continued by the Soviet government until very recently.

   D. banned worldwide since 1957.

47. Nuclear waste storage in the United States is handled

   A. in temporary storage at individual plants.

   B. in the permanent storage depot managed by the federal government.

   C. by dumping at sea.

   D. by shipping overseas to Surinam and Venezuela.

48. Yucca Mountain, Nevada, is the site of a

   A. proposed breeder reactor project.

   B. proposed national nuclear waste repository.

   C. the most notorious radioactive leak in history.

   D. leading nuclear free zone.

49. Magnetic confinement is a theoretical method for

   A. storing nuclear waste.   C. facilitating a fusion reaction.

   B. preventing leaks at power plants.   D. All of these.

50. Nuclear fusion is a _____ technology.

   A. proven and common   C. technologically easy but publicly objectionable

   B. ideal but so far unachievable   D. long-time standard

CHAPTER 22
SUSTAINABLE ENERGY

1. The main problem with fossil fuels is that they

   A. don't work well.

   B. won't supply the entire world if developing countries begin using their share of fossil fuels.

   C. can't supply us for another twenty years even at minimal usage.

   D. are so plentiful that we have no incentive to find other nonpolluting energy sources.

2. Amory Lovins of the Rocky Mountain Institute estimated that raising the efficiency of the US car and light truck fleet by _____ mile(s) per gallon would cut oil consumption by about 295,000 barrels a day.

   A. 1   B. 10   C. 15   D. 20

3. Most of our energy waste results from

   A. a failure to turn off lights.

   B. technological inefficiency.

   C. the fact that more efficient energy conversion is not possible.

   D. overwhelming public ignorance of conservation issues.

4. Which of the following statements is *false*?

   A. Improving standards of living has been repeatedly demonstrated to require increased energy consumption.

   B. An average house built today requires only half the energy used by a new home in 1974.

   C. Technology exists for automobiles to average 100 mpg at highway speeds and over 65 mpg in the city.

   D. All of these are true.

5. Superinsulated houses built now in Sweden use only ___ percent of the energy used by a modern American home.

   A. 75   B. 50   C. 25   D. 10

6. Energy efficiency is a measure of

   A. heat produced by a barrel of fuel.

   B. energy stored in a unit of fuel.

   C. energy produced compared to energy consumed.

   D. total energy consumed.

7. Net energy yield differs from energy efficiency in that net yield takes into account

   A. lifetime energy costs of equipment, infrastructure, and disposal.

   B. energy lost in conversion from heat to electricity.

   C. energy saved in waste heat capture.

   D. lifetime energy consumption of all users of the energy produced by a plant or generator.

8. In terms of generating electricity, fuel cells are _____ efficient than thermal-conversion machines because the chemical energy of a fuel is _____.

   A. less, converted into electricity with an intermediate combustion cycle.

   B. less, converted directly into electricity without an intermediate combustion cycle.

   C. more, converted into electricity with an intermediate combustion cycle.

   D. more, converted directly into electricity without an intermediate combustion cycle.

9. Net energy yield is a good way to assess efficiency of nuclear power because

   A. nuclear power is an unusually expensive energy source.

   B. fuel production, transport, construction, and waste disposal consume vast amounts of energy.

   C. nuclear power uses extremely large amounts of fuel.

   D. nuclear electricity production requires energy to initiate reactions.

10. Which of the following statements is *false*?

   A. Capturing waste heat in a thermal-electric plant can increase efficiency from 30 percent to 80 or 90 percent.

   B. The net energy yield of nuclear power may be negative, with total energy input less than output.

   C. Net yields and overall conversion efficiencies are the best way to evaluate energy sources.

   D. Only 40 percent of the energy in coal is turned into energy at a coal-fired power plant.

11. Utility companies are investing in public education and incentive programs to reduce energy use because

   A. it is cheaper for them to invest in energy conservation than build new power plants.

   B. they are worried about the finite supply of fossil fuel.

   C. the high cost of global warming would be prohibitive for them.

   D. of the need to improve public relations by helping consumers reduce their monthly bills.

12. The idea of cogeneration is to actively use _____ at electricity generating plants.

   A. solar as well as coal energy to produce electricity   C. two kinds of fuel, e.g., coal and oil

   B. warm water as well as steam to produce electricity   D. both electricity and waste steam heat

13. A glass greenhouse on the south side of a building is an example of

   A. parabolic collection.   C. passive heat absorption.

   B. an active solar heating system.   D. eutectic heat exchange.

14. Which of the following solar energy use has been used by people for thousands of years?

   A. Parabolic solar collection   C. Passive heat absorption

   B. Active solar heating system   D. Eutectic heat exchange

15. Active solar energy systems involve

   A. large volumes of massive heat absorbers.   C. photovoltaic cells.

   B. pumps and moving fluids.   D. eutectic materials.

16. Eutectic chemicals release heat when they

   A. solidify.   B. evaporate.   C. absorb water.   D. liquefy.

17. Parabolic mirrors _____ sunlight on a collecting medium.

   A. selectively reflect the brightest   B. deflect the most   C. diffuse intense   D. focus intense

18. The most effective way developed so far to produce solar energy concentrated enough to run an industrial furnace or turbine is to use

   A. parabolic mirrors.   C. passive heat absorption.

   B. eutectic materials.   D. photovoltaic cells.

19. In 1997 the _____ company invested money into a solar cell manufacturing facility. This action is _____.

    A. Shell Oil, typical for a fossil fuel company because they are invested in energy sources.

    B. British Petroleum, typical for a fossil fuel company because they are invested in energy sources.

    C. British Petroleum, atypical for a fossil fuel company because they usually block renewable energy.

    D. Shell Oil, atypical for a fossil fuel company because they usually block renewable energy.

20. The quickest and easiest way to save money on energy bills is to

    A. install a new furnace and water heater.   C. put new insulation in your home.

    B. modify your energy-using behavior.   D. buy a more efficient automobile.

21. The two greatest energy users in the average American home are

    A. the furnace and water heater.   C. lighting and space heating.

    B. the refrigerator and water heater.   D. small appliances and space heating.

22. Photovoltaic cells work because solar energy striking their surface

    A. causes the cells to liquefy as they heat.

    B. releases electrons, causing an electric potential in attached wires.

    C. is collected in the form of photons and sent through attached wires.

    D. causes an uneven magnetic charge to develop.

23. Photovoltaic electricity costs are _____ coal or nuclear-powered electricity.

    A. substantially less than   C. incomparably more expensive than

    B. unlikely to become as cheap as   D. likely to be cheaper in the near future than

24. The term "living off the grid" refers to being separated from

    A. the grid-like layout of urban streets.   C. the electric and energy utility systems.

    B. the daily schedule of city life.   D. All of these.

25. Renewable energy makes up ____ percent of total world energy use.

    A. 18   B. 5   C. 25   D. 50

26. Plants store solar energy by

    A. changing phase.   C. creating the chemical bonds of sugar molecules.

    B. creating kinetic energy.   D. transforming it into electrical energy.

27. Which of the following is normally considered a biomass fuel?

    A. wood   B. peat   C. waste wood chips   D. All of these

28. Since fuelwood is their primary source of energy for cooking, many people living in the cities of less-developed countries.

    A. spend about a quarter of their household income on buying fuelwood.

    B. spend an enormous amount of time gathering fuelwood.

    C. are growing trees for sustainable harvesting.

    D. are spending their money to convert to an alternate fuel.

29. Very few living trees are cut down for fuel in _____ because twigs, branches and crop residues are used for fuel. However, in _____ the forests are nearly gone and even fruit trees are cut for fuel.

    A. Pakistan, India   B. Pakistan, Haiti   C. Haiti, Pakistan   D. India, Haiti

30. In the United States and Canada, the most common problem with using wood as a major heat source is

    A. the cost.

    B. wood shortages.

    C. that it separates people from the utility grid.

    D. carbon monoxide production.

31. Manure or dung makes a good fuel except that it is

    A. scarce.

    B. not clean.

    C. often needed as fertilizer.

    D. difficult to burn.

32. Methane is produced by

    A. bacteria.

    B. living animals.

    C. anaerobic decomposition.

    D. All of these.

33. Burning methane from dung

    A. is more efficient than burning the dung directly.

    B. provides more heat than burning the dung directly.

    C. allows the dung to also be used as a fertilizer.

    D. Both A and C.

    E. All of these.

34. Mixed ethanol and gasoline is often called _____. The added ethanol _____ and is a good substitute for lead anti-knocking agents.

    A. methanol, raises fuel efficiency

    B. methane, lowers fuel prices

    C. gasohol, raises octane levels

    D. natural gas, raises fuel prices

35. Since the 1920s, hydropower production has

    A. risen, but not as fast as fossil fuel use.

    B. fallen due to disinterest.

    C. fallen due to a lack of available sites.

    D. become our most important energy source.

36. The total world production of hydropower is currently equal to ___ percent of the total world potential.

    A. 100   B. 10   C. 125   D. 50

37. Siltation and falling water quality are especially significant problems with

    A. microhydro dams.

    B. minihydro dams.

    C. huge dams on major rivers.

    D. All of these equally.

38. A major proposed Canadian hydropower project that could have serious environmental and social consequences is the

    A. Aswan High Dam.

    B. Three Gorges Dam.

    C. Itaipu Dam on the Parana River.

    D. James Bay project.

39. Low-head hydropower involves _____ dams on _____ rivers.

    A. large, major   B. small, minor   C. large, minor   D. small, major

40. Some highly efficient turbines can be submerged directly in a river and require only _____ to operate.

    A. run-of-the-river flow

    B. low-head dams

    C. a low, natural waterfall

    D. a slow trickle of water

41. A microhydro generator is most likely to be installed by a(n)

    A. small town.

    B. individual household.

    C. regional utility grid.

    D. All of these are equally likely to use micro-hydro.

42. Windmills played a critical role in the settlement of

    A. Appalachia.   C. the Great Plains.

    B. Central California.   D. the Rocky Mountains.

43. The world's largest wind power producers are

    A. Australia and India.   C. Brazil and Japan.

    B. the United States and Denmark.   D. Japan and France.

44. Windmills that operate best in light winds are those that have

    A. many blades.   C. no generator attached.

    B. two or three large blades.   D. two or four very small blades.

45. In the United States, the state with the largest wind farm is

    A. Texas.   B. California.   C. Nebraska.   D. Oklahoma.

46. Geothermal energy uses _____ to produce usable heat or electricity.

    A. naturally occurring hot groundwater   C. molten rock from below ground

    B. artificially heated water injected below ground   D. underground radioactive decay

47. Tidal power stations operate by using

    A. the differential heat of inshore and offshore waters.

    B. electrolytic decomposition of saltwater.

    C. turbines that spin in the flow of tide water.

    D. All of these together.

48. One of the environmental consequences of a large tidal station (such as one through the Bay of Fundy) is

    A. saltwater flooding of aquifers.

    B. heavy erosion of the sea floor.

    C. destroyed equipment due to the high energy of the tidal action.

    D. Both A and B.

    E. All of these.

49. Ocean thermal electric conversion (OTEC) uses _____ to produce usable energy.

    A. warm surface water and cold deep seawater   C. fossil fuel-heated seawater

    B. hot water from below the seafloor   D. heat from deep-ocean thermal vents

50. Ocean thermal electric conversion systems would operate best in

    A. cold, polar seas.   C. cold, temperate seas.

    B. warm, tropical seas.   D. warm, shallow freshwater lakes.

CHAPTER 23
SOLID, TOXIC, AND HAZARDOUS WASTE

1. The story of the ship Khian Sea is a graphic demonstration of

    A. the consequences of overpopulation.   C. the growing difficulty of waste disposal.

    B. shortages of space and resources.   D. the extreme volume of waste in developing countries.

2. According to the EPA, the United States produces about _____ tons of solid waste per year.

    A. 100 million   B. 11 billion   C. 1 million   D. 2 billion

3. The trouble with the large amounts of agricultural waste we produce is that it

    A. cannot be recycled.   C. reduces agricultural productivity.

    B. is classified as toxic and hazardous waste.   D. produces vast amounts of nonpoint source pollution.

4. "Waste stream" is a term describing

    A. the steady production of all waste products.

    B. production of all domestic and commercial waste.

    C. production of solid waste specifically.

    D. the intermittent production of particular wastes.

5. In recent decades, unregulated open dumps have _____ in developing countries.

    A. nearly disappeared.   C. remained the primary disposal method.

    B. mostly become regulated.   D. been replaced by incineration and methane generation.

6. Mexico City faces extreme waste disposal problems because that city

    A. is growing faster than infrastructure can be built.

    B. produces more garbage per person than any other.

    C. is very far from any disposal sites.

    D. produces a unique kind of waste.

7. Motor oil can be toxic at concentrations of only 1 part per million, which means that _____ of fresh water.

    A. 1 quart of oil can pollute 1 million gallons

    B. 1 liter of oil can pollute 4 million liters

    C. 1 barrel of oil can pollute 1 million gallons

    D. 1 quart of oil can pollute 1 million quarts

8. Many cities in the United States continued ocean dumping of municipal waste until

    A. 1900.   B. 1988.   C. 1965.   D. 1945.

9. Landfills differ from open dumps in that

    A. landfills are smaller.   C. landfilled waste is compacted and covered.

    B. dumps are cleaner and smell less.   D. Landfills and dumps do not differ at all.

10. The percentage of US cities that will run out of landfill space before 1996 is

    A. more than 50 percent.   C. 30 percent.

    B. nearly 75 percent.   D. just under 10 percent.

11. Choosing the site of a landfill depends on

    A. local topography and drainage patterns.   D. permeability of underlying rock formations.

    B. proximity to aquifer recharge zones.   E. All of these.

    C. neighborhood and community attitudes.

12. If less-developed countries can make money while more-developed countries can rid themselves of waste, why would an organization such as *Greenpeace* be opposed to exporting wastes from developing countries?

    A. Local people in the developing country probably don't know what is in the waste.

    B. People in the developing country may not have the resources to test for toxic materials in the waste.

    C. The practice can involve corrupt government officials who allow the wastes to be dumped illegally.

    D. All of these are reasons *Greenpeace* is opposed to exporting wastes from developing countries.

13. Many states, countries, and corporations dispose of their waste overseas because it is

    A. extremely cheap.   C. the best way environmentally.

    B. the safest method.   D. the only possible method.

14. The main method for disposing of municipal wastes in the United States is _____ while _____ is the main method in Japan.

    A. incineration, recycling   C. landfilling, recycling

    B. recycling, landfilling   D. landfilling, incineration

15. Energy recovery is another term for _____ waste.

    A. recycling   C. preventing the production of

    B. burning   D. A combination of A, B, and C.

16. Refuse-derived fuel differs from normal garbage in that it

    A. is sorted.   B. has coal added.   C. is unsorted.   D. is selectively collected.

17. Refuse-derived fuel has a _____ energy content than raw refuse, but requires energy _____ before burning.

    A. higher, enrichment   C. higher, to sort

    B. lower, enrichment   D. lower, to sort

18. A mass burn is the incineration of

    A. agricultural waste.   C. hazardous substances.

    B. sorted garbage.   D. shredded, unsorted trash.

19. Incinerator ash is

    A. a good source of agricultural fertilizer.   C. pure carbon, with no nutrients.

    B. tainted with highly concentrated toxic substances.   D. tainted with toxins in some rare cases.

20. Ash left from incineration represents ____ percent of the original waste volume.

    A. 2   B. 3 - 7   C. 10 - 20   D. 30 - 50

21. Which of the following is not a major toxic pollutant produced by incinerators?

    A. dioxins   B. lead   C. cadmium   D. aromatic hydrocarbons

22. One of the problems with incinerators is that due to recycling

    A. there may not be enough trash to feed them.

    B. there are not enough funds to support their high costs of operation since most money has gone to recycling.

    C. the energy content of the raw trash is much higher, leading to safety problems.

    D. jobs are being lost because sorting is no longer needed.

23. One of the sources of dangerous heavy metal emissions is from incinerating

    A. plastics.   C. residue from household cleaning products.

    B. bleached paper containing chlorine.   D. batteries.

24. Using a refillable beverage container (returnable bottles) would be an example of _____ materials.

    A. reusing   B. recycling   C. reducing   D. All of these.

25. Recycling, in terms of solid waste management, means

    A. reusing materials.   C. keeping intact but putting to a new use.

    B. melting or shredding to make new products. D. All of these.

26. Which of the following represents the "three Rs" of waste disposal in *descending* order of energy expenditure?

    A. reuse, reduce, recycle   C. recycle, reuse, reduce

    B. reduce, recycle, reuse   D. reuse, recycle, reduce

27. Urban curbside recycling costs cities

    A. a great deal, but citizens approve the expense anyway.   C. more than any other disposal method.

    B. nothing at all because materials always pay for expenses. D. far less than landfilling or incinerating.

28. The United States currently landfills ____ percent of all solid waste.

    A. 80   B. 50   C. 30   D. 10

29. Recycling aluminum is most important for saving

    A. raw materials (ore).   B. energy.   C. landfill space.   D. All of these.

30. Composting is a waste disposal method that

    A. is useful only for single households.   C. vastly reduces total waste volumes.

    B. is more environmentally costly than landfilling. D. is technologically complex.

31. The following should not be put in compost

    A. rotten, smelly garden vegetables.   C. shredded paper products.

    B. sticks.   D. oil and meat products.

32. Individual efforts to reduce the volume of the waste stream

    A. have enormous cumulative effects.

    B. are useful mainly in demonstrating to corporations that we care.

    C. have little effect but make people feel better.

    D. matter very little.

33. Photodegradable plastics break down
   A. when exposed to heat.   C. as they age.
   B. when exposed to light.   D. when exposed to pressure.

34. Biodegradable plastics incorporate _____ to speed breakdown processes.
   A. special types of hydrocarbons   C. cornstarch
   B. week structural components   D. water

35. The most often overlooked of the "three Rs" is
   A. recycle.   B. reuse.   C. redefine.   D. reduce.

36. Hazardous waste is anything that
   A. causes human health threats.
   B. severely contaminates the environment.
   C. is toxic, carcinogenic, mutagenic, corrosive, or explosive.
   D. All of these.

37. The original pool of money available for Superfund cleanup projects
   A. was reserved for future cleanups.   C. was only intended to be used on nontoxic dumps.
   B. far exceeds needed funds.   D. was about 1/10 as much as needed.

38. The National Priority List is a list of sites that
   A. we currently have money to deal with.
   B. deserve research for possible cleanup.
   C. will probably never be cleaned up.
   D. seriously require cleanup to prevent further environmental and health damage.

39. Which of the following is one of the factors that led to the 1995 amendments of CERCLA?
   A. A site for a children's playground and an industrial site have different criteria for cleanup.
   B. The provisions were not rigorous enough.
   C. The policy to rely on site-specific cleanup levels was not working and national standards needed to be set.
   D. No one was liable for clean up of a contaminated site.

40. A brownfield is
   A. the area and property extending 200 meters around a landfill
   B. contaminated property that is not used to its full potential.
   C. property contaminated by a sewage treatment plant.
   D. property that was formerly contaminated and is now safe enough to be used for housing developments

41. The questions of ____ and _____ are among the biggest problems in cleaning up hazardous waste sites.
   A. liability, degree of purity required
   B. degree of purity required, appropriate technology,
   C. appropriate technology, liability
   D. appropriate technology, location

42. Contamination in the Love Canal was from a(n)

   A. active petrochemical plant.

   B. major toxic waste disposal firm.

   C. long-abandoned toxic dump.

   D. neighboring county whose groundwater seeped into the canal.

43. Toxic landfills are frequently located in _____ areas.

   A. wilderness   B. urban   C. rural   D. nonpopulated

44. In waste lagoons, hazardous waste is

   A. stored in cement containment ponds.   C. poured into the sea.

   B. contained in submerged barrels.   D. dumped in illegal, uncontained, leaky ponds.

45. Illegal dumping and storage of hazardous waste

   A. continues to threaten public health.

   B. has completely stopped since the Superfund Act.

   C. has not stopped completely but is rare.

   D. has become a problem mainly since the Superfund Act.

46. The old adage, "One person's trash is another one's treasure" is a potential option for industry to reduce

   A. disposal costs.   D. air pollution.

   B. purchasing costs.   E. All of these.

   C. hazardous wastes.

47. Chemical processing is a way of _____ hazardous waste for safe disposal.

   A. reducing the volume of   C. incinerating

   B. neutralizing   D. filtering and precipitating

48. Biological treatments of hazardous waste involves _____ hazardous substances.

   A. using bacteria to absorb and detoxify   C. using microorganisms to disperse

   B. the genetic alteration of species suffering from   D. None of these is correct.

49. Secure landfills are those that

   A. have no groundwater below them.   C. are built like a bathtub with a lid.

   B. accept no toxic substances.   D. are sealed entirely with durable plastic.

50. Secure landfills are usually sealed with

   A. clay.   B. sand.   C. dirt.   D. gravel.

CHAPTER 24
URBANIZATION AND SUSTAINABLE CITIES

1. Nearly ___ percent of the world's population lives in cities today.
   A. 10   B. 25   C. 50   D. 85

2. Urbanization began to grow especially quickly after the
   A. development of agriculture.   C. beginning of the twentieth century.
   B. invention of record keeping, commerce, and religion.   D. industrial revolution.

3. The most useful definition of a city is based on
   A. the land uses involved.   C. geographical area.
   B. functions.   D. size.

4. _____ of the world's population has always lived in _____, at least since the beginning of written history.
   A. At least half, urban areas   C. The vast majority, urban areas
   B. At least half, rural communities   D. The vast majority, rural communities

5. In rural areas, the majority of people
   A. are involved in harvesting natural resources.   C. are economically dependent on cities.
   B. work in trade and manufacturing.   D. work in information and goods exchange.

6. A collection of rural households linked by custom, culture, or family, is known as a(n)
   A. city.   B. urban area.   C. village.   D. farm.

7. Cities are distinguished by their
   A. sheer size.
   B. differentiated, specialized jobs and functions.
   C. large groups of interdependent households.
   D. strong traditions and cultural character.

8. A city with a population greater than _____ is considered a megacity.
   A. 1 million   B. 200 thousand   C. 10 million   D. 30 million

9. An example of a megacity is
   A. Mexico City.   B. The Paris Basin.   C. Bos-Wash.   D. All of these.

10. The urban core of a large city is usually considered the center of
    A. social activity.   B. economic activity.   C. political activity.   D. All of these.

11. The urbanization experience of many developing countries is similar to the United State's _____ that occurred in the nineteenth and early twentieth century.
    A. demographic rural shift   C. rural-to-urban shift
    B. demographic transformation   D. urban-to-rural shift

12. In developed countries of Europe and North America, about _____ of people live in cities.
    A. 3/4   B. 1/2   C. 1/3   D. 1/4

13. The largest city in the world is now
    A. London.   B. Mexico City.   C. Los Angeles.   D. Tokyo.

14. The principal problem with rapid urban growth, especially in developing countries, is

    A. finding skilled labor.

    B. physically finding room for people to live.

    C. the building of infrastructure can't keep up with increasing needs.

    D. All of these are equally difficult.

15. Natural increase is an especially important factor in urban areas of

    A. Latin America and Asia.   C. Europe.

    B. the United States.   D. the former Soviet region.

16. Natural increase factors in urban growth result from _____ while immigration results from _____.

    A. improved medical care, better sanitation   C. improved medical care, push and pull factors

    B. better sanitation, improved medical care   D. push and pull factors, improved medical care

17. Which of the following is a push factor for urban growth?

    A. jobs in rural manufacturing

    B. unemployment in farming communities

    C. better access to education at big universities

    D. high unemployment in cities

18. Which of the following is a pull factor for urban growth?

    A. jobs in rural manufacturing.

    B. unemployment in farming communities.

    C. better access to education at big universities.

    D. high unemployment in cities.

19. Televisions and other mass media contribute to urban growth because

    A. people must move close to town to get TV reception.

    B. there are so many jobs in media.

    C. TV is used to advertise about labor shortages.

    D. TV makes urban life appear luxurious and accessible.

20. Which of the following statements is *false*?

    A. Even crowded, squalid living conditions in expanding Third World cities are sometimes better than what people left in the countryside.

    B. When governments set commodity prices to make urban life easier, rural populations often suffer, leading to further migration to cities.

    C. Agricultural mechanization is a major pull factor in urbanization of developing countries.

    D. Political instability can play a major role in urban growth.

    E. All of these are true.

21. Air pollution in major cities of developing countries is

    A. usually negligible.

    B. responsible for extremely high rates of respiratory diseases.

    C. rapidly becoming less of a problem.

    D. not well understood.

22. The diseases that are caused by water pollution in the major cities of developing countries are mainly due to the

   A. lack of waste treatment systems to accommodate the population.

   B. high amount of runoff that includes pesticides, fertilizers, and animal waste.

   C. high number of industries that dump their wastes into surface water.

   D. practice of swimming in water contaminated by toxic chemicals.

23. Slums are usually dwelling places that are

   A. illegal and built by squatters.

   B. legal but have inadequate living conditions.

   C. condemned by the city but illegally occupied.

   D. small but up to code.

24. The principal difference between shantytowns and slums is that shantytowns are

   A. maintained by the city.   C. illegal and built by residents.

   B. built by the city but condemned.   D. legal but below code.

25. Squatter towns are often dangerous places to live because the land they are on is

   A. unstable, polluted, or near industrial sites.   C. in the densest parts of the city.

   B. owned by powerful political figures.   D. None of these.

26. Which of the following statements is *false*?

   A. Most future urban growth is expected to occur in developing countries.

   B. Rural areas are always safer places to live, in terms of violent crime, than urban areas.

   C. Squatter towns, while illegal, are sometimes very large and highly organized places.

   D. All of these are true.

27. The main problem facing major US city centers is

   A. the growth of shantytowns.

   B. runaway air pollution and an absence of sewage treatment facilities.

   C. the loss of tax dollars and jobs to the suburbs.

   D. a great deal of new infrastructure and no population to use it.

28. When compared to less-developed countries, shantytowns are _____ found in more developed countries due to the _____.

   A. not, lack of poverty

   B. also, same conditions of poverty and lack of infrastructure

   C. not, high levels of public support for a nation's poor

   D. also, lack of initiative among poorer people

29. In many US cities, poor, undereducated, minority, and other less powerful groups are often concentrated

   A. in urban centers.   C. outside of the city entirely.

   B. at city margins.   D. in a ring of satellite settlements around a city.

30. Texas *colonias* are examples of

    A. urban redesign projects in the United States.

    B. shantytowns in the United States.

    C. rural ghost towns resulting from rapid migration to cities.

    D. sustainable projects in the United States to help urban people help themselves.

31. The Lake Calumet Industrial District on Chicago's South Side is an excellent example of the cleanup

    A. and use of brownfields.   C. and elimination of a squatter town.

    B. of a shantytown.   D. and elimination of a shantytown.

32. What is the source of funding for the cleanup of projects in The Lake Calumet Industrial District?

    A. State funds for job retraining.

    B. Local residents have raised the funds through donations.

    C. Federal funds from the Superfund.

    D. Fines levied on companies for illegal dumping.

33. In the United States, a massive nation-wide urban renewal program began in the

    A. 1850s.   B. 1930s.   C. 1950s.   D. 1980s.

34. The urban renewal programs of the 1950s and 1960s are credited with

    A. building freeways to ease the movement of poor people to more pleasant suburbs.

    B. strengthening poor urban communities with new, improved housing projects.

    C. replacing concert halls and other amenities with new housing units.

    D. further destabilizing poor urban communities.

35. Which of the following statements is *true*?

    A. Noise can produce physiological as well as psychological responses.

    B. Tinnitus occurs with about equal frequency anywhere in the world.

    C. An essential component of urban renewal is reducing noise.

    D. The most dangerous noise is that in a city.

36. The main thing that bothers city residents about their environment is

    A. pollution.   B. noise.   C. crime.   D. congestion.

37. A sound measured at 1 decibel is

    A. extremely loud.   C. extremely quiet.

    B. the average noise level on a city street.   D. moderately quiet.

38. Tinnitus, or ringing in the ears, may affect as many as ___ percent of Americans.

    A. 12   B. 23   C. 52   D. 94

39. Tinnitus, or ringing in the ears, results from

    A. prolonged exposure to loud noises.   C. genetically-caused ear degeneration.

    B. age.   D. prolonged exposure to any noise at all.

40. In the Sudan 70 year olds have no significant hearing loss. This is attributed mainly to

    A. their nutritious diet.   C. the lack of pollution in the environment.

    B. their genetic makeup.   D. the lack of noise in the environment.

41. One of the most important things influencing land use is the

    A. building of mass transit systems.   C. siting of cities.

    B. building of freeways.   D. siting of industry.

42. Transportation plays a _____ role in urban growth and urban health.

    A. negligible   C. critical

    B. sometimes important, sometimes unimportant   D. modest

43. City planning was first invented by

    A. Pierre L'Enfant and Baron von Hausmann in the 1700s.   C. Greek city states perhaps 2500 years ago.

    B. transportation planners of the industrial revolution.   D. urban renewal architects in the 1950s.

44. "New towns" are designed to

    A. incorporate the best aspects of rural and urban life.

    B. improve industrial activity in urban centers.

    C. keep separate the income classes so as to prevent crime.

    D. urbanize rural communities.

45. The idea of a technopolis is

    A. very similar to that of garden cities.

    B. focused on skyscrapers (vertical expansion).

    C. to incorporate industrial and residential activities harmoniously.

    D. to incorporate green spaces in cities.

46. Most major American cities are most like which of the following models?

    A. the garden city   C. the technopolis

    B. new towns   D. Pierre L'Enfant's radiating boulevard model

47. Suburbs are known for

    A. uniform, single family detached houses.   C. presence of artistic and cultural opportunities.

    B. affordable housing for minorities.   D. creating sense of community and identity.

48. Traditional suburban development

    A. is usually only house lots and streets.

    B. typically consists of identical parcels of land without open space.

    C. usually is required by local zoning ordinances.

    D. consumes agricultural land and wildlife habitat.

    E. All of these are true.

49. Which of the following is *not* a characteristic of a revitalized city?

    A. a vital nightlife   D. traffic congestion

    B. convenient shopping and services   E. All of these are characteristic of a revitalized city.

    C. less automobile dependency

50. Curitiba, Brazil, is famous for its

    A. creative solutions to environmental problems.

    B. runaway population growth.

    C. particularly disastrous rainforest destruction.

    D. complete environmental breakdown due to uncontrolled industry.

CHAPTER 25
WHAT THEN SHALL WE DO?

1. In the twenty years from 1975-1995, the spills in the Niger Delta were about _____ as the Exxon Valdez spill in Alaska.

   A. half as much   B. the same   C. twice as much   D. five times as much

2. In Nigeria natural gas is

   A. used as a resource by the Shell Oil Company.   C. burned off as a waste product.

   B. used by the local people.   D. sold to neighboring countries.

3. The main target(s) of the Nigerian military campaign to silence environmental protection and social justice was/were

   A. Ken Siro-Wiwa.   C. traditional village chiefs.

   B. General Sani Abacha.   D. Shell employees living in Nigeria.

4. The goal to encourage postsecondary students to pursue careers related to the environment is part of the

   A. 1990 National Environmental Education Act.

   B. 21st Century Environmental Education Law.

   C. Goals 2000 Education Act.

   D. goals of President Clinton for the 21st Century.

5. Environmental literacy consists of being able to

   A. read environmental journals.   C. carry out ecological models and experiments.

   B. understand the basic principles of ecology.   D. write and publish in environmental journals.

6. The US government has become interested in widespread environmental literacy because

   A. the collective action of all citizens makes any policy function or fail.

   B. widespread agreement makes collecting environmental taxes much easier.

   C. the actions of average citizens are harmful toward the environment.

   D. All of these.

7. As more environment-oriented jobs become available, the number of students prepared for them is

   A. staying the same.   C. decreasing.

   B. increasing.   D. increasing dramatically.

8. On a national level, environmental job opportunities are

   A. changing very little.   C. being exported overseas.

   B. shrinking.   D. expanding.

9. Businesses are now willing to become "green" because doing so

   A. improves their public image.   C. saves money.

   B. is expensive but makes good advertising.   D. improves their image and saves money.

10. Many businesses are exploring and adopting the "design for the environment." This approach emphasizes

    A. preventing environmental problems to save money and stay competitive in future markets.

    B. public relations about their environmental policies.

    C. recycling their products.

    D. hiring more environmental science and environmental studies graduates.

11. The market for technology used in cleaning up environmental disasters and dirty industries is expected to be especially large in

    A. South Africa.   C. Central Africa.

    B. Eastern and Central Europe.   D. the Amazon region.

12. Which of the following events is probably the most significant in increasing the job market for environmentally related careers?

    A. The public's emphasis on recycling.

    B. The high rate of extinction.

    C. The Goals 2000 Education Act.

    D. The shift of businesses to decrease their environmental impact.

13. The cost of litigation for past environmental oversights encourages many corporations to

    A. prevent future pollution.   C. decrease spending on environmental problems.

    B. hire better lawyers.   D. dissolve their environmental departments.

14. The terms nontoxic, biodegradable, recyclable, natural, organic, and environmental friendly are used

    A. as standards for merchandising environmental products.

    B. as excellent indicators of products that do not harm the environment.

    C. by advertising to sell products.

    D. by the Green Party and Blue Angels to endorse a product.

15. Which of the following is a *true* statement?

    A. If a product advertises that it won't hurt the environment it is better to spend the extra money to buy it.

    B. Organic shampoos are better for the environment and for you.

    C. Any business that goes to the considerable trouble of advertising itself as "green" can usually be counted on to be environmentally conscious.

    D. Simply buying fewer things is an important means of protecting the environment.

    E. All of these are true statements.

16. The idea of precycling is to

    A. consume less energy and materials in the first place.

    B. sort all recyclable materials before disposal.

    C. reuse manufactured items such as shopping bags or clothing.

    D. export more materials than we import.

17. Which of the following is *not* a form of precycling?

    A. riding the bus to work instead of driving

    B. refusing to buy disposable items

    C. buying a new car every few years to ensure high fuel efficiency

    D. buying fewer clothes and shoes

18. The German Blue Angel and US Green Seal are

    A. a set of new environmental quality goals.   C. measures of corporate responsibility.

    B. environmental endorsements of products.   D. newly established political parties.

19. Making intelligent environmental decisions as a consumer

    A. is impossible because there are so many green products on the market.

    B. is futile because it doesn't have an impact.

    C. requires attention but is important.

    D. is something few people are interested in.

20. If you buy a product that is "natural" you can be assured that the product

    A. is nontoxic to humans.   D. contains no pesticides.

    B. is better for the environment.   E. None of these.

    C. contains no harmful ingredients.

21. In which of the following situations would it probably be less environmentally damaging for you to use paper bags at the grocery store?

    A. When paper bags are reused by the grocery store.

    B. When I use plastic grocery bags for my trash instead of buying separate plastic trash bags.

    C. When paper and plastic bags are both recycled.

    D. None of these.

    E. Both B and C.

22. Life-cycle analysis is useful because energy and environmental hazards are associated with _____ of products.

    A. use as well as production   C. both transport and production

    B. production but not use   D. production, transport, use, and disposal

23. Environmental groups for secondary and postsecondary (college) students help participants

    A. come together to multiply the efforts of people with the same goals and ideals.

    B. develop their organizational skills.

    C. become deep ecologists.

    D. learn how to become effective radical environmentalists.

    E. Both A and B.

24. The "group of 10" environmental organizations are most useful in

    A. spearheading truly radical environmental change.

    B. inspiring individual direct actions by all members.

    C. having strong, respected, and organized influence on national environmental policy setting.

    D. initiating student environmental activism on local environmental issues.

25. The Sierra Club would probably have the philosophy that environmental problems _____ while Sea Shepherd would probably view problems as _____.

A. are environmental crises requiring immediate attention, situations that can be overcome by working with the established system.

B. can be overcome by working with the established system, environmental crises requiring immediate attention.

C. Both the Sierra Club and Sea Shepherd would probably view problems as environmental crises requiring immediate attention.

D. Both the Sierra Club and Sea Shepherd would probably view problems as situations that can be overcome by working with the established system.

26. Philosopher Arne Naess used the term deep ecology to describe a

A. profound change in attitude and behavior toward environmental issues.

B. highly scientific approach in understanding ecological concepts.

C. widespread, popular movement in understanding environmental issues.

D. less serious approach compared to shallow ecology.

27. Social ecology is _____ deep ecology.

A. violently opposed to   C. less green than

B. greener than   D. more humanist than

28. Which group below is most identified with direct action for environmental causes?

A. the Audubon Society   C. the Wise Use Movement

B. Earth First!   D. the Natural Resources Defense Council

29. Monkeywrenching may be

A. problematic but clearly legal.   D. both B and C.

B. illegal but possibly correct.   E. All of these.

C. environmentally correct but sometimes dangerous to human life.

30. Why would the "group of 10" environmental organizations be criticized?

A. They are militant and extremist groups that lead to environmental revolutions.

B. They oppose most environmental protection.

C. They tend to compromise and cooperate with the establishment.

D. Their membership is small and they have focused and limited influence.

31. The Wise Use Movement

A. advocates complete environmental protection.

B. opposes most environmental protection.

C. advocates monkeywrenching.

D. is dedicated to buying land for wilderness preservation.

32. Which of these groups is dedicated to opening all public lands to development and resource extraction?

A. Earth First!   C. Sahara Club

B. the Nature Conservancy   D. Natural Resources Defense Council

33. Who made the famous declaration that "poverty is the greatest danger to the environment"?

A. Indira Ghandi, the prime minister of India   C. Dave Foreman, the leader of Earth First!

B. Bill Clinton, the president of the United States   D. Murray Bookchin, the proponent of social ecology

34. A country that is more likely to act in favor of environmental protection rather than focus on acquiring money and material goods has _____ values.

    A. postmodernist   B. Marxist   C. postmaterialistic   D. postindustrial

35. Some of the highest levels of public support for environmental protection would most likely be found in

    A. Brazil.   B. the Netherlands.   C. Ireland.   D. Greece.

36. One of the key factors in a sustainable future based on improving human well-being and protecting our common environment is

    A. technology transfer from developed to developing countries.

    B. environmental and resource protection.

    C. increased aid for developing countries.

    D. All of these.

37. Which of the following would probably *not* be a focus of a NGO?

    A. Creating and enforcing national environmental laws.

    B. Initiating radical or innovative development strategies.

    C. Greening major international corporations.

    D. Applying large funds to steering international policies.

38. The country with the biggest, best established political Green Party is

    A. China.   B. Canada.   C. Germany. D. Brazil.

39. The requirement that cars must be designed so they can be repaired or recycled rather than thrown away is a component of the

    A. Green Party's political agenda.   C. Japanese energy-efficiency laws.

    B. Dutch Green Plan.   D. US auto manufacturers goals.

40. Which federal agency is responsible for Wildlife Refuges and Wild and Scenic Rivers?

    A. Agriculture Department   C. Environmental Protection Agency

    B. US Forest Service   D. Department of the Interior

41. The EPA is responsible for _____ while the Department of Agriculture administers _____.

    A. regulating air and water pollution, the national forests and Soil Conservation Service

    B. the national forests and Soil Conservation Service, regulations of air and water pollution

    C. national parks and wild refuges, Public Health Service and occupational safety and health

    D. nuclear energy and fossil fuel, Public Health Service

42. When writing to your elected officials it is important to

    A. be polished, use the right key words and type your letter.

    B. write about at least two issues to make the letter worthwhile.

    C. follow-up with positive feedback or thanks when your issues are supported.

    D. write a letter that is approximately one and a half pages long.

    E. All of these.

43. An environmental impact statement is required for any

    A. major new pollution emissions.   C. possible health threat to people.

    B. major building projects.   D. All of these.

44. Under the Freedom of Information Act a letter to your legislators is considered _____ and minutes of meetings are considered _____.

    A. public correspondence, private   C. public correspondence, public

    B. private correspondence, public   D. private correspondence, private

45. A major drawback of international treaties and conventions is that

    A. there is too much time spent with government-to-government networking.

    B. there is too much time spent with person-to-person networking.

    C. they generally lack enforcement powers.

    D. All of these are drawbacks of international treaties and conventions.

46. Which of the following statements is *true*?

    A. The best thing about sustainable development is that it is carried out without significant investments of money or technology.

    B. Nongovernmental organizations have become significant players in international environmentalism and development.

    C. No important international agreement has ever been violated once it was passed by the international community.

    D. Public concern about environmental protection is always higher where pollution is most severe.

47. A green plan that can serve as a model for the rest of the world because of its comprehensive and long-term nature is that of

    A. the United States.   D. the Netherlands.

    B. Germany.   E. England.

    C. Japan.

48. Improved product quality, energy conservation, and integrated life-cycle management are all components of

    A. a business's environmental plan.   D. All of these could be true.

    B. the Dutch Green Plan.   E. Both A and B could be true.

    C. the US Green Plan.

49. How is the following viewpoint attempting to bias the reader?

    Despite the hysterics of a few pseudo-scientists, there is no reason to believe in global warming.

    A. The writer is using language that ridicules the view that the global warming threat is real.

    B. The writer is attempting to link environmental concerns with an unpopular political ideology instead of using evidence.

    C. The writer is using language that conveys emotion combined with evidence that is not referenced.

    D. The writer is attempting to use reason and logic to convince the reader.

50. The values of respect for all life, ecosystem protection and restoration, human rights, equitable sharing of resources, and democratic decision-making are all components of the

    A. 1979 Convention on Long-Range Transboundary Air Pollution.

    B. 1997 Earth Charter principles.

    C. 1989 Accord on Chlorofluorocarbon Emissions.

    D. 1945 establishment of the United Nations.

ANSWER KEY

Chapter 1

1. C	12. D	23. B	34. A	45. D	56. C
2. D	13. A	24. C	35. B	46. B	57. D
3. D	14. D	25. A	36. D	47. D	58. A
4. A	15. B	26. C	37. C	48. C	59. A
5. D	16. C	27. D	38. C	49. A	60. C
6. B	17. E	28. A	39. D	50. B	61. D
7. D	18. B	29. C	40. A	51. A	
8. C	19. A	30. B	41. B	52. C	
9. A	20. D	31. C	42. A	53. D	
10. C	21. A	32. B	43. D	54. B	
11. A	22. C	33. B	44. A	55. B	

Chapter 2

1. D	11. A	21. C	31. A	41. B	51. A
2. A	12. A	22. C	32. C	42. C	52. A
3. B	13. A	23. D	33. A	43. D	53. C
4. C	14. C	24. B	34. D	44. C	54. B
5. D	15. D	25. B	35. B	45. B	55. D
6. A	16. A	26. A	36. B	46. D	56. B
7. D	17. C	27. B	37. A	47. C	57. D
8. A	18. A	28. C	38. D	48. D	
9. C	19. B	29. C	39. A	49. A	
10. B	20. A	30. B	40. D	50. B	

Chapter 3

1. D	13. B	25. A	37. B	49. B	61. D
2. B	14. D	26. D	38. E	50. C	62. C
3. D	15. C	27. B	39. A	51. A	63. D
4. A	16. B	28. C	40. C	52. D	64. B
5. B	17. A	29. D	41. B	53. C	65. E
6. C	18. B	30. B	42. D	54. A	66. D
7. A	19. C	31. A	43. A	55. D	67. A
8. B	20. E	32. B	44. D	56. A	68. D
9. D	21. C	33. D	45. A	57. B	69. B
10. A	22. A	34. C	46. C	58. B	70. A
11. A	23. C	35. C	47. A	59. D	
12. C	24. B	36. B	48. D	60. C	

Chapter 4

1.	B	12.	D	23.	C	34.	D	45.	D	56.	A
2.	A	13.	B	24.	A	35.	A	46.	B	57.	C
3.	C	14.	A	25.	D	36.	C	47.	B	58.	A
4.	B	15.	B	26.	A	37.	A	48.	D	59.	C
5.	D	16.	C	27.	B	38.	D	49.	B	60.	D
6.	D	17.	B	28.	D	39.	A	50.	A	61.	B
7.	D	18.	C	29.	C	40.	C	51.	D	62.	A
8.	A	19.	D	30.	A	41.	B	52.	B	63.	C
9.	B	20.	B	31.	D	42.	D	53.	B	64.	B
10.	D	21.	C	32.	C	43.	B	54.	C	65.	C
11.	C	22.	B	33.	D	44.	D	55.	D		

Chapter 5

1.	B	11.	C	21.	D	31.	C	41.	A	51.	B
2.	C	12.	C	22.	B	32.	A	42.	C	52.	D
3.	A	13.	D	23.	D	33.	B	43.	D	53.	A
4.	B	14.	B	24.	C	34.	C	44.	B	54.	B
5.	C	15.	A	25.	A	35.	B	45.	A	55.	C
6.	D	16.	B	26.	C	36.	A	46.	C	56.	C
7.	B	17.	D	27.	D	37.	C	47.	A	57.	A
8.	D	18.	B	28.	B	38.	B	48.	D		
9.	C	19.	A	29.	E	39.	D	49.	B		
10.	B	20.	C	30.	D	40.	B	50.	C		

Chapter 6

1.	D	11.	C	21.	C	31.	B	41.	D	51.	C
2.	A	12.	D	22.	C	32.	C	42.	A	52.	B
3.	C	13.	A	23.	A	33.	A	43.	C	53.	B
4.	A	14.	D	24.	B	34.	B	44.	C	54.	C
5.	C	15.	C	25.	A	35.	A	45.	A	55.	A
6.	D	16.	C	26.	B	36.	D	46.	B	56.	A
7.	C	17.	B	27.	D	37.	C	47.	A	57.	C
8.	A	18.	A	28.	C	38.	E	48.	B	58.	D
9.	B	19.	D	29.	B	39.	A	49.	C	59.	B
10.	A	20.	B	30.	E	40.	B	50.	B	60.	D

Chapter 7

1. C	12. A	23. B	34. C	45. C	56. C
2. A	13. B	24. D	35. D	46. A	57. A
3. C	14. B	25. A	36. C	47. D	58. D
4. B	15. D	26. B	37. A	48. B	59. E
5. D	16. A	27. B	38. B	49. A	60. C
6. C	17. B	28. C	39. A	50. B	61. B
7. D	18. C	29. A	40. D	51. D	62. C
8. C	19. A	30. C	41. B	52. B	63. B
9. B	20. D	31. B	42. D	53. B	64. D
10. C	21. C	32. C	43. A	54. C	
11. C	22. D	33. A	44. D	55. A	

Chapter 8

1. C	12. A	23. B	34. D	45. B	56. A
2. C	13. B	24. C	35. D	46. D	57. D
3. A	14. A	25. D	36. B	47. C	58. A
4. C	15. D	26. C	37. C	48. C	59. D
5. D	16. C	27. A	38. D	49. A	60. B
6. C	17. D	28. B	39. D	50. A	61. C
7. A	18. C	29. A	40. A	51. B	
8. C	19. B	30. C	41. C	52. C	
9. D	20. A	31. B	42. A	53. C	
10. B	21. B	32. D	43. A	54. A	
11. D	22. D	33. C	44. D	55. B	

Chapter 9

1. D	12. C	23. B	34. C	45. D	56. C
2. E	13. B	24. A	35. C	46. B	57. A
3. D	14. D	25. D	36. D	47. A	58. A
4. A	15. A	26. B	37. A	48. B	59. D
5. C	16. B	27. C	38. D	49. A	60. C
6. D	17. B	28. A	39. A	50. D	61. B
7. B	18. A	29. D	40. B	51. C	62. A
8. C	19. C	30. B	41. B	52. C	63. C
9. C	20. C	31. A	42. C	53. A	64. D
10. D	21. A	32. B	43. A	54. B	65. C
11. A	22. D	33. D	44. D	55. C	

Chapter 10

1. B	11. B	21. B	31. B	41. D	51. D
2. C	12. A	22. C	32. D	42. C	52. D
3. A	13. B	23. B	33. C	43. C	53. C
4. B	14. C	24. A	34. C	44. D	54. A
5. C	15. E	25. B	35. A	45. A	55. B
6. B	16. B	26. C	36. B	46. C	56. D
7. C	17. A	27. B	37. D	47. B	57. B
8. C	18. C	28. D	38. B	48. C	58. A
9. D	19. D	29. A	39. A	49. B	59. D
10. A	20. E	30. A	40. B	50. B	60. C

Chapter 11

1. A	11. D	21. D	31. C	41. C	51. A
2. C	12. C	22. A	32. A	42. A	52. C
3. B	13. A	23. D	33. B	43. B	53. B
4. A	14. C	24. B	34. D	44. D	54. C
5. C	15. B	25. A	35. C	45. A	55. E
6. B	16. D	26. C	36. D	46. D	56. A
7. E	17. C	27. D	37. D	47. C	57. D
8. C	18. B	28. C	38. C	48. B	58. B
9. D	19. A	29. D	39. B	49. D	59. D
10. C	20. C	30. A	40. A	50. B	60. C

Chapter 12

1. B	11. A	21. D	31. B	41. A	51. D
2. C	12. C	22. C	32. D	42. D	52. C
3. B	13. B	23. D	33. B	43. D	53. C
4. A	14. A	24. B	34. A	44. B	54. D
5. A	15. B	25. B	35. B	45. B	55. B
6. B	16. D	26. A	36. D	46. D	56. A
7. C	17. C	27. C	37. C	47. A	57. D
8. B	18. B	28. D	38. B	48. D	58. C
9. D	19. A	29. A	39. C	49. B	59. B
10. D	20. A	30. C	40. C	50. A	60. B

Chapter 13

1. D	12. D	23. B	34. D	45. D	56. B
2. C	13. B	24. D	35. C	46. A	57. A
3. B	14. E	25. C	36. B	47. D	58. C
4. C	15. A	26. A	37. D	48. A	59. D
5. D	16. B	27. D	38. A	49. C	60. A
6. B	17. C	28. C	39. D	50. D	61. B
7. A	18. C	29. B	40. B	51. B	62. C
8. C	19. D	30. A	41. D	52. A	
9. D	20. A	31. D	42. B	53. D	
10. B	21. B	32. B	43. C	54. A	
11. A	22. A	33. B	44. A	55. C	

Chapter 14

1. A	13. A	25. A	37. C	49. B	61. B
2. B	14. B	26. C	38. A	50. D	62. C
3. C	15. C	27. D	39. B	51. B	63. A
4. A	16. B	28. A	40. D	52. C	64. D
5. D	17. D	29. B	41. A	53. D	65. C
6. C	18. B	30. D	42. C	54. C	66. A
7. D	19. A	31. A	43. B	55. C	67. B
8. A	20. B	32. C	44. D	56. A	
9. B	21. D	33. D	45. E	57. D	
10. C	22. B	34. B	46. D	58. B	
11. A	23. C	35. A	47. D	59. A	
12. D	24. C	36. D	48. C	60. B	

Chapter 15

1. D	11. B	21. B	31. B	41. B	51. A
2. B	12. A	22. D	32. C	42. D	52. B
3. A	13. C	23. A	33. A	43. A	53. B
4. D	14. D	24. B	34. E	44. D	54. A
5. B	15. C	25. C	35. A	45. B	55. D
6. D	16. B	26. C	36. B	46. D	56. A
7. C	17. D	27. B	37. C	47. D	57. C
8. B	18. D	28. C	38. D	48. C	58. B
9. A	19. A	29. D	39. A	49. A	59. A
10. C	20. C	30. C	40. C	50. D	60. C

Chapter 16

1.	B	10.	B	19.	A	28.	A	37.	C	46.	D
2.	C	11.	C	20.	C	29.	A	38.	B	47.	B
3.	D	12.	E	21.	D	30.	D	39.	D	48.	C
4.	A	13.	C	22.	C	31.	A	40.	B	49.	D
5.	B	14.	A	23.	A	32.	B	41.	A	50.	D
6.	D	15.	B	24.	D	33.	A	42.	C		
7.	B	16.	A	25.	B	34.	D	43.	C		
8.	C	17.	D	26.	C	35.	C	44.	A		
9.	A	18.	B	27.	B	36.	A	45.	A		

Chapter 17

1.	C	10.	A	19.	B	28.	E	37.	A	46.	B
2.	A	11.	B	20.	B	29.	A	38.	C	47.	E
3.	B	12.	D	21.	A	30.	B	39.	D	48.	A
4.	A	13.	C	22.	B	31.	A	40.	A	49.	C
5.	D	14.	A	23.	D	32.	C	41.	B	50.	D
6.	B	15.	B	24.	C	33.	D	42.	B	51.	E
7.	D	16.	D	25.	D	34.	A	43.	C	52.	D
8.	C	17.	C	26.	A	35.	B	44.	A		
9.	B	18.	D	27.	B	36.	B	45.	D		

Chapter 18

1.	C	12.	C	23.	C	34.	D	45.	C	56.	C
2.	A	13.	A	24.	A	35.	C	46.	B	57.	D
3.	B	14.	C	25.	B	36.	D	47.	D	58.	A
4.	C	15.	A	26.	D	37.	B	48.	B	59.	D
5.	D	16.	C	27.	D	38.	E	49.	B	60.	C
6.	A	17.	B	28.	C	39.	A	50.	A	61.	D
7.	A	18.	D	29.	A	40.	D	51.	C	62.	B
8.	D	19.	A	30.	D	41.	B	52.	B	63.	A
9.	C	20.	C	31.	B	42.	C	53.	D		
10.	B	21.	D	32.	A	43.	A	54.	B		
11.	A	22.	A	33.	A	44.	B	55.	C		

Chapter 19

1. D	10. C	19. A	28. C	37. D	46. B
2. A	11. A	20. C	29. C	38. B	47. A
3. D	12. B	21. A	30. D	39. A	48. D
4. A	13. D	22. B	31. B	40. A	49. E
5. B	14. C	23. D	32. B	41. B	50. C
6. C	15. B	24. A	33. C	42. D	51. B
7. D	16. A	25. D	34. B	43. C	
8. A	17. A	26. A	35. C	44. D	
9. B	18. C	27. A	36. C	45. C	

Chapter 20

1. B	10. B	19. A	28. D	37. A	46. A
2. E	11. C	20. C	29. E	38. D	47. B
3. A	12. D	21. D	30. D	39. B	48. D
4. C	13. B	22. C	31. B	40. C	49. C
5. D	14. A	23. D	32. D	41. A	50. A
6. B	15. C	24. C	33. A	42. B	
7. A	16. D	25. B	34. D	43. D	
8. C	17. B	26. D	35. B	44. A	
9. A	18. C	27. A	36. C	45. C	

Chapter 21

1. B	10. B	19. D	28. D	37. C	46. C
2. A	11. D	20. B	29. C	38. A	47. A
3. C	12. D	21. A	30. D	39. B	48. B
4. D	13. C	22. C	31. E	40. D	49. C
5. B	14. B	23. B	32. B	41. A	50. B
6. D	15. A	24. C	33. C	42. B	
7. A	16. B	25. A	34. A	43. D	
8. C	17. A	26. B	35. B	44. B	
9. B	18. C	27. A	36. A	45. D	

Chapter 22

1. B	10. C	19. C	28. A	37. C	46. A
2. A	11. A	20. B	29. B	38. D	47. C
3. B	12. D	21. A	30. D	39. B	48. D
4. A	13. C	22. B	31. C	40. A	49. A
5. D	14. C	23. D	32. D	41. D	50. B
6. C	15. B	24. C	33. E	42. C	
7. A	16. A	25. B	34. C	43. B	
8. D	17. D	26. C	35. A	44. A	
9. B	18. A	27. D	36. B	45. B	

Chapter 23

1. C	10. A	19. B	28. A	37. D	46. E
2. B	11. E	20. C	29. D	38. D	47. B
3. D	12. D	21. D	30. C	39. A	48. A
4. A	13. A	22. A	31. D	40. B	49. C
5. C	14. C	23. D	32. A	41. A	50. A
6. A	15. B	24. A	33. B	42. C	
7. D	16. A	25. B	34. C	43. B	
8. B	17. C	26. C	35. D	44. D	
9. C	18. D	27. D	36. C	45. A	

Chapter 24

1. C	10. D	19. D	28. B	37. C	46. C
2. D	11. C	20. C	29. A	38. D	47. A
3. B	12. A	21. B	30. B	39. A	48. E
4. D	13. B	22. A	31. A	40. D	49. E
5. A	14. C	23. B	32. D	41. B	50. A
6. C	15. A	24. C	33. C	42. C	
7. B	16. C	25. A	34. D	43. C	
8. C	17. B	26. B	35. A	44. A	
9. D	18. C	27. C	36. B	45. B	

Chapter 25

1.	D	37.	A
2.	C	38.	C
3.	A	39.	B
4.	A	40.	D
5.	B	41.	A
6.	A	42.	C
7.	C	43.	D
8.	D	44.	B
9.	D	45.	C
10.	A	46.	B
11.	B	47.	D
12.	D	48.	E
13.	A	49.	A
14.	C	50.	B
15.	D		
16.	A		
17.	C		
18.	B		
19.	C		
20.	E		
21.	A		
22.	D		
23.	E		
24.	C		
25.	B		
26.	A		
27.	D		
28.	B		
29.	D		
30.	C		
31.	B		
32.	C		
33.	A		
34.	C		
35.	B		
36.	D		